Biological & Inorganic Copper Chemistry
Volume II

Biological & Inorganic Copper Chemistry Volume II

Proceedings of the Second Conference on Copper Coordination Chemistry held at the State University of New York at Albany, July 23-27, 1984

Edited by

Kenneth D. Karlin

Department of Chemistry
State University of New York at Albany

and

Jon Zubieta

Department of Chemistry
State University of New York at Albany

Adenine Press, P.O. Box 355
Guilderland, New York 12084

Adenine Press
Post Office Box 355
Guilderland, New York 12084

Cover illustration: Structure of a tetrachloro-*o*-catecholato- and phenoxo-bridged dicopper(II) complex, by K.D. Karlin, Y. Gultneh, T. Nicholson and J. Zubieta as a model for intermediates in coper-catalyzed oxidation of catechols

Library of Congress Cataloging-in-Publication Data

Conference on Copper Coordination Chemistry
   (2nd : 1984 : Albany, N.Y.)
   Biological & inorganic copper chemistry.

   Includes bibliographies and indexes.
   1. Copper proteins—Congresses.   2. Copper—
Congresses.   3. Coordination compounds—Congresses.
I. Karlin, Kenneth D., 1984-   .   II. Zubieta, Jon,
1945-   .   III. Title.   IV. Title: Biological and
inorganic copper chemistry.
QP552.C64C65   1984   546'.65   85-32334
ISBN 0-940030-11-X (v. 1)
ISBN 0-940030-15-2 (v. 2)

Made in New York, USA

Preface

These volumes explore the relationships of the biological and inorganic roles of copper by presenting contributions from spectroscopists, biochemists and inorganic coordination chemists. The books have evolved from the scientific discussions of the Second Conference on Copper Coordination Chemistry held at the State University of New York at Albany, July 23-27, 1984.

A previous volume in this series, published in 1983, provides an introduction to the field of the bioinorganic and general catalytic chemistry of copper. The evolution of our understanding of the role of copper in these processes has so accelerated that a mass of significant new chemistry has been developed since the publication of this original volume. The past three years have witnessed a refinement of structural and spectroscopic implications of the metal binding sites in type 1 and 2 copper proteins, with relevant structural analogues evolving in sophistication. Likewise, the rapid progress in the development of binuclear copper systems has profound implications upon the nature of the interaction of molecular oxygen with copper both in enzymes and in abiological systems.

The persistent theme of these volumes is that the evolution of the coordination chemistry of copper provides the fundamental insights required for the detailed understanding of the structural and spectroscopic properties of copper sites in proteins and of the interactions of molecular oxygen with reduced copper.

E.I. Solomon prefaces the volume with an overview of the role of copper coordination chemistry in the development of fundamental concepts of both biological and abiological catalysis, spectroscopy, and structural chemistry.

The volume opens with contributions exploring the chemical and spectroscopic properties of a variety of copper-containing proteins. The fine details of the type 1 or blue copper binding site are discussed in contributions by D.R. McMillen and A.G. Sykes. Applications of nuclear magnetic resonance spectroscopy and EXAFS to the elucidation of the copper(II) sites in superoxide dimutase are presented by C. Luchinat and N.J. Blackburn, while the role of zinc(II) and the essential arginyl residue of Zn/Cu SOD is examined by J.S. Valentine.

R.A. Scott and S.P. Cramer discuss structural studies of the binuclear copper site of cytochrome c oxidase. The functional diversity of binuclear copper sites is illustrated in the contrasting role of hemocyanin, where the copper site cooperativity is explored in a discussion by C.A. Reed. The binding of Cu(II) to Poly(L-Lysine) is discussed by F.T. Greenaway. The strategy of chemical modification of metal sites in proteins is the unifying theme of presentations by M.M. Morie-Bebel, D.M. Dooley, and J.M. Rifkind, who apply this technique in investigations of proteins as diverse as laccase, superoxide dimutase and modified hemoglobin.

The second major subdivision of the volume describes recent developments in the exciting area of medicinal applications of copper chemistry. The specific antitumor activity of copper preparations and the possible mechanisms of this activity are represented by contributions from S.-H. Chiou and coworkers and from W.E. Antholine and D.H. Petering. J.R.J. Sorenson and coworkers present an overview of the medicinal uses of copper complexes. Site-specific metal mediated Haber-Weiss mechanism in paraquat toxicity is proposed by R. Kohn and M. Chevion.

The first volume concludes with the discussion of the physical and spectroscopic properties of copper complexes and provides the bridge between the study of biological materials and the fundamental physico-chemical principles gleaned from small molecule or "model" studies. The general magnetic and electronic properties of a variety of copper (II) complexes are developed in detail by the contributers. Magnetic interactions in chain compounds and EPR properties of cluster compounds are discussed by W.E. Hatfield and G. Kokoszka respectively. O. Kahn discusses spin polarization effects in ligand bridged copper (II) ions. Novel analytical applications of electron paramagnetic resonance provide the focus of contributions by J.S. Hyde and W.E. Antholine and by H. Gampp and A.D. Zuberbühler. Electronic and magnetic properties associated with diverse phenomena-mixed-valence complexes, cooperative Jahn Teller interactions and antiferromagnetic coupling, are examined by D.N. Hendrickson, D. Reinen and C.P. Landee, respectively.

The second volume focuses on the synthesis and characterization of copper complexes that mimic some aspects of the structural or functional roles of copper proteins or of abiological copper catalysts. A major theme of the presentations is the persistence of analogies between the biological and the simple chemical catalytic systems.

The "activation" of molecular oxygen provides the topic for the introductory section of the volume. Contributions by J.S. Thompson and L. Wilson focus on the reversible reactions of dioxygen with mononuclear copper complexes. Binuclear complexes which mimic tyrosinase or hemocyanin activity represent exciting new chemistry in the presentations of S.M. Nelson, T.N. Sorrell, and K.D. Karlin. Copper catalyzed oxidation of phenols, an important industrial process, is explored in synthetic systems by J.E. Lyons and D.A. Haitko. The reactivity of copper clusters toward dioxygen is developed by G. Davies, while the mechanistic feature of the reactions of α-diketones with metallic copper are presented by G. Speier.

The second major subdivision presents the general topic of copper coordination chemistry with an emphasis on protein models. Models for copper sites in cytochrome c oxidase are discussed by J.K. Hurst and H. Toftlund. Binuclear complexes are discussed in relation to type 3 copper proteins, to synthetic copper binding polymers, and to a variety of homo- and hetero-binuclear systems by J. Reedijk, K.S. Murray and E. Sinn, respectively. The more general inorganic and structural properties of copper(II) complexes are developed in contributions by D.E. Fenton, J.M. Latour and G. Davies.

The volume concludes with a discussion of organometallic copper complexes, species of general interest in the development of organic synthetic processes. G. Van Koten focuses on the structural chemistry of organocuprate reagents. Polyhydride clusters are employed in numerous synthetic processes; K.G. Caulton discusses the rational synthesis of copper polyhydride species. The theme of aggregation is pursued by G. Doyle in a contribution on the synthesis of other types of copper containing clusters.

The contributions to these volumes are representative of the current trends in the development of the bioinorganic and more classical coordination chemistry of copper and reflect our major thesis that underlying the apparent diversity of physico-chemical data there exists a unity of fundamental chemical design. Once again, we hope that these volumes will serve as a useful compendium of the most recent research trends in this area and as a focus for discussion and further research activity.

The 1984 Copper Symposium and these volumes were only made possible through the generous support of a variety of University, State, and industrial sources. We wish to thank the SUNY Conversations in the Discipline Program, the SUNYA Office of the Vice President for Research, and the Research Foundation of the State of New York for financial assistance. We were particularly gratified by the supportive response from industry and wish to thank Allied Corporation, Bioanalytical Systems Inc., Bristol-Myers Company, Exxon Research & Engineering Co., Galbraith Laboratories, General Electric, International Copper Research Association, Inc., the Standard Oil Company (SOHIO), Sun Tech Inc., and Texaco Co. We hope that the fruitful collaboration between the University and industrial sectors represented by the success of this endeavor continue to flourish in years to come.

Finally, we would like to thank the contributors, who met our numerous deadlines without protest and who dealt stoically with the delays occasioned by editorial miscues. In conclusion, K.D.K. thanks Nancy and Matthew for their patience and affection and J.Z.thanks Susan, Chloe and Christa for bearing up when the long hours were showing.

Kenneth D. Karlin
Jon Zubieta
November, 1985
State University of New York (SUNY) at Albany

Foreword

The coordination chemistry of copper has played a major role in the development of both basic concepts of physical inorganic chemistry and important catalytic reactions, particularly those involving dioxygen and carbon monoxide activation. Since the 1950's, detailed spectroscopic and magnetic studies on high symmetry transition metal complexes have provided the experimental framework for ligand field theory. Strong emphasis has been placed on copper (II) as the d^9 (one hole) configuration allows a most rigorous correlation to theory. A few key studies of particular note are: The temperature dependence of the EPR spectrum of copper (II) doped in $Zn(H_2O)_6 \cdot SiF_6$, which first clearly demonstrated that a Jahn-Teller effect was active; the use of EPR on square planar copper (II) complexes to obtain g values, hyperfine and superhyperfine coupling parameters, which in turn gave experimental estimates of the covalent mixing in the anti-bonding "d" molecular orbitals of these complexes; the dependence of the $d \Rightarrow d$ transition energies on geometry and ligand type, provided an accurate test of the ligand field approximation of separating radial and angular contributions to the energies and further allowed the investigation of possible chemical insight from the values of these radial integrals; further, the $d \Rightarrow d$ combined with the charge transfer transitions in high symmetry copper complexes have enabled an experimental evaluation of various levels of molecular orbital calculations for metal ions (extended Huckel, HF-SCF-LCAO at different levels of approximation and SCF-X α -SW); finally, the classic magnetochemistry studies of cupric acetate monohydrate and related binuclear copper(II) complexes have led to deep insight into antiferromagnetic coupling, superexchange pathways, and magneto structural correlations (i.e. changes in exchange coupling with bridging geometry and ligand type).

The reactivity of copper active sites play critical roles in heterogeneous, homogeneous and enzymatic catalysis. In heterogeneous catalysis, the conversion of synthesis gas to methanol at low temperature and pressure is achieved through a copper-promoted ZnO catalyst. This catalyst is also used commercially in the water gas shift reaction. In addition, cuprous oxide has been found to be an effective selective oxidation catalyst which uses dioxygen to oxidize propylene, apparently through a π-allyl intermediate. Little is known about the oxidation state, ligation or geometry of any of these surface copper active sites. Even less is known on a molecular level about the copper chloride catalyst systems involved in the apparently homogeneous oxidation of organic molecules with dioxygen. At this point, the most well defined active sites are those found in copper proteins. High resolution crystal structures are now available for Cu-Zn superoxide dismutase and the Blue Copper proteins, and structures are underway on hemocyanin, ascorbate oxidase, and ceruloplasmin. For hemocyanin, tyrosinase and laccase, chemical and spectroscopic studies have led to the generation of spectroscopically effective models for their active sites; hemocyanin and tyrosinase containing a binuclear copper unit involved in reversible oxygen binding and oxygenation, and laccase a trinuclear copper site which appears to be important in the irreversible reduction of dioxygen to water.

It is clear from the contributions to these volumes and from the proceedings of the "Albany Meeting" which are the basis for this series, that the areas of copper coordination chemistry including spectroscopy, synthesis and catalysis, have come together and are providing fundamental geometric and electronic structural insight into these active sites on a molecular level. The first volume of this set includes physical inorganic studies on protein active sites and parallel studies on small molecule high-symmetry complexes which serve as electronic structural analogues. The second volume focuses on the synthesis and characterization of structurally defined copper complexes which model specific features of the active site and allow one to systematically investigate structural contributions to reactivity. As is demonstrated by the depth and quality of the papers in this collection, much attention is now focused toward active sites in copper proteins and structure-function correlations are rapidly developing. These should encourage parallel molecular level studies of copper coordination chemistry related to the less well defined active sites in heterogeneous and homogeneous catalytic systems in the near future.

Edward I. Solomon
Stanford University
November, 1985

CONTENTS

Volume I

CONTENTS

Volume II

Coordination Chemistry; Protein Models

Organometallic Copper Complexes

Biological & Inorganic Copper Chemistry,
ISBN 0-940030-11-X, Eds., K. D. Karlin & J. Zubieta, Adenine Press, ©Adenine Press, 1985

Copper-Dioxygen Chemistry. Synthesis, Properties and Reactions of Cu(II)-Superoxide and -Peroxide Complexes

Jeffery S. Thompson
Central Research and Development Department
E.I. du Pont de Nemours and Co.
Experimental Station
Wilmington, DE 19898

Abstract

The syntheses, spectral properties, and reactivities of a series of Cu(II)-dioxygen adducts are discussed. In all cases, the adducts are prepared by the reaction of molecular oxygen with a Cu(I)-ethylene complex. Three types of complexes have been prepared, corresponding to reduction of molecular oxygen by one, two, and four electrons. A Cu(II)-superoxide complex is obtained from the reaction of ethylene(hydrotris(3,5-dimethyl-1-pyrazolyl)borato)copper(I) with molecular oxygen. Similarly, the reaction with ethylene(N,N,N′,N′-tetraethylethylene-diamine)copper(I) perchlorate yields a μ-peroxodicopper(II) complex. Small molecules such as ethylene and carbon monoxide displace the bound dioxygen. Reactions of Cu(I)-ethylene complexes with less sterically crowded ligands yield di-μ-hydroxy or di-μ-methoxy complexes (reactions carried out in methanol). The choice of ligands in the copper coordination sphere appears to be critical in preparing stable Cu(II)-dioxygen adducts. Three types of reactions have been observed: loss of oxygen to yield a Cu(I) complex, decomposition to Cu(II)-hydroxy dimers or similar compounds, and hydroxylation of the coordinated ligand.

Introduction

Our recent research summarized in this contribution has centered on the synthesis and characterization of properties and reactivities of copper-dioxygen complexes. These adducts have often been proposed as intermediates in copper autoxidation reactions (1) and in the reactions of copper oxidases (2), but there are few well-characterized examples (3). Extensive kinetic studies of copper autoxidation reactions (1) suggest initial formation of a superoxide species, followed by a second one-electron transfer to form a peroxide species, which then decomposes by several pathways to water or hydroxide (further reduction or disproportionation); these reactions, shown in eq. 1, are generally very fast. Superoxide has not been observed in these reactions (1). Hydrogen peroxide is often produced in such autoxidations, but copper-dioxygen complexes can generally only be inferred as intermediates. Our work (4) has yielded stable Cu(II)-oxygen complexes with each of the reduced

1

$$O_2 \xrightarrow{\text{1e}} O_2^- \xrightarrow{\text{1e}} O_2^= \xrightarrow{\text{2e/4H}^+} 2H_2O \tag{1}$$

$$\phantom{O_2 \xrightarrow{\text{1e}} O_2^- \xrightarrow{\text{1e}} O_2^=}\, \underset{\text{2H}^+}{\xrightarrow{\hspace{1.2cm}}} H_2O + 1/2\,O_2$$

species shown in eq. 1, corresponding to reduction of dioxygen by one, two and four electrons. These complexes allow us to explore the spectral properties and reactivities of copper-dioxygen complexes.

Synthetic Approach

Our approach to the synthesis of copper-dioxygen complexes involves reacting molecular oxygen with a Cu(I) complex having a ligand that is easily displaced without oxidation. The starting materials for the complexes described here are Cu(I)-ethylene complexes recently reported by us (5-7). The compounds prepared in this manner are intended to establish the structural chemistry, physical properties, and reactivities of copper-dioxygen adducts, rather than to model active sites of copper proteins; however, the results from this study give some insight into how copper oxidases activate molecular oxygen.

This synthetic approach allows us to easily change the other ligands in the copper coordination sphere. Choice of ligand has a profound effect on the type of complex that can be isolated. These ligand effects are similar to those observed with other transition metal-dioxygen systems, for which restraints imposed by the ligands have been shown to control the metal ion/dioxygen ratio and the reactions of the bound dioxygen (8). Similarly, ligand effects have been observed in kinetic studies of copper autoxidation reactions (1).

Copper(II)-Superoxide Complex

Reacting molecular oxygen with the Cu(I)-ethylene complex Cu(HB(3,5-Me$_2$pz)$_3$)-(C$_2$H$_4$), I, (HB(3,5-Me$_2$pz)$_3$ = hydrotris(3,5-dimethyl-1-pyrazolyl)borate) recently reported by us (5) in acetone at room temperature yields an intensely reddish-purple precipitate (eq. 2). A microcrystalline sample of the same color, II, obtained by recrystallization at $-40°$C from oxygen-saturated dichloromethane-diethyl ether, is indefinitely stable under nitrogen or oxygen at $-40°$C, but slowly turns green on standing at room temperature. Spectroscopic and analytical data suggest the formulation Cu$_2$(HB(3,5-Me$_2$pz)$_3$)$_2$(O) for this green material; this type of complex has been obtained in other reactions of cuprous complexes with molecular oxygen (9). Dichloromethane solutions of II turn green fairly rapidly at room temperature,

$$Cu(HB(3,5-Me_2pz)_3)(C_2H_4) \xrightarrow[O_2]{} Cu(HB(3,5-Me_2pz)_3)(O_2) + C_2H_4 \tag{2}$$

but may be handled easily at reduced temperatures. A green product isolated from CH_2Cl_2-solutions at room temperature is the Cu(II) complex $Cu(HB(3,5\text{-}Me_2pz)_3)(Cl)$, based on analytical and spectroscopic data (4a).

Analytical and spectroscopic data are consistent with the formulation of *II* as a Cu(II)-superoxide complex, $Cu(HB(3,5\text{-}Me_2pz)_3)(O_2)\cdot XEt_2O$. The material does not give rise to an EPR signal at liquid nitrogen temperatures, but does have an NMR spectrum consistent with the indicated formulation. These results support the assignments of the copper and oxygen oxidation states. Both Cu(II) and superoxide ions have an unpaired electron; coordination of these ions should lead to strong coupling of spins and formation of an EPR silent, but NMR detectable, complex. There is no broadening of the ^1H NMR resonances, suggesting strong coupling of spins. Formation of an EPR silent complex was observed for a Cu(II)-superoxide complex prepared directly (10).

Other formulations for the copper-dioxygen adducts would also give rise to an EPR silent complex, but visible absorption and infrared data support the $Cu(II)\text{-}O_2^-$ assignment. The visible spectrum of *II* obtained in dichloromethane at $-14°C$ consists of a relatively intense band at 524 nm ($\epsilon = 600\ M^{-1}cm^{-1}$) with a broad shoulder on the low energy side that tails into the near infrared region. This spectrum resembles other Cu(II) complexes with this polypyrazolylborate ligand (11). We tentatively assign the 524 nm band to a ligand-to-metal charge transfer band because of its intensity and position and the broad, lower energy shoulder to d-d bands because of the similarity in band position and intensity to that of the Cu(II)-p-nitrophenolate complex $Cu(HB(3,5\text{-}Me_2pz)_3)(OC_6H_4NO_2)$ previously reported (11).

Infrared data for the complexes prepared from $^{16}O_2$ and $^{18}O_2$, *IIa* and *IIb*, confirm the presence of a superoxide species. The infrared spectrum of *IIa* is essentially unchanged from those of *I* and the analogous carbonyl complex (without the bands attributable to these small molecules). No band appears that can be identified as an O-O stretching vibration. The spectrum of *IIb* has a new, relatively weak band at $1015\ cm^{-1}$, but is otherwise identical to that of *IIa*. We have assigned this band to an $^{18}O\text{-}^{18}O$ stretch. A similar band should appear in the spectrum of *IIa* at higher energy, but a strong band from the polypyrazolylborate ligand at $1060\ cm^{-1}$ obscures this region. Oxygen stretching vibrations in this region are characteristic of unsymmetrically bound superoxide ions (12).

The reaction chemistry of *II* (Scheme I) is consistent with formation of a Cu(II)-dioxygen complex. Addition and removal of molecular oxygen cause the metal ion to shuttle between the cuprous and cupric states, as shown by the gain and loss of the intense color. Adding molecular oxygen to *I* produces *II*; this reaction is reversed by bubbling ethylene through the mixture to yield *I* and a green Cu(II) material, which has not yet been fully characterized. Reacting *II* with excess acetonitrile gives a similar result: production of a Cu(I)-acetonitrile complex and this green product. Less than stoichiometric amounts of molecular oxygen are obtained from

SCHEME I

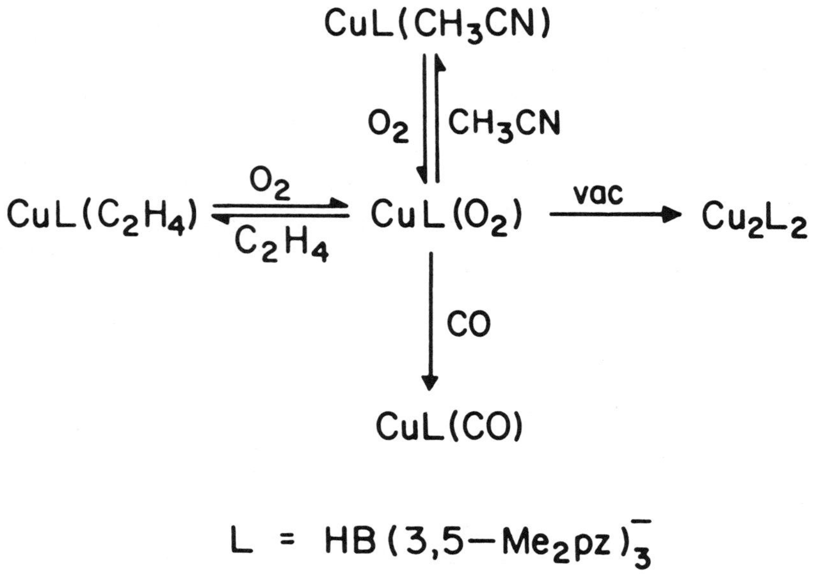

$$CuL(CH_3CN)$$

$$O_2 \upharpoonleft\!\!\downharpoonright CH_3CN$$

$$CuL(C_2H_4) \underset{C_2H_4}{\overset{O_2}{\rightleftharpoons}} CuL(O_2) \xrightarrow{vac} Cu_2L_2$$

$$\downarrow CO$$

$$CuL(CO)$$

$$L = HB(3,5-Me_2pz)_3^-$$

this reaction; the presence of molecular oxygen has been confirmed by mass spectral analysis of the collected gases. Solutions of the acetonitrile complex prepared in this manner turn the same reddish-purple color of *II* when exposed to molecular oxygen. Carbon monoxide displaces the bound dioxygen from *II* to form the Cu(I)-carbonyl complex $Cu(HB(3,5-Me_2pz)_3)(CO)$, previously reported (13). Finally, removing solvent from solutions of *II* under high vaccuum produces a light green solid, from which the Cu(I) complex $Cu_2(HB(3,5-Me_2pz)_3)_2$ is obtained on recrystallization (13). In each of these reactions, a Cu(I) complex is formed by displacing bound dioxygen; no reducing agent has been added. This reversible oxygen binding is strong evidence for the presence of an O_2 species in this complex.

Cu(II)-Peroxide Complex

Adding molecular oxygen to the Cu(I)-ethylene complex $[Cu(TEEN)(C_2H_4)]ClO_4$, *IV*, (TEEN=N,N,N',N'-tetraethylethylenediamine) in methanol yields a dark blue solution (eq. 3), which is sensitive to reaction conditions and easily lost if not handled properly. The following steps were devised to permit consistent prep-

$$2[Cu(TEEN)(C_2H_4)]ClO_4 \xrightarrow[O_2]{H_2O} [Cu_2(TEEN)_2(H_2O)(O_2)](ClO_4)_2 + C_2H_4 \quad (3)$$

aration of the complex. The starting ethylene complex was prepared just prior to use from copper(II) perchlorate hexahydrate and copper dust, as described elsewhere (7,8). After filtration to remove excess copper dust, the methanol solution was stirred open in a dry box under a nitrogen flush and then cooled in Dry Ice. Oxygen was then flushed vigorously through the flask, which was maintained at $-78°C$ for one hour and then at $-40°C$ overnight. A deep blue color developed. A blue powder, which can be handled at room temperature without any apparent decomposition, was obtained from this methanol solution by vapor diffusion of oxygen-saturated diethyl ether at $-40°C$. Methanol solutions can be handled briefly at room temperature, but decompose on standing.

Analytical and spectroscopic data (4b) on the product isolated from the above procedure suggest the formulation $[Cu_2(TEEN)_2(H_2O)(O_2)](ClO_4)_2$, a μ-peroxodicopper(II) complex, V (eq. 3). This material is EPR silent at $-160°C$, a result consistent with the formation of a Cu(II) dimer. There are several examples in the literature of EPR silent, dimeric Cu(II) complexes with the TEEN ligand (14). The visible absorption spectrum consists of a broad band centered at 630 nm, which can be assigned to d-d bands on the basis of its intensity and position and is characteristic of square planar Cu(II) complexes in general and of Cu(II)-TEEN complexes in particular (15). In addition, a new band appears at approximately 240 nm that is lacking in the spectra of the Cu(II) decomposition products of V (vide infra). In this regard, the spectral features of V resemble those of peroxylaccase, rather than oxyhemocyanin (16). Two dimeric Cu(II) complexes derived from V have a strong band in this region (vide infra). The infrared spectrum of V shows bands at 3570, 1670, and 1620 cm^{-1} that can be assigned to a water molecule. These bands shift to lower energy when the complex is prepared in methanol-d_4 with a trace amount of D_2O. Infrared and Raman studies of the $^{16}O_2$ and $^{18}O_2$ derivatives are in progress.

The reaction chemistry of V (Scheme II) is consistent with the formation of a Cu(II)-dioxygen adduct and is dominated by two types of reactions: displacement of molecular oxygen to form a Cu(I) complex and disproportionation of the peroxide moiety to form a Cu(II) complex. Addition of molecular oxygen displaces ethylene from the copper coordination sphere to produce V; this reaction is reversed by

SCHEME II

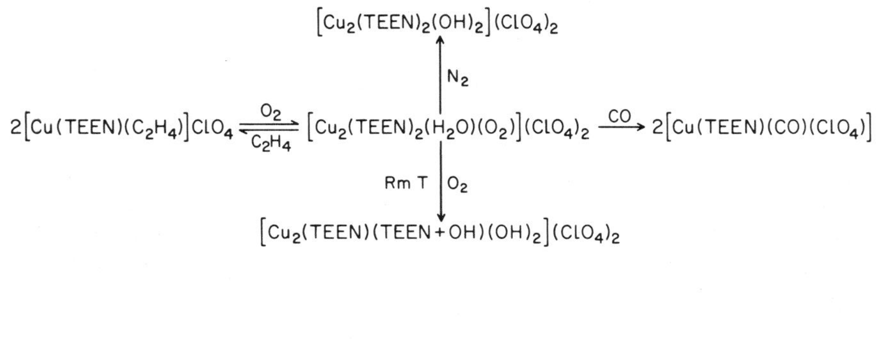

$$[Cu_2(TEEN)_2(OH)_2](ClO_4)_2$$

$$\uparrow N_2$$

$$2[Cu(TEEN)(C_2H_4)]ClO_4 \underset{C_2H_4}{\overset{O_2}{\rightleftharpoons}} [Cu_2(TEEN)_2(H_2O)(O_2)](ClO_4)_2 \xrightarrow{CO} 2[Cu(TEEN)(CO)(ClO_4)]$$

$$Rm\ T \downarrow O_2$$

$$[Cu_2(TEEN)(TEEN+OH)(OH)_2](ClO_4)_2$$

bubbling ethylene through the solution to produce the starting material. This sequence of reactions must be done at room temperture, without initial stirring of the ethylene complex under a nitrogen flush. Similarly, bubbling carbon monoxide through a methanol solution of V yields the Cu(I)-carbonyl complex [Cu(TEEN)(CO)ClO$_4$] (6). In each case, dioxygen appears to be displaced to yield a Cu(I) complex; no reducing agent is added.

The second reaction type of V is disproportionation of the peroxide moiety to yield a di-μ-hydroxydicopper(II) complex, [Cu$_2$(TEEN)$_2$(OH)$_2$](ClO$_4$)$_2$, VI, which has been prepared directly (14). This complex precipitates from solution when V is stirred under a nitrogen atmosphere. Two likely pathways to VI are shown in eq. 4 and 5. When ^{18}O$_2$ is used, the bridging hydroxides do not appear to contain ^{18}OH$^-$; therefore the reaction shown in eq 5 is the more likely. Similar reactions have been proposed from kinetic studies of copper autoxidation reactions (1).

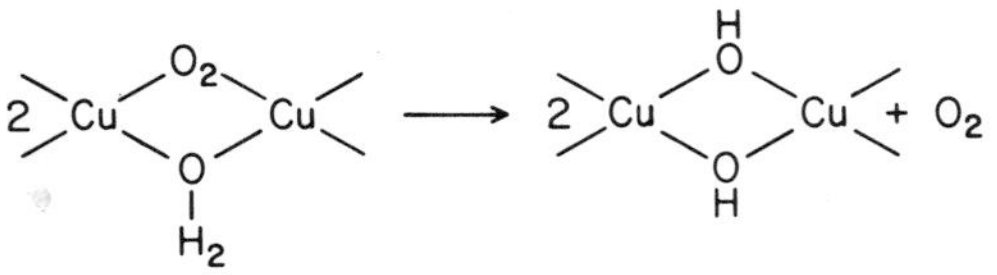

$$2 \, \text{Cu} \overset{O_2}{\underset{\underset{H_2}{O}}{}} \text{Cu} \longrightarrow 2 \, \text{Cu} \overset{\overset{H}{O}}{\underset{\underset{H}{O}}{}} \text{Cu} + O_2 \qquad (4)$$

$$\text{Cu} \overset{O_2}{\underset{\underset{H_2}{O}}{}} \text{Cu} \overset{H_2O}{\longrightarrow} \text{Cu} \overset{\overset{H}{O}}{\underset{\underset{H}{O}}{}} \text{Cu} + H_2O_2 \longrightarrow 1/2 \, H_2O + 1/2 \, O_2 \qquad (5)$$

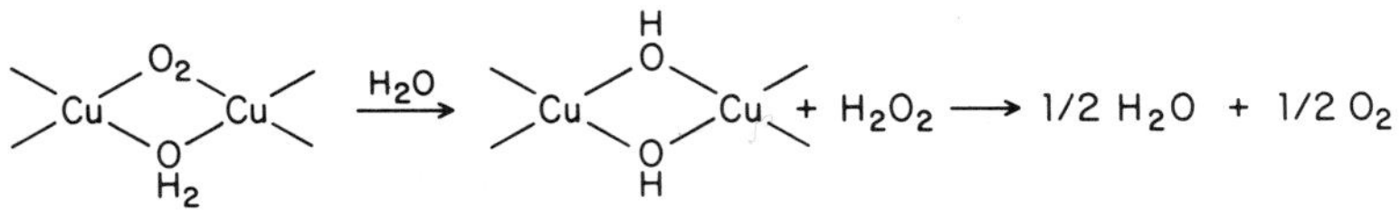

The reaction chemistry of V under an oxygen atmosphere at ambient temperatures differs from that under nitrogen described above. From this reaction, we have isolated and characterized analytically, spectroscopically, and crystallographically (for the BF$_4$ salt) a second di-μ-hydroxydicopper(II) complex in which one of the eight ethyl groups of the TEEN ligand has been hydroxylated (Figure 1) (18). The hydroxyl group is coordinated to one of the Cu(II) ions in an axial position to form a five-coordinate complex. The origin of the hydroxyl group has not yet been unequivocally determined, but the available data suggest molecular oxygen. Oxidation of the TEEN ligand has been suggested in the autoxidation reactions of other Cu(I)-TEEN complexes (19).

Copper(II)-Hydroxy and -Methoxy Compounds

Use of ligands less sterically crowded than those shown above in reactions with molecular oxygen yields Cu(II) complexes and water or hydroxide ions, corresponding to fully reduced molecular oxygen (eq 1). The starting materials and products for autoxidation reactions of a number of Cu(I) complexes are shown in Table I. Although no intermediates have yet been fully characterized, these reactions probably involve formation of a peroxide complex and/or free hydrogen peroxide followed

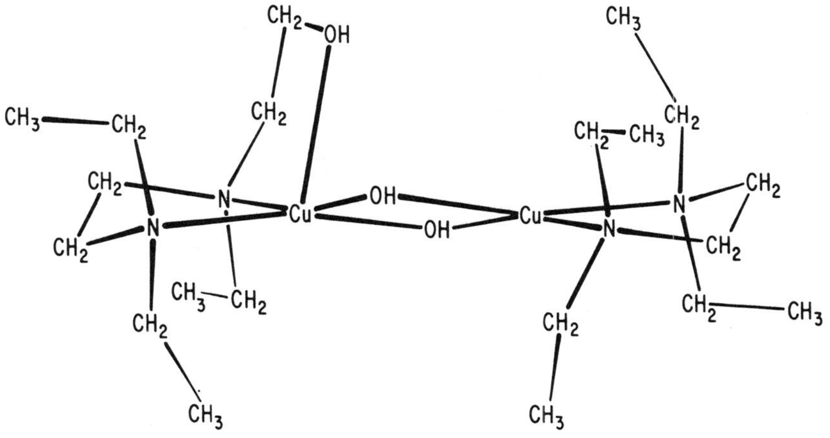

Figure 1. Structure of $[Cu_2(TEEN)(TEEN+OH)(OH)_2]^{2+}$.

by disproportionation to yield hydroxy- or methoxy-bridged Cu(II) dimers. All of these reactions were performed in methanol with trace amounts of water present.

The complexes shown in Table I are catalytically active in the oxidation of catechols to the corresponding benzoquinones. Many copper complexes catalyze this reaction (20), but a detailed understanding of this reaction is lacking. The complexes reported here appear to carry out this reaction by a pathway involving partial reduction of the copper complex and activation of substrate to attack by dioxygen. The Cu(II) dimer $[Cu_2(NHpy_2)_2(OCH_3)_2](ClO_4)_2$ reacts with one equivalent of 3,5-di-*tert*-butylcatechol to produce a Cu(I) complex (presumably $[Cu(NHpy_2)ClO_4]_x$) and a Cu(II)-semiquinone complex $[Cu(NHpy_2)(3,5-di-tert-butylsemiquinone)]ClO_4$, *VII*, which has been characterized analytically, spectroscopically, and crystallographically (21). The Cu(II) ion is coordinated to two pyridyl nitrogen atoms from the 2,2'-dipyridylamine ligand and to two oxygen atoms of the semiquinone ligand. In addition, a perchlorate anion is coordinated in an axial position and weakly bridges two of these units. The C-O bond lengths of 1.29-1.30A are characteristic of

Table I
Cu(II) Products from Autoxidation Reactions of Cu(I) Complexes[a]

Reactant	Product
$[Cu(TMEN)(C_2H_4)]ClO_4$	$[Cu_2(TMEN)_2(OH)(OCH_3)](ClO_4)_2$
$[Cu(TEEN)(C_2H_4)]ClO_4$	$[Cu_2(TEEN)_2(OH)_2](ClO_4)_2$
$[Cu(NHpy_2)(C_2H_4)]ClO_4$	$[Cu_2(NHpy_2)_2(OCH_3)_2](ClO_4)_2$
$[Cu(Bipy)(C_2H_4)]ClO_4$	$[Cu_2(Bipy)_2(OCH_3)_2](ClO_4)_2$
$[Cu(OP)(C_2H_4)]ClO_4$	$[Cu_2(OP)_2(OCH_3)_2](ClO_4)_2$
$[Cu(pyridine)_4]ClO_4$	$[Cu_2(pyridine)_4(OCH_3)_2](ClO_4)_2$

[a]TMEN=N,N,N',N'-tetramethylethylenediamine; Bipy=2,2'-dipyridyl; OP=1,10-phenanthroline.

semiquinone complexes (22). This complex can also be prepared by reacting the Cu(I) ethylene complex $[Cu(NHpy_2)(C_2H_4)]ClO_4$ with 3,5-di-*tert*-butylbenzoquinone; the cuprous ion transfers one electron to the benzoquinone to produce *VII*, which will also catalyze the oxidation of catechols, as determined by literature procedures (20). The next step in this oxidation reaction with our complexes is not yet clear, but appears to require attack of oxygen on the coordinated semiquinone to produce the benzoquinone and $[Cu_2(NHpy_2)_2(OCH_3)_2](ClO_4)_2$. Our work establishes that the oxidation reaction proceeds in one-electron transfer steps and supports earlier observations that a copper-bound dioxygen species is not required to carry out this oxidation.

Conclusions

Our initial results on the synthesis and characterization of properties and reactivities of copper-dioxygen complexes establish several important aspects of copper-dioxygen coordination chemistry. Stable compounds with dioxygen reduced by one and two electrons can be prepared and characterized by a variety of techniques, with the proper choice of ligands and reaction conditions. The oxidation states of both metal ion and oxygen moiety have been clearly established spectroscopically for both the superoxide and peroxide complexes, although the details of these structures require further characterization. Cu(II)-superoxide species have been proposed as an initial reduction product in copper autoxidations, but have not been observed; peroxide complexes have been suggested or detected spectroscopically in such reactions (3). The remarkable feature of *II* and *VI* is their stability to further reduction of the dioxygen species, in light of the overwhelming tendency of Cu(I) complexes to reduce molecular oxygen completely. For both of these complexes, the choice of other ligands in the copper coordination sphere is critical for the isolation of the dioxygen complexes. The bulky substituents of the $HB(3,5-Me_2pz)_3^-$ and TEEN ligands minimize molecular aggregation that lead to further reduction of dioxygen. In this regard, the coordination chemistry of copper-dioxygen complexes is similar to that of other transition metal-dioxygen complexes (8).

The reactions of these complexes fall into three categories: loss or displacement of dioxygen to generate a Cu(I) complex, further reduction of the dioxygen species with formation of Cu(II) complexes, and oxygenation of organic molecules. Bound dioxygen is displaced by small molecules that stabilize the cuprous oxidation state (ethylene, carbon monoxide, and acetonitrile). Although this displacement reaction does not model the reversible oxygen binding of many copper proteins, it demonstrates that O-O bond is not broken on coordination to copper ions and that copper complexes are not necessarily irreversibly oxidized by dioxygen. The most common reaction for the cuprous complexes described here and elsewhere is the complete reduction of dioxygen. A likely pathway involves formation and disproportionation of hydrogen peroxide.

Copper-bound dioxygen has been suggested as a potent oxidizing agent, but there are few well-characterized examples (3). Our work shows that when the disproportionation reaction is suppressed (eq 4 and 5) and the substrate held in the proper orientation, oxygenation can take place. In this regard, the oxygenation of the TEEN ligand is similar to a single turnover of a copper oxygenase; the copper ions hold both the oxygen molecule and substrate close enough for the reaction to occur, much in the same way envisioned for the active site of a copper protein.

References and Footnotes

1. a) A.D. Zuberbuhler in *Copper Coordination Chemistry: Biochemical and Inorganic Perspectives,* Ed., K.D. Karlin and J. Zubieta, Adenine Press, Guilderland, N.Y., pp. 237-258 (1983). b) H. Gampp and A.D. Zuberbuhler, *Met. Ions Biol. Syst. 12,* 133-189 (1981). c) A.D. Zuberbuhler, *Met. Ions Biol. Syst. 5,* 325-368 (1976).

2. a) E.I. Solomon in *Copper Coordination Chemistry: Biochemical and Inorganic Perspectives,* Ed., K.D. Karlin and J. Zubieta, Adenine Press, Guilderland, N.Y., pp. 1-22 (1983). b) G.L. Woolery, L. Powers, M. Winkler, E.I. Solomon, and T.G. Spiro, *J. Am. Chem. Soc. 106,* 86-92 (1984). c) M.S. Co, K.O. Hodgson, T.K. Eccles, and R. Lontie, *J. Am. Chem. Soc. 103,* 984-986 (1981). d) R.S. Himmelwright, N.C. Eickman, C.D. LuBien, and E.I. Solomon, *J. Am. Chem. Soc. 102,* 5378-5388 (1980). e) M.E. Winkler, K. Lerch, and E.I. Solomon, *J. Am. Chem. Soc. 103,* 7001-7003 (1981).

3. a) K.D. Karlin, R.W. Cruse, Y. Gultneh, J.C. Hayes, and J. Zubieta, *J. Am. Chem. Soc. 106,* 3372-3374 (1984). b) C.L. Merrill, T.J. Thamann, T.M. Loehr, N.S. Ferris, W.H. Woodruff, and L.J. Wilson, *J. Chem. Soc. Dalton Trans.* 2207-2222 (1984). c) J.E. Bulkowski and W.E. Summers in *Copper Coordination Chemistry: Biochemical and Inorganic Perspectives,* Ed., K.D. Karlin and J. Zubieta, Adenine Press, Guilderland, N.Y., pp. 445-456 (1983).

4. a) J.S. Thompson, *J. Am. Chem. Soc. 106,* 4057-4059 (1984). b) J.S. Thompson, *J. Am. Chem. Soc. 106,* 8308-8309 (1984).

5. J.S. Thompson, R.L. Harlow, and J.F. Whitney, *J. Am. Chem. Soc. 105,* 3522-3527 (1983).

6. J.S. Thompson and R.M. Swiatek, *Inorg. Chem., 24,* 110-113 (1985).

7. J.S. Thompson and J.F. Whitney, *Inorg. Chem., 23,* 2813-2819 (1984).

8. A.E. Martell, *Accounts Chem. Res. 15,* 155-162 (1982).

9. a) G. Davies and M.A. El-Sayed in *Copper Coordination Chemistry: Biochemical and Inorganic Perspectives,* Ed., K.D. Karlin and J. Zubieta, Adenine Press, Guilderland, N.Y., pp. 281-309 (1983). b) G. Speier and Z. Tyeklar, *J. Chem. Soc. Dalton Trans.* 1995-2000 (1983). c) S. Bhaduri and N.Y. Sapre, *J. Chem. Soc. Dalton Trans.* 2585-2586 (1981). d) C. Lapinte, H. Riviere, and A. Roselli, *J. Chem. Soc. Chem. Commun.* 1109-1110 (1981). e) C. Jallabert, C. Lapinte, and H. Riviere, *J. Mol. Catal. 7,* 127-136 (1980). f) H. Gampp and A.D. Zuberbuhler, *J. Mol. Cata. 7,* 81-88 (1980).

10. M. Nappa, J.S. Valentine, A.R. Miksztal, H.G. Schugar, and S.S. Isied, *J. Am. Chem. Soc. 101,* 7744-7746 (1979).

11. J.S. Thompson, T.J. Marks, and J.A. Ibers, *J. Am. Chem. Soc. 101,* 4180-4192 (1979).

12. a) K. Nakamoto, *Infrared and Raman Spectra of Inorganic and Coordination Compounds,* 3rd. ed., Wiley, N.Y., pp. 297-299 (1978). b) R.D. Jones, D.A. Summerville, and F. Basolo, *Chem. Rev. 79,* 139-179 (1979). c) G. McLendon and A. Martell, *Coord. Chem. Rev. 19,* 1-39 (1976). d) J. Valentine, *Chem. Rev. 73,* 235-245 (1973).

13. C. Mealli, C.S. Arcus, J.L. Wilkinson, T.J. Marks, and J.A. Ibers, *J. Am. Chem. Soc. 98,* 711-718 (1976).

14. a) M. Nasakkala, *Ann. Acad. Sci. Fenn. Sec. AII 181,* 1-72 (1977). b) E.D. Estes, W.E. Hatfield, and D.J. Hodgson, *Inorg. Chem. 13,* 1654-1657 (1974).

15. a) J. S. Thompson and J.C. Calabrese, unpublished observation. b) The Cu(II) complexes Cu(TEEN)(NO$_3$)$_2$ has a visible absorption spectrum very similar to that of V. This material crystallizes in the orthorhombic space group Pnna with four molecules per unit cell of dimensions a=11.617(5)A, b=15.658(3)A, and c=8.730(3)A. Least squares refinement of 96 variables led to a value of the conventional R index of 0.039 and R$_w$ of 0.037 for 1146 reflections having F$_o^2$>2 (F$_o^2$). The cupric ion is coordinated to two nitrogen atoms of the TEEN ligand and to an oxygen atom from each nitro group in a square planar arrangement.

16. a) E.I. Solomon in *Metal Ions in Biology,* Vol. 3, Ed., T.G. Spiro, Wiley-Interscience, N.Y., pp. 41-108 (1981). b) M.E. Winkler, D.J. Spird, C.D. LuBien, T.J. Thamann, and E.I. Solomon, *Biochem. Biophys. Res. Commun. 107,* 727-734 (1982). c) O. Farver, M. Goldberg, and I. Pecht, *Eur. J. Biochem 104,* 71-77 (1980).

17. T. Shibahara and M. Mori, *Bull. Chem. Soc. Jap. 51,* 1374-1379 (1978).

18. J.S. Thompson and T.H. Tulip, manuscript in preparation.

19. M.R. Churchill, G. Davies, M.A. El-Sayed, J.A. Fournier, J.P. Hutchinson, and J.A. Zubieta, *Inorg. Chem. 23,* 783-787 (1984).

20. a) M.M. Rogic, M.D. Swerdloff, and T.R. Demmin in *Copper Coordination Chemistry: Biochemical and Inorganic Perspectives,* Ed., K.D. Karlin and J. Zubieta, Adenine Press, Guilderland, N.Y., pp. 259-279 (1983). b) G. Speier and Z. Tyeklar, *J. Mol. Cat. 9,* 23-235 (1980). c) T.R. Demmin, M.D. Swerdloff, and M.M. Rogic, *J. Am. Chem. Soc. 103,* 5795-5804 (1981). d) N. Oishi, Y. Nishida, K. Ida, and S. Kida, *Bull. Chem. Soc. Jpn. 53,* 2847-2850 (1980).

21. J. S. Thompson and J.C. Calabrese, *Inorg. Chem., 24,* 3167-3171 (1985).

22. C.G. Pierpont and R.M. Buchanan, *Coord. Chem. Rev. 38,* 45-87 (1981).

Biological & Inorganic Copper Chemistry,
ISBN 0-940030-11-X, Eds., K. D. Karlin & J. Zubieta, Adenine Press, ©Adenine Press, 1985

Reversible Reactions of Dioxygen with Synthetic Copper(I) Complexes Under Ambient Conditions

John A. Goodwin, David M. Stanbury, and Lon J. Wilson
Department of Chemistry
Rice University
Houston, Texas 77251, U.S.A.

Robert A. Scott
School of Chemical Sciences
University of Illinois at Urbana-Champaign
Urbana, Illinois 61801, U.S.A.

Abstract

The {bis-2,6-[1-(2-imidazol-4-ylethylimino)ethyl]pyridine}copper(I) cation, $[Cu^I(imidH)_2DAP]^+$, has been previously reported to react reversibly with O_2 under ambient conditions in solution whereas the related {bis-2,6-[1-(2-pyridin-2-ylethylimino)ethyl]pyridine}copper(I) cation, $[Cu^I(py)_2DAP]^+$, is unreactive toward O_2 under similar conditions. In a continuing study of these unusual copper(I) compounds and their reactivity toward O_2, magnetochemical, resonance Raman spectroscopic, EXAFS, and kinetic measurements have been performed on deoxy and oxygenated solutions of the complexes to characterize the nature of the copper-dioxygen interaction. Furthermore, the synthesis of the related copper(I) derivatives, $[Cu^I(imidR)(py)DAP]^+$, $[Cu^I(imidH)(py)DAP]^+$, $[Cu^I(imidR)_2DAP]^+$ and $[Cu^I(imidH)-(imidR)DAP]^+$, with R = p-$CH_2(C_6H_4)CH_3$, has been achieved in order to examine the role, if any, of the imidazole nitrogen proton in the reversible oxygenation process.

Introduction

The current interest in modelling the active site of hemocyanin has recently culminated in notable advances. With the microenvironment of the copper centers of the protein quite well established (1), it has been possible to devise a few corroborative model systems which are reasonably satisfying in their duplication of the static structure of the deoxy-copper(I) state. Within the present ken of metalloprotein modelling, synthetic systems necessarily focus upon particular aspects of the biomolecules of interest, such as ligand environment or reactivity. With the emphasis of such systems upon the accurate protrayal of the microenvironment of the copper centers in hemocyanin (2-6), there is a compromise in relegating the protein's reactivity to a position of distinct secondary importance. But even within the limitations imposed by the synthetic ligand structure, low temperatures have

11

permitted the observation of the oxy forms of copper(I) species such as those reported by Karlin (2) and Thompson (6). Our own studies of copper(I)-dioxygen interactions have focused on reversible reactions which occur under ambient conditions, but here the known protein ligand structure has been compromised somewhat further.

Our copper(I)-dioxygen modelling studies were initiated almost eight years ago (before the active site structure of hemocyanin was so well established) by the synthesis and characterization of the {bis-2,6-[1-(imidazol-4-ylethylimino)ethyl]-pyridine}copper(I) cation, [Cu^I(imidH)$_2$DAP]$^+$, in Figure 1A, which was found to react reversibly with dioxygen in solution at room temperature and pressure (7a,b).

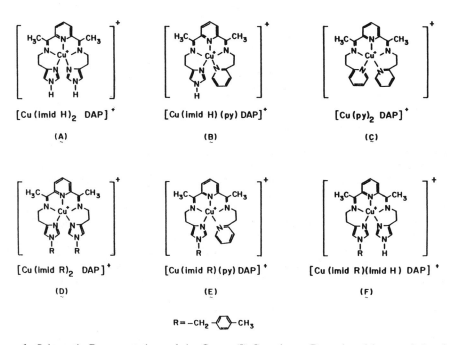

Figure 1. Schematic Representations of the Copper(I) Complexes. Reproduced by permission from reference 7e.

Less striking, but no less curious, was the finding that the {bis-2,6-[2-pyridin-2-ylethylimino)ethyl]-pyridine}copper(I) cation, [Cu^I(py)$_2$DAP]$^+$, in Figure 1C, did not exhibit a reversible reaction, but rather remained quite inert toward dioxygen under identical reaction conditions. Furthermore, the additional findings that both the red deoxy-[Cu^I(imidH)$_2$DAP]$^+$ complex and the green oxygenated product are essentially epr-silent at 100 K and that the reaction stoichiometry is two moles of copper to one mole of dioxygen led us to propose this system as a potential model for the hemocyanin active site, primarily from the standpoint of reactivity, but also within reasonable limits, structure (7b,c). In subsequent studies, several similar Schiff base copper(I) complexes (Figures 1B,D,E, and F) were synthesized to investigate further the electronic and structural parameters of the copper complexes, and their effects upon the dioxygen reaction and its reversal; in this study characterization of the oxygenated species was extended by electrochemical, solid-solution magnetic susceptibility measurements, and low-temperature resonance Raman spectroscopy studies (7e).

In the present paper, we present additional resonance Raman and mass spectrometry results for oxy-[Cu(imidH)$_2$DAP]$^{n+}$, as well as preliminary EXAFS structural results for the deoxy-[Cu^I(imidH)$_2$DAP]$^+$ and oxy-[Cu(imidH)$_2$DAP]$^{n+}$ species. Finally, the new Raman and EXAFS results are used, along with previous findings on all the copper(I) species in Figure 1, to propose and analyze various structural and electronic possibilities for the reversibly oxygenated and irreversibly oxidized products of these unusual copper(I) complexes.

Results and Discussion

Synthesis and Characterization of the Complexes

Although the field of nitrogen-ligated copper(I) complexes has expanded greatly in recent protein modelling studies, before the current surge of interest, little was known. Obviously, imidazole and imidazole-like ligands are prime candidates in this regard, and therefore our initial efforts were directed at exploring polyfunctional ligands containing imidazole moieties. Polyfunctional ligands were deemed desirable to help prevent disproportionation and to insure compound integrity in solution for labile copper(I). For convenience of synthesis, Schiff base chemistry was also employed, and the preparation of the [Cu^I(imidH)$_2$DAP]$^+$ cation from two mole equivalents of histamine (imidH) with one mole of 2,6-diacetylpyridine (DAP) and one mole of [Cu^I(CH$_3$CN)$_4$]$^+$, was among the first of our attempted syntheses (7a). Since then, we have also prepared the related copper(I) species shown in Figure 1, as well as their copper(II) and zinc(II) analogues (7e). Our early work used ClO$_4^-$ as the counter ion (7a,b) but two minor laboratory explosions convinced us to employ BF$_4^-$ salts instead. Furthermore, we now usually prepare the copper(I) analogues by electrochemical reduction of their copper(II) counterparts rather than by direct chemical synthesis. Elemental analysis, as well as solution conductivity measurements in various solvents are consistent with mononuclear complexes in all cases, including those of copper(I). The zinc(II) complexes all give ^{1}H nmr spectra in solution consistent with the proposed pentacoordinate molecular structures, as exemplified by the spectrum of the [Zn^{II}(py)(imidR)DAP]$^{2+}$ cation in Figure 2. Of all the copper(I) complexes, only [Cu^I(py)$_2$DAP]$^+$ is insensitive enough to dioxygen to yield a high quality ^{1}H nmr spectrum, and the spectrum is consistent with the pentacoordinate molecular structure proposed in Figure 1(7b), although rapid (faster than nmr time scale) fluxionality involving coordination numbers lower than five cannot be ruled out at this time. Of course, the same is also true of the zinc(II) complexes. Low-temperature ^{1}H nmr studies, presently in progress, are aimed at addressing the possibility of molecular fluxionality in solution for these molecules.

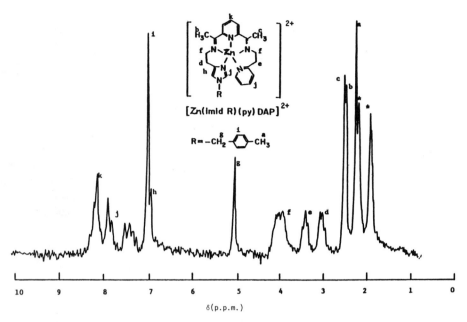

Figure 2. ^{1}H nmr Spectrum of [Zn^{II}(imidR)(py)DAP]$_2$ in CD$_3$CN Relative to SiMe$_4$. Reproduced by permission from reference 7e.

Although the copper(I) structures in Figure 1 imply that the ligands are pentadentate and fully coordinated, this has been established by X-ray crystallography for only the [Cu^{II}(imidH)$_2$DAP]$^{2+}$ and [Zn^{II}(imidH)$_2$DAP]$^{2+}$ cations (7d). Thus far, no copper(I) X-ray structures have become available due to small crystal size and handling problems of single crystals of the compounds in the required absence of dioxygen. However, preliminary EXAFS data are now available for [Cu^I(imidH)$_2$DAP]$^+$, as discussed below, so that structural data are finally beginning to emerge for these potentially pentadentate ligands with copper(I). Structural information of this nature for the copper(I) precursors is probably of key importance in understanding their reversible reaction with dioxygen, especially since copper(I) is generally thought to favor lower coordination numbers than copper(II). For example, the [(imidH)$_2$DAP] ligand in its free base form probably exists in the "cyclized" structure shown below (8); apparently copper(II) and zinc(II) are capable of stabilizing the uncyclized ligand by realizing its full pentacoordinate potential, but for copper(I) where five-coordination is relatively rare, other possible modes of coordination may occur. It is not clear whether the [(py)$_2$DAP] ligand of [Cu^I(py)$_2$DAP]$^+$ in Figure 1C is also capable of cyclizing in its free base form.

Reactivity with Dioxygen

In its stoichiometric reaction with one mole of dioxygen (1 atm. O$_2$;RT) in aceto-nitrile, two moles of red [Cu^I(imidH)$_2$DAP]$^+$ undergoes a change in its electronic spectrum over a 10-15 minute period as shown in Figure 3A. Then, upon immediate sparging of the solution with N$_2$, the absorbance at 512 nm, characteristic of the copper(I) species, may be recovered by *ca.* 85%. This oxygenation and deoxygenation cycling may be repeated several times with gradual loss due to a decomposition process which yields brown solutions and solids which have not been well characterized. However, it has been observed that this decomposition is retarded and that reversibility is enhanced somewhat by lower temperatures (*ca.* 250K). To one degree or another, all the other copper(I) complexes in Figure 1, save the [Cu^I(py)$_2$DAP]$^+$ cation, show similar reversibility patterns with dioxygen under ambient conditions in solution, with reversibility factors ranging over *ca.* 50-80%. Of course, none of the copper(II) or zinc(II) complexes shows any evidence of reaction with dioxygen in solution under similar conditions, and the parent copper(I) complex, [Cu^I(imidH)$_2$DAP]$^+$, displays no reactivity toward CO. Any hypothesis regarding the rate and reversibility of the oxygenation reaction of [Cu^I(imidH)$_2$DAP]$^+$ must be tempered by the observation that trace amounts of [Cu^I(CH$_3$CN)$_4$]$^+$ catalyze the reaction dramatically.

The [Cu^I(py)$_2$DAP]$^+$ complex is unique in that it is essentially unreactive toward dioxygen under ambient conditions, except in a very slow, irreversible reaction (over several hours) which shows greater than a two-to-one (Cu:O$_2$) stoichiometry.

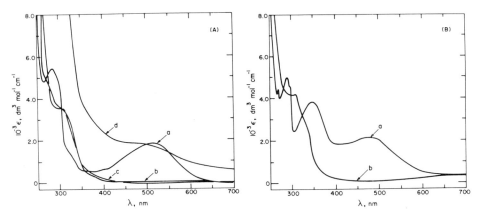

Figure 3. Electronic Absorption Spectra in CH$_3$CN of the Copper Complexes (10^{-4}M). (A) [Cu(imidH)$_2$-DAP]$^{n+}$ and (B) [Cu(py)$_2$DAP]$^{n+}$ as a) Deoxy-Cu^I, b) Cu^{II}, c) Oxy-Cu^I, and d) Redeoxy

The electronic absorption spectra of $[Cu^I(py)_2DAP]^+$ and $[Cu^{II}(py)_2DAP]^{2+}$ in solution are shown in Figure 3B for comparison with their $[Cu^{I,II}(imidH)_2DAP]^{+,2+}$ counterparts. The copper(II) complexes both display d-d absorption transitions at *ca.* 700 nm, but these bands are too weak ($\epsilon \sim 150$ dm^3 mol^{-1}cm^{-1}) to observe for the spectral conditions of Figure 3 (7b,e).

A red, solid sample of $[Cu^I(imidH)_2DAP]BF_4$ is relatively inert to dioxygen on the open bench, but it does become greenish in color under prolonged exposure. However, a homogeneous-appearing solid sample of green oxygenated $[Cu^I(imidH)_2DAP]^+$ can be obtained by quickly lyophilizing a freshly oxygenated solution, and this solid, if fresh, can be converted to a reddish-appearing solid by heating above 100°C *in vacuo*. This qualitative observation is of interest as background information to a mass spectrometry study of a thusly obtained oxygenated solid sample of $[Cu^I(imidH)_2DAP]ClO_4$. In the experiment, a freshly prepared oxygenated sample was placed in a mass spectrometry probe which was gradually heated, while continuously monitoring m/e=32 and m/e=16. Figure 4 shows plots of ion current at constant m/e = 32 vs. scan number and constant m/e = 16 vs. scan number (2 sec., 3°/scan). As seen from the m/e = 32 data, the ion current remains steady up until a surge occurs at about 195°C at scan number 65, whereas the m/e=16 data show an additional surge at scan number 35. The resulting solid sample, when removed from the probe, was found to be red, as is $[Cu^I(imidH)_2DAP]ClO_4$ before exposure to dioxygen. Since a solid sample of $[Zn^{II}(imidH)_2DAP]ClO_4$ showed no surge in ion current for m/e = 32, even up to scan number 100, this result can be

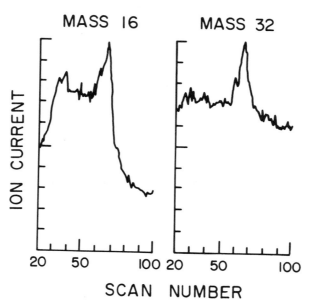

Figure 4. Mass Spectral Data for a Solid Sample of Oxy-[Cu(imidH)$_2$DAP]$^{n+}$ as the ClO$_4^-$ salt. Ion Current vs. Scan Number (2 sec., 3° C/scan) monitored at m/e=16 and m/e=32.

construed to indicate reversible dioxygen evolution (O_2^+) from the solid state material. The surge in ion current for m/e = 16 at scan number 65 (195°C) is consistent with O^+ production from O_2^+, and the scan number 35(95°) surge in ion current possibility arises from dehydration of the compound and the production of O^+ from water. A similar observation of possible O_2^+ release from a solid sample of oxygenated $[Cu^I(L\text{-bisp})]^+$, shown immediately below, has recently been reported by Casella and Ibers (9).

Electrochemistry

Cyclic voltammograms for $[Cu^{II}(py)_2DAP]^{2+}$ and $[Cu^{II}(imidH)_2DAP]^{2+}$ under argon are shown in Figure 5. For $[Cu^{II}(py)_2DAP]^{2+}$ in acetonitrile the Cu^{II}/Cu^I couple is reversible and occurs at −0.14 V vs. SCE with a peak-to-peak separation of 60 mV(Figure 5b), whereas the $[Cu^{II}(imidH)_2DAP]^{2+}$ cation reduces at a 150 mV more negative half-wave potential of −0.29 V. However, for $[Cu^{II}(imidH)_2DAP]^{2+}$, the reduction is only quasi-reversible, with the peak-to-peak separation strongly dependent on scan rate (Figure 5a). In these cyclic voltammograms, ferrocene has been employed as an internal standard for verification by its known half-wave potential (+0.40 V vs. SCE) and reversibility (59 mV). At this time, it is not known why the Cu^{II}/Cu^I couples for these two compounds differ so much in their electrochemical reversibilities, but they may correspond to fundamental structural differences between the complexes. Table I lists $E_{1/2}(Cu^{II}/Cu^I)$ and FWHM results from differential pulse polarography experiments for all the copper(II) compounds of Figure 1. As seen from the table, the $E_{1/2}$'s vary smoothly from −0.29 V for $[Cu^{II}(imidH)_2DAP]^{2+}$ to −0.14 v vs. SCE for $[Cu^{II}(py)_2DAP]^{2+}$. The fact that the mixed-ligand-arm species such as $[Cu^{II}(imidH)(imidR)DAP]^{2+}$, $[Cu^{II}(imidH)(py)DAP]^{2+}$, and $[Cu^{II}(imidR)-(py)DAP]^{2+}$, all exhibit distinct half-wave potentials demonstrates that they are, indeed, discrete species in solution and not mixtures of compounds.

All of the imidazole-containing copper(II) species in Figure 1 and Table I react, to some degree or another, in a reversible fashion with dioxygen under ambient conditions, whereas $[Cu^I(py)_2DAP]^+$ does not. Since only 10 mV separates the $E_{1/2}(Cu^{II}/Cu^I)$ potentials of $[Cu^{II}(py)_2DAP]^{2+}$ and $[Cu^{II}(imidR)(py)DAP]^{2+}$, the abrupt

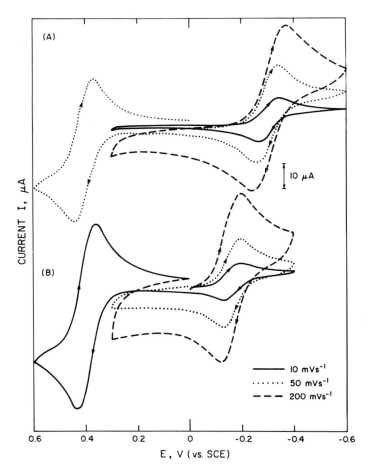

Figure 5. Cyclic Voltammograms of Cu^{II}/Cu^I Couples for the Copper(II) Complexes (10^{-4}M) in CH_3CN with TBABF$_4$ (0.1 M) at a Platinum-wire Working Electrode under Argon. (A) [Cu(imidH)$_2$DAP]$^{2+,+}$, and (B) [Cu(py)$_2$DAP]$^{2+,+}$, with Ferrocene (E$_{1/2}$ = +0.40 V vs. SCE) as an Internal Reference.

Table I

Half-wave Potentials as Determined by Differential Pulse Polaragraphy in CH_3CN[a]

Compound[b]	E$_{1/2}$(Cu^{II}/Cu^I)[c] (V vs. SCE)	FWHM(mV)
[Cu^{II}(imidH)$_2$DAP]$^{2+}$	−0.29	125
[Cu^{II}(imidH)(imidR)DAP]$^{2+}$	−0.26	108
[Cu^{II}(imidR)$_2$DAP]$^{2+}$	−0.25	140
[Cu^{II}(imidH)(py)DAP]$^{2+}$	−0.18	210
[Cu^{II}(imidR)(py)DAP]$^{2+}$	−0.15	150
[Cu^{II}(py)$_2$DAP]$^{2+}$	−0.14	105

[a]Scan rate = 1 mVs^{-1}; modulation amplitude = 50 mV; drop time = 0.5 sec.
[b]Copper(II) complexes as BF$_4$$^-$ salts at 10^{-3}M.
[c]Platinum wire working electrode; supporting electrolyte, TBABF$_4$, 10^{-1}M.

loss in dioxygen reversibility for $[Cu^I(py)_2DAP]^+$ is probably not adequately explained by the difference in the Cu^{II}/Cu^I redox potentials, although, in general, the more negative the potential, the greater the tendency for reversibility of the oxygenation reaction for the compounds in Table I. Perhaps more important in this regard is the absence or presence of an imidazole moiety. The electrochemical behavior of the *in situ* generated copper (I) complexes of Figure 1 in the presence of dioxygen has been discussed elsewhere and will not be reviewed here (7b,c,e).

Nature of the Copper(I)-Dioxygen Species in Solution

Structural information for $[Cu^I(imidH)_2DAP]^+$ and its oxygenated form in solution has recently been obtained by EXAFS experiments. In Figure 6A, copper K edge data for deoxy-$[Cu^I(imidH)_2DAP]^+$ and oxy-$[Cu(imidH)_2DAP]^{n+}$ are presented for comparison. Data for $[Cu^{II}(imidH)_2DAP]^{2+}$ are not shown in the figure for the purpose of clarity, since they are essentially an exact overlay of the oxy compound data. This result establishes for the first time that oxy-$[Cu(imidH)_2DAP]^{n+}$ contains copper in its 2+ oxidation state. For the FT data of Figure 6B, the most intense

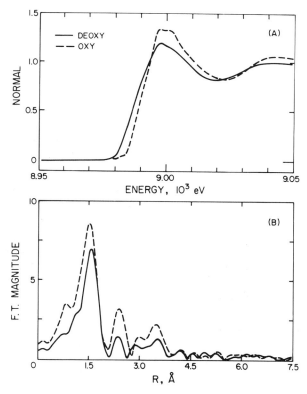

Figure 6. EXAFS Data for $[Cu(imidH)_2DAP]^{n+}$ in CH_3CN at $-30°$ C. (A) Copper K Edges of the Oxy(-------) vs the Deoxy (———) Forms. (B) Fourier Transforms of Oxy(-------) and Deoxy (———) Data. (k = 3.0-13.0 $Å^{-1}$, k^3 weighting)

first-shell peak for the oxy compound is more intense than for the deoxy copper(I) compound. In addition, all of the first shell distances are slightly shorter for the oxy species, which is consistent with copper(II) formation during oxygenation. The greater peak intensities for the oxy compound could be interpreted to correspond to an increase in coordination number during the oxygenation process or it might be explained simply by a decrease in the Debye-Waller factors for copper(II) when compared to copper(I). Thus, from these data there is no unambiguous evidence to support (or to refute) the notion that the coordination sphere for copper increases upon oxygenation of deoxy-$[Cu^I(imidH)_2DAP]^+$. For our previously stated "working model" of a μ-dioxygen or μ-peroxo bridging species for the oxy compound (7b,e), an expansion in the coordination number of each copper atom upon oxygenation is implicit, unless it is assumed that a ligand arm dissociates to maintain the same

"WORKING MODEL"

coordination number (O substituting for N) as in the deoxy compound. Furthermore, a μ-peroxo hypothesis is attractive since it is consistent with: 1) the 2:1 $(Cu:O_2)$ reaction stoichiometry, 2) a formal 2+oxidation state for copper, 3) our full temperature dependent magnetic susceptibility study which suggested an *anti*ferromagnetic exchange interaction of $-J \sim 70$ cm^{-1} between S$=\frac{1}{2}$ copper(II) centers and 4) the near epr silence of the oxy species at 100 K (7).

Short of an X-ray crystal structure of the oxy compound, one of the most direct confirmations of the μ-peroxo hypothesis would be identification of a $\nu_{(o-o)}$ stretching mode by Raman or resonance Raman (r.R.) spectroscopy. Figures 7A and B show resonance Raman data obtained for the parent $[Cu^I(imidH)_2DAP]^+$ compound in its deoxy, oxy($^{16}O_2$, $^{18}O_2$), and redeoxy forms, as well as one spectrum of the copper(II) complex. The actual band positions, intensities and experimental conditions, are presented in Tables II and III. Although no characterizable LMCT band corresponding to a copper(II)-O_2^{2-} chromophore is apparent in the visible or near uv region of the electronic spectrum of the oxy compound (Figure 2A), some resonance enhancement was achieved by irradiation at 5145 Å and 4579 Å where weak absorbances due to unassigned transitions occur. As seen from the data in Figure 7, the r.R. spectrum of deoxy-$[Cu^I(imidH)_2DAP]^+$ is clearly different from that of the oxy compound. Unfortunately, no Raman-active $\nu_{(o-o)}$ stretching frequency is obvious in the spectrum. In particular, the region of special interest for an O_2^{2-} (peroxide-like) stretching frequency would be ca. 700-800 cm^{-1} (10). However, this region of the spectrum for the oxy compound is featureless. When the green oxygenated solution is sparged

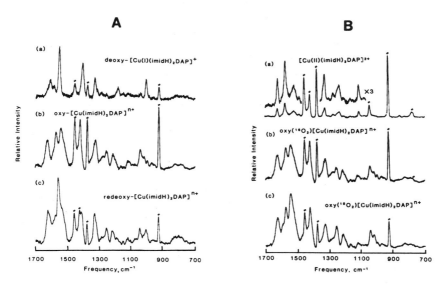

Figure 7. Resonance Raman Spectra Obtained at 77 K for 0.1 M Solutions in CH_3CN of (A) a) Deoxy-[Cu^I(imidH)$_2$DAP]$^+$ Using 514.5 nm Excitation, b) Oxy-[Cu(imidH)$_2$DAP]$^{n+}$ and c) Redeoxy-[Cu(imidH)$_2$DAP]$^{n+}$ Using 457.9 nm Excitation. (B) a) [Cu^{II}(imidH)$_2$DAP]$^{2+}$ Using 514.5 nm Excitation, b) $^{16}O_2$-Oxygenated [Cu(imidH)$_2$DAP]$^{n+}$ and c) $^{18}O_2$-Oxygenated [Cu(imidH)$_2$DAP]$^{n+}$ Using 457.9 nm Excitation. Solvent Bands are Marked #. Reproduced from reference 7e by permission.

with N_2, the red, redeoxy-[Cu^I(imidH)$_2$DAP]$^+$ solution is obtained, and the r.R. spectrum of a frozen aliquot of this sample contains vibrational bands for both oxy and deoxy-[Cu^I(imidH)$_2$DAP]$^+$. Thus, the r.R. data display the same partial reversibiltiy of the dioxygen reaction that was also noted in the electronic spectroscopy study of Figure 2. In addition to the reaction with $^{16}O_2$, deoxy-[Cu^I(imidH)$_2$DAP]$^+$ has been oxygenated with $^{18}O_2$ and its r.R. spectrum is shown in Figure 7B. Since the spectrum

Table II
Resonance-Raman Spectral Data[a,b] for the Deoxy, Oxy,
and Redeoxy Forms of [Cu(imidH)$_2$DAP]BF$_4$, 0.1 M in CH_3CN at 77 K

deoxy-[Cu(imidH)$_2$DAP]$^+$ (514.5 nm)[c]	1002m, 1038w, 1183m, 1330m, 1373w, 1409s, 1465m, 1557s, 1588m, 1613m
[$^{16}O_2$]oxy-[Cu(imidH)$_2$DAP]$^{n+}$ (457.9 nm)[c]	821w, 1013w, 1116w, 1163w, 1212m, 1254m, 1275m, 1321s, 1540s, 1573s, 1623s
redeoxy-[Cu(imidH)$_2$DAP]$^{n+}$ (457.9 nm)[c]	819w, 1002m, 1011m, 1068w, 1117m, 1148w, 1186w, 1215m, 1253m, 1284w, 1316(sh), 1329s, 1413s, 1538(sh), 1557s, 1610(sh), 1622s

[a] s = Strong, m = medium, w = weak, and (sh) = shoulder.
[b] Reproduced by permission from Reference 7e.
[c] Excitation wavelength.

Table III
Resonance-Raman Spectral Data[a,b] for [Cu(imidH)$_2$DAP]$^{2+}$ and the $^{16}O_2$-
and $^{18}O_2$-Oxygenated Forms of [Cu(imidH)$_2$DAP]$^+$ in CH$_3$CN at 77K

[Cu(imidH)$_2$DAP]$^{2+}$ (514.5 nm)[c]	822w, 853w, 1015m, 1110m, 1164w, 1202w, 1234m, 1274w, 1352s, 1336(sh), 1521s, 1577s, 1626s
[$^{16}O_2$]oxy-[Cu(imidH)$_2$DAP]$^{n+}$ (457.9 nm)[c]	821w, 1013w, 1039m, 1116w, 1163w, 1212m, 1254m 1275w, 1325s, 1422s, 1544s, 1573s, 1623s
[$^{18}O_2$]oxy-[Cu(imidH)$_2$DAP]$^{n+}$ (457.9 nm)[c]	822w, 1015m, 1039m, 1116w, 1164w, 1212m, 1253m, 1275w, 1325m, 1421s 1524s, 1575s, 1595(sh), 1626s

[a]s = Strong, m = medium, w = weak, and (sh) = shoulder.
[b]Reproduced by permission from Reference 7e.
[c]Excitation wavelength.

for the $^{16}O_2$ and $^{18}O_2$ oxy compounds are essentially identical, no isotope effect is revealed. Very recently, room temperature r.R. experiments performed on deoxy-[Cu^I(imidH)(imidR)DAP]$^+$, and its oxy ($^{16}O_2$, $^{18}O_2$), and redeoxy forms, also failed to detect a $\nu_{(o-o)}$ stretching frequency for this derivative (11). Here, however, it is important to note that the absence of an assignable $\nu_{(o-o)}$ stretch from these initial r.R. isotope studies does not necessarily mean that the oxy compounds do not contain Cu-O$_2$ or Cu-O$_2$-Cu units, since detection of an $\nu_{(o-o)}$ stretch can be very dependent on experimental and resonance conditions.

Alternatives to the simple μ-Peroxo Hypothesis

With the above EXAFS and r.R. experiments having fallen short of confirming our [Cu^{II}-O$_2{}^{2-}$-Cu^{II}] "working model" as the stable oxygenated species, other explanations for the reversible dioxygen reaction must also be considered. At least three explanations would seem to have some merit. First, the oxygenation process could involve some kind of imidazole-nitrogen "proton-involvement" scheme whereby [Cu^I(imidH)$_2$DAP]$^+$ could react with dioxygen to yield hydrogen peroxide as shown immediately below:

$$2[Cu^I(imidH)_2DAP]^+ + O_2 \rightleftarrows H_2O_2 + 2[Cu^{II}(imidH)(imid)DAP]^+$$

In such a scheme, proton abstraction occurs to give H$_2$O$_2$ and a mono-deprotonated oxidized copper(II) product. In fact, a similar deprotonation mechanism has recently been proposed for the reaction of dioxygen with tris(2,2-bi-2-imidazoline)iron(II) (12). The final [Cu(II)(imidH)(imid)DAP] product would need to be dimerized or polymerized to explain the observed reduction in epr intensity of the oxy product and the removal of dioxygen would than have to cause spontaneous reduction to [Cu^I(imidH)$_2$DAP]$^+$ to complete the reversible oxygenation cycle. The liklihood of this mechanism was explored by synthesizing N^1-para-xylyl substituted histamine, which was then incorporated into the copper(I) complex, $[Cu^I(imidR)_2DAP]^+$ shown in Figure 1D. The fact that this copper(I) complex also shows a reversible reaction with dioxygen diminishes the "proton involvement" mechanism as a viable possibility. The unsymmetrical species $[Cu^I(imidH)(py)DAP]^+$, $[Cu^I(imidR)(py)DAP]^+$, and $[Cu^I(imidR)(imidH)DAP]^+$, shown in Figure 1B,E, and F, respectively, were also prepared in the interest of obtaining compounds of intermediate dioxygen reactivity, and in pursuit of isolating a more stable and characterizeable product, since equilibria and decomposition hinder this characterization for the parent compound's oxygenated product.

A second possibility involves a reversible oxidation of the imidazole moieties of the copper(I) complexes. While imidazoles are quite difficult to oxidize, "drastic" oxidation of the methylbenzylimidazoles by concentrated potassium permanganate solution removes the benzene moiety of the compound with the formation of 4,5-imidazoledicarboxylic acid (13). Subsequent decarboxylation, with heating, yields the unsubstituted imidazole compound. A well-documented mechanism involving the oxidation of the imidazole ring structure (14-16), using dioxygen as the oxidant, might be invoked to explain the observed reactivity of these copper(I) complexes toward dioxygen. When in the presence of dyes, such as rose bengal or methylene blue, and visible light, $^3O_2$ is photosensitized to $^1O_2$, which then reacts with imidazoles to yield several photooxidized products, including an endoperoxide (14). While some substituted endoperoxides undergo a reverse Diels-Alder reaction at low temperature to regenerate a portion of $^1O_2$ and the starting material, the majority of substituted endoperoxides do not regenerate starting imidazoles but form a complex

mixture of products. Unsubstituted imidazole undergoes a very slow photooxidation (requiring about two weeks), and irradiation usually causes irreversible degradation of the heterocycle. In addition, the oxygenation of histidine requires greater than one mole of dioxygen per mole of substrate destroyed and yields several complicated products (15,16). This photooxidation procedure has also been employed to elucidate structure-function relationships in the hemocyanins. In the photochemical irradiation of *octopus vulgaris* hemocyanin (17,18), using various external photosensitizers, tryptophanyl and histidyl side chain residues are selectively photooxidized, forming endoperoxide-like intermediates; fluorescence emission spectra of the photooxidized protein indicate that in addition to histidine, a tryptophanyl residue may be located near the copper-dioxygen binding site in hemocyanin (17). To examine the possibility of endoperoxide formation (perhaps catalyzed by copper(I)) in the present oxygenation reaction, the oxygenation of the $[Cu^I(imidH)_2DAP]^+$, $[Cu^I(imidR)_2DAP]^+$, $[Cu^I(imidR)(imidH)DAP]^+$, and $[Cu^I(imidH)(py)DAP]^+$ species has been examined in the dark, but no noticeable difference in the red to green oxygenation cycle was observed. Thus, light has no apparent effect on the oxygenation reaction, and the imidazole photooxidation reaction mechanism seems, at best, a remote possibility.

Finally, Nelson and coworkers have proposed (19) an oxidative dehydrogenation mechanism for binuclear compounds in which the copper(I) centers are coordinated to secondary amines, as could be the case for the "cyclized" [(imidH)_2DAP] ligand structure discussed above. A scheme, similar to that proposed by Nelson is reproduced directly below. In the scheme, oxidation of the copper centers occurs during (reversible?) formation of a μ-peroxo species; this is followed by ligand oxidation to

imine bonds with the concomitant production of water, and finally, regeneration of the copper(I) centers in a dead-end mechanism. At present, we have no evidence supporting this or any other ligand oxidation mechanism, but identification of the brown-colored materials which are ultimately produced in the reactions of all of these copper(I) complexes with dioxygen should address this possibility; such studies are currently underway.

A Solid State Structure of the Copper(I)-Dioxygen Species?

The molecular structure of these reversibly formed copper(I)-dioxygen species is of central importance in all this chemistry, and our recent attempts to grow crystals of these oxygenated materials for a definitive X-ray structural study have been quite encouraging. The fact that these materials can be obtained and handled for reasonable periods of time under ambient conditions makes the quest for the single crystal an undeniably tantalizing goal.

Acknowledgements

The authors would like to thank the Robert A. Welch Foundation (D.M.S. and L.J.W.) and the National Institutes of Health (L.J.W. and R.A.S.) for support of this reseach. The XAS experiments were carried out at Stanford Synchrotron Radiation Laboratory (SSRL) which is supported by the Department of Energy, Office of Basic Energy Sciences and the NIH, Biotechnology Resource Program, Division of Research Resources.

References and Footnotes

1. See for example: R.S. Himmelwright, N.C. Eickman, C.D. LuBien, and E.I. Solomon, *J. Am. Chem. Soc., 102,* 5378 (1980); J.M. Brown, L. Powers, B. Kincaid, J.A. Larrabee, and T.G. Spiro, *ibid, 102,* 4210 (1980); G.L. Woolery, L. Powers, M. Winkler, E.I. Solomon, and T.G. Spiro, *ibid., 106,* 86 (1984).
2. K.D. Karlin, Y. Gultneh, R.W. Cruse, J.C. Hayes, and J. Zubieta, *J. Am. Chem. Soc., 106,* 3372, (1984).
3. T. N. Sorrell, D. L. James, and C. J. O'Conner, *Inorg. Chem., 23,* 190 (1984).
4. J. E. Bulkowski, P. L. Burk, M. Ludman, and J.A. Osborn, *J. Chem. Soc. Chem. Comm.,* 498 (1977); P.L. Burk, J.A. Osborn, M. Youinou, Y. Agnus, R. Louis, and R. Weiss, *J. Am. Chem. Soc., 103,* 1273 (1981).
5. Y. Nashida, K. Takahashi, H. Kuramoto, and S. Kida, *Inorg. Chim. Acta, 54,* 103 (1981).
6. J. S. Thompson, *J. Am. Chem. Soc., 106,* 4057 (1984).
7. a) M.G. Simmons and L.J. Wilson, *J. Chem. Soc. Chem. Comm.,* 634 (1978). b) M.G. Simmons, C. L. Merrill, L. J. Wilson, L. A. Bottomley, and K. M. Kadish, *J. Chem. Soc. Dalton,* 1827 (1980). c) L.J. Wilson, C.L. Merrill, M.G. Simmons, J.M. Trantham, L. A. Bottomley, and K. M. Kadish, *Invertebrate Oxygen Binding Proteins,* J. Lamy and J. Lamy, Ed., Marcel Dekker, Inc., New York, p. 571 (1981). d) J. D. Korp, I. Bernal, C. L. Merrill, and L. J. Wilson, *J. Chem. Soc. Dalton,* 1951 (1981). e) C. L. Merrill, T. J. Thamann, T. M. Loehr, N.S. Ferris, W. H. Woodruff, and L. J. Wilson, *J. Chem. Soc. Dalton,* 2207 (1984).
8. L. Casella and J. M. Gullotti, *J. Am. Chem. Soc., 103,* 6338 (1981).
9. L. Casella, M. E. Silver, and J. A. Ibers, *Inorg. Chem., 23,* 1409 (1984).
10. T. J. Thamman, J. S. Loehr, and T. M. Loehr, *J. Am. Chem. Soc., 99,* 4187 (1977).
11. Preliminary results from experiments performed in collaboration with Professor W. H. Woodruff, Department of Chemistry, University of Texas at Austin.
12. M. G. Burnett, V. McKee, and S. M. Nelson, *J. Chem. Soc. Chem. Comm.,* 599 (1980).
13. K. Hofmann, *Imidazole and Its Derivatives,* Interscience, New York, Ch. 8, p. 254 (1953).
14. H. H. Wassermann, K. Stiller, and M. B. Floyd, *Tet. Letters,* 3277 (1968).
15. T. Matsuura and I. Saito, *J. Chem. Soc. Chem. Comm.,* 693 (1967).
16. L. Weil, S. James, and A. R. Buchert, *Arch. Biochem. Biophys., 46,* 266 (1953).
17. G. Jori, B. Salrato, and L. Tallandini, *Structure and Function of Haemocyanins,* J. V. Bannister, Ed., Springer-Verlag, Berlin, p. 156 (1977).
18. M. Deley and R. Lontie, *ibid.,* p. 164.
19. S. M. Nelson, *Copper Coordination Chemistry: Biochemical and Inorganic Perspectives,* Karlin and Zubieta, Eds., Adenine Press, New York (1982).

Biological & Inorganic Copper Chemistry,
ISBN 0-940030-11-X, Eds., K. D. Karlin & J. Zubieta, Adenine Press, ©Adenine Press, 1985

Substrate Binding and Dioxygen Activation at Dicopper Sites

S. Martin Nelson, Jadwiga Trocha-Grimshaw,
Aidan Lavery, Kieran P. McKillop
Department of Chemistry,
Queen's University,
Belfast BT9 5AG, N. Ireland

Michael G.B. Drew
Department of Chemistry
The University, Reading RG6 2AD, U.K.

Introduction

The synthesis of di- and polynuclear complexes in which the ligand maintains the metal centres in close proximity is an important objective in transition metal chemistry. Interest in such systems arises in part because of their potential as multi-metal-centred catalysts in both biological and non-biological reactions, particularly those involving di- or multi-electron transfer. It is well established that the biological action of many metalloproteins is associated with the occurrence of the metal atoms in pairs or clusters. Prominent among these are copper proteins containing di-copper (Type 3) sites (1). These include the O_2-transport protein hemocyanin, and oxygenase and oxidase enzymes such as tyrosinase. Recent studies (1,2) on these two proteins and their derivatives have greatly advanced our knowledge of the active site chemistry and have allowed the identification of probable requirements in worthwhile model compounds for these and other Type 3 copper proteins. These requirements include

(i) a binucleating capability on the part of the synthetic ligand which permits a relatively close approach (3-4 Å) of the copper atoms. Retention of the integrity of the bimetallic unit in solution is an important associated requirement;

(ii) accessibility of both Cu(I) and Cu(II) oxidation states;

(iii) coordinative unsaturation in the di-Cu(I) state;

(iv) a coordination polyhedron for each metal ion which includes two (or three) nitrogen donors;

(v) the provision of a bridging group (cf. the endogenous bridge of the natural systems) which mediates antiferromagnetic coupling between the metal ions in the oxidised state and which accounts for the ESR silence of the native proteins.

In recent years a variety of binucleating ligands have been synthesised which form di-copper complexes which exhibit some or all of the features specified above (3-14). Among the synthetic di-copper complexes are those that show reversible O_2-binding activity (4,8) and others that display monoxygenase (9) and oxidase (7,13,14) activity. In this paper we review some recent investigations on the chemistry of di-copper complexes of macrocycles $L^1(R=H)$ and $L^2(R=Me)$. It will be shown that several of the complexes satisfy the requirements noted above and, additionally, function as catalysts for the oxidation of selected organic substrates.

Synthesis of the Macrocycles

For some years we have been engaged in the synthesis of binucleating macrocyclic ligands derived from the cyclic [2+2] condensation of dicarbonyl compounds (e.g. 2,6-diacetylpyridine, 2,5-diformylfuran) with a range of diprimary amines (15,16). Among the most interesting of these is the 20-membered macrocyle L^1 formed from 2,5-diformylfuran and 1,3-diaminopropane (17). As for most other macrocyclic Schiff base ligands of this class L^1 and L^2 are best synthesised by a template method which uses the large alkaline earth metal ions Ca^{2+}, Sr^{2+} or Ba^{2+}. In these cases the macrocylces are isolated as the 1:1 complexes (Ca, Sr and Ba) or as the 2:1 ligand:metal complex (Ba only). The structure of the cation $[Ba(L^1)_2(H_2O)_2]^{2+}$ has been determined (17). The Ba^{2+} ion is bonded to all six heteroatoms of one macrocycle but only to three of the second macrocycle, this being severely folded so that one furan di-imine moiety is uncoordinated. Two water molecules are also bonded to the Ba^{2+} ion giving an overall coordination number of eleven. The alkaline earth cation in all these complexes may be replaced by two Cu(I) or by two Cu(II) ions to give a series of di-copper complexes in good yield.

Di-copper(I) Complexes

Treatment of any of the alkaline earth complexes of L^1 (or L^2) with an excess of

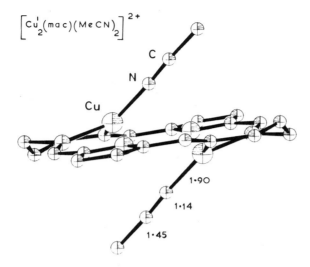

Figure 1. The structure of the cation $[Cu_2L^1(MeCN)_2]^{2+}$ showing the three-coordinate geometry of the Cu(I) ions.

$[Cu(MeCN)_4]ClO_4$ in MeOH:MeCN mixed solvent in the absence of O_2 afforded the yellow crystalline complex $[Cu_2L^1(MeCN)_2][ClO_4]_2$ *1*. In this complex (Figure 1) the two Cu(I) ions are three-coordinate with a distorted trigonal planar geometry, the two metal ions being displaced 0.23 Å, on opposite sides, from the N_3 planes. Cu−N bond lengths lie between 1.958 (18) and 1.919 (16) Å and the N−Cu−N angles between 101° and 103°. The Cu...Cu separation is 3.35 Å. The complex appears to bind carbon monoxide reversibly in MeCN solution as judged by the reversible orange ⇔ yellow colour changes and by CO-uptake measurements. A precise stoichiometry for the reaction has not yet been established but it appears that in the temperature range 0-21°C the di-Cu(I) complex is in equilibrium with the bis(CO) adduct, in which, presumably, the coordinative number of each metal ion has increased to four.

The MeCN molecules in $[Cu_2L^1(MeCN)_2]^{2+}$ can be readily replaced by other monodentate donors such as pyridine and triphenylphosphine. Treatment with halide or pseudohalide ion afforded the neutral complexes $[Cu_2L^1X_2]$ *2* (X = Cl, Br, I, SCN, SeCN). X-ray analysis of the thiocyanato complex has shown that the Cu(I) ions are four-coordinate, the two SCN^- ions linking the metal ions via the sulphur atom only (18). This is the first and only structurally defined example of a symmetrical sulphur-atom-only thiocyanate bridge. Its occurrence here can presumably be traced to the close proximity of the two metal ions (2.796 Å in this molecule) which precludes the formation of the conventional lengthways three-atom bridge.

The apparent difficulty in accommodating a linear three-atom bridge between the metal centres does not extend to non-linear three-atom bridges nor to two-atom bridges, however. Thus, reaction of $[Cu_2L^1(MeCN)]^{2+}$ with bis(diphenylphosphino)-

methane (dppm) afforded the complex $[Cu_2L^1(dppm)]^{2+}$ *3* shown from analytical and ^1H and ^{31}P NMR measurements to contain the bridging dppm molecule. Again, treatment with pyridazine afforded the complex $[Cu_2L^2(pyridazine)_2][ClO_4]_2$ *4* shown by X-ray analysis to contain two tetrahedral Cu(I) ions linked by bridging pyridazine molecules (Figure 2). It is noteworthy that in both the di-μ-thiocyanato and di-μ-pyridazine di-Cu(I) complexes the two bridges are symmetrically positioned on opposite sides of a roughly planar 'Cu₂(macrocycle)' moiety. The Cu...Cu separation in the di-μ-pyridazine complex *4* is, as expected, somewhat larger, at 3.15 Å, than in the thiocyanate.

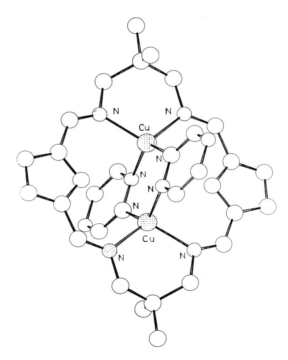

Figure 2. The structure of the cation $[Cu_2L^2(pyridazine)_2]^{2+}$ showing the approximate tetrahedral coordination of the Cu(I) ions.

Di-Cu(II) Complexes

When the transmetallation of the alkaline earth metal complexes of L^1 was carried out using $Cu^{II}(ClO_4)_2 \cdot 6H_2O$ instead of Cu(I) salts, the product was the complex $CuL^1(OH)_2(ClO_4)_2 \cdot H_2O$ *5*. Electronic spectra (ν_{max} 14,700 cm^{-1}) suggest a tetragonal coordination for the Cu(II) ions in this complex in which the two metal ions are bridged by two OH$^-$ groups (19). However, the detailed structure remains uncertain. The occurrence of antiferromagnetic interaction is evidenced by the reduced magnetic moment (1.37 μ_β per Cu ion at 293K) and its further reduction on cooling

(0.70 μ_β at 90K) but the temperature dependence does not conform well to that required for coupled pairs of S = ½ spins (20). It may be that there are additional intermolecular interactions between metal ions of adjacent macrocyclic units. Some support for intermolecular aggregation in this complex is provided by the results obtained when the ClO_4^- counter ions are replaced by the bulkier BPh_4^- ions. Thus, the complexes $[Cu_2L^1(OR)_2(MeCN)_2][BPh_4]_2$ *6*, and also $[Cu_2L^1(OR)_2(NCS)_2]$ *7*, (R = Me, Et, ^nPr) have ligand field spectra (ν_{max} 14,000, 9350 cm^{-1}) suggestive of a trigonal bipyramidal coordination and magnetic properties which do conform to the theoretical equation (20) expected for interacting pairs of Cu(II) ions, with the singlet-triplet separation 2J in the range -600 to -700 cm^{-1}. Confirmation of the presence of two trigonal bipyramidal Cu(II) ions bridged by two alkoxo groups was obtained by the structure determination (19) of one member of the series, $[Cu_2L^1(OEt)_2(NCS)_2]$. In this structure, shown in Figure 3, the two metal ions are displaced by 0.57 Å on opposite sides of the macrocycle so that each bridging ethoxide occupies an axial site in the coordination sphere of one metal ion and an equatorial site of the other. The NCS$^-$ ions are terminally bound, via the nitrogen atom, one to each Cu(II) ion. In this complex the two Cu(II) ions are 3.003 Å apart (19). It should be noted that in none of the copper complexes of L^1 or L^2 are the furan oxygen atoms coordinated though they are (Ba-O, 2.86 Å) in the complex $[Ba(L^1)_2(H_2O)_2][Co(NCS)_4]$ and, presumably, other complexes with alkaline earth metal ions (17).

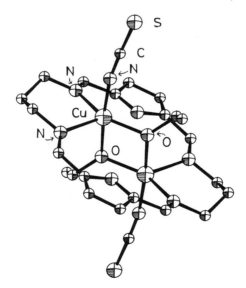

Figure 3. The structure of $[Cu_2L^1(OEt)_2(NCS)_2]$

It has been noted that the di-Cu(1) site in macrocycle L^1 can accommodate both single atom and two-atom (and even non-linear three-atom) bridging units with relatively minor adjustments in the metal-metal separation. The preference of the di-Cu(1) site for one-atom or two-atom bridge is relevant to the question of the mode of coordination of dioxygen since both μ-1,1-$[O_2]^{2-}$ and μ-1,2-$[O_2]^{2-}$ structures *8* and *9* can be envisaged.

$$O^{2-}$$
$$|$$
$$O$$
$$Cu^{II} \qquad Cu^{II}$$
$$8$$

$$O —— O^{2-}$$
$$Cu^{II} \qquad\qquad Cu^{II}$$
$$9$$

The symmetrical two-atom bridging peroxide structure (*9*) in the one generally assumed to occur in μ-peroxo complexes. It is well established, for example, in μ-peroxo-di-cobalt(III) complexes (21) and, as judged by optical and CD spectra (2), is the favoured structure for oxyhemocyanin in which the Cu...Cu separation is ~ 3.6 A (22). The significantly smaller Cu...Cu distances in the di-copper complexes of L^1 may render the μ-1,1-$[O_2]^{2-}$ structure *8* the preferred one in these cases, however. In order to probe the ability of the di-copper site in the oxidised $[Cu(II)_2]$ form to accommodate a two-atom bridge complex *5* was treated with pyrazole. The complex $[Cu_2L^1(pz)_2][ClO_4]_2$ *10* (pz = pyrazolate anion) was obtained. Initial indications derived from analytical data and IR spectra that this complex contains two bridging pyrazolate anions were reinforced by magnetic susceptibility and ESR data. Variable temperature magnetic susceptibility results established that the two Cu(II) ions are fairly strongly coupled with $2J = -290$ cm^{-1}. ESR spectra also revealed a half-band $\Delta M = 2$ transition at g ~ 4.4 in addition to the main band $\Delta M = 1$ signal at g ~ 2.2. A single crystal X-ray analysis (23) confirmed the presence of the bridging pyrazolate anions and further showed that, in contrast to the situation found for the di-Cu(1) complexes *2* and *4*, the bridges are disposed on the same side of the macrocycle, this being folded into a saddle-shaped conformation (Figure 4).

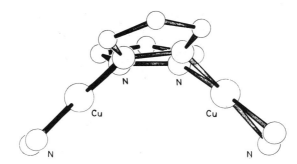

Figure 4. The structure of the di-μ-pyrozolyl di-Cu(II) bridging unit in $[Cu_2L^1(pz)_2]^{2+}$

This arrangement allows the two Cu(II) ions to achieve a nearly perfect square planar arrangement each being bonded to two macrocycle nitrogens (average Cu−N, 2.023 Å) and two pyrazolate nitrogens (average Cu−N, 1.949 Å). The two square planes intersect at an angle of 85.2°. The smallness of this angle means that despite the two-atom bridges the Cu...Cu separation is still only 3.39 Å.

Reduction of the Di-Cu(II) to Di-Cu(I) Complexes

It was found that the di-Cu(II) complexes *5*, *6* and *7* containing hydroxo or alkoxo bridges undergo reduction to di-Cu(I) complexes simply by heating their solutions in MeCN or MeCN/ROH mixed solvent. For complexes *5* and *6* the product is the complex *1* while for complex *7* the product is the di-μ-thiocyanate *2*. Experiments conducted on the complexes of type (*6*) in the solid state established that the $[Cu(II)]_2$ to $[Cu(I)]_2$ reduction is accompanied by oxidation of the OR^- groups. Thus, mass spectral and IR analysis of the evolved vapours revealed the presence of the corresponding alcohol and aldehyde consistent with a

$$2RCH_2O^- \Rightarrow 2RCH_2O\cdot \Rightarrow RCH_2OH + RCHO$$

Cu(II)-mediated oxidation of the bridging ligands to alkoxide radicals followed by disproportionation (16).

The ease of the $[Cu(II)_2]$ to $[Cu(I)_2]$ reduction can be traced to geometrical factors. Molecular models together with consideration of the structures of complexes *1*, *2*, *4*, *7* and *10* show that when the 'Cu$_2$L'' moiety is in its prefered planar conformation there is a very severe degree of steric hindrance between the bridging groups and the uncoordinated furan oxygens if the coordination about each metal is 'square'. This steric interaction can be relieved most effectively if the metal ions adopt a tetrahedral geometry with one bridging ligand positioned above the macrocycle plane and the other below, as, in fact, was found in the di-Cu(I) complexes *2* and *4*. However, a tetrahedral coordination is not acceptable for Cu(II) which much prefers a square based or trigonal bipyramidal coordination and these can be achieved only at the expense of macrocycle bond angle strain. Thus, in the di-μ-pyrazolyl complex *10* each Cu(II) achieves a square planar coordination by severe macrocycle folding while in the di-μ-alkoxo complexes *6* and *7* the macrocycle is forced into a non-planar stepped conformation in order that the metal ions acquire the trigonal bipyramidal arrangement. Thus, it is apparent that the most strain-free structures are those in which the bridged metal atoms each have a tetrahedral geometry within the cavity of a roughly planar macrocycle.

Substrate Oxidation

The observation of hydroxide and alkoxide bridging ligand oxidation which accompanies the $[Cu(II)_2]$ to $[Cu(I)_2]$ reduction suggested that if the reduction were carried out in the presence of an oxidisable substrate then the substrate might become oxidised in preference to the bridging ligand. This proved to be the case for a range of substrates containing labile hydrogen. Thus, for example, H_2O_2 may be oxidised to O_2, thiols to disulphides, catechols to *o*-quinones, hydroquinone to *p*-quinone, ascorbic acid to dehydroascorbic acid, benzoin to benzil, hydrazobenzene to azobenzene, phenylacetylene to diphenyl-diacetylene, and 2,6-di-tert-butylphenol to the coupled para, para dimer. When carried out in dimethylformamide (DMF) or dimethylacetamide (DMA) in the presence of O_2 several of the oxidations proved to be catalytic in the di-Cu(I) complex *1* or the di-Cu(II) complexes *5* and *6* with, as shown by O_2-uptake measurements, a O_2/substrate (2HX or H_2X_2) stoichiometry of 0.5 (19). Figure 5 shows typical results for the catalytic oxidation of 3,5-di-tert-butylcatechol. Significantly, complexes *2* and *7* are inactive as catalysts, reflecting

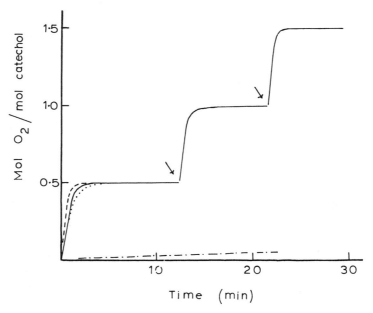

Figure 5. Uptake of O_2 (1 atm initial pressure) by solutions of 3,5-di-tert-butylcatechol) in dimethylformamide (7×10^{-3}M) containing different copper complexes (3.5×10^{-4}M) at 30°C: $Cu_2L^1(OH)$-$(ClO_4)_2 \cdot H_2O$ (——); $[Cu_2L^1(OEt)_2(MeCN)_2]$ $[BPh_4]_2$ (-------); $[Cu_2L^1(MeCN)_2]$ $[BPh_4]_2$ (·······); $Cu(ClO_4)_2 \cdot 6H_2O$ (7×10^{-4}M) (-·-·-·-). The arrows denote fresh additions of catechol.

the need for coordinative unsaturation in the reduced state. It is also significant that (mononuclear) $Cu(ClO_4)_2 \cdot 6H_2O$ showed very poor catalytic activity (see Figure 5) reflecting the importance of a 'built-in' dicopper site. A possible mechanism for the catalytic cycle for the oxidation of a catechol to o-quinone is outlined in Figure 6. This Scheme involves the participation of both the di-Cu(I) and di-Cu(II) species in the catalytic cycle. It also emphasises the role of the di-copper site in the binding of dioxygen (assumed in this diagram to be bound in the μ-1,2-peroxo mode) and in providing a pathway for the dielectronic reduction to peroxide thereby by-passing the energetically unfavourable formation of superoxide. The Scheme also implies a steric match between the two functional groups of the substrate catechol and the dimetallic active site although there is no independent evidence that this is the

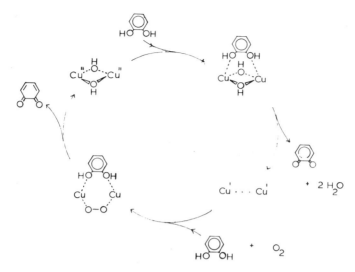

Figure 6. Possible mechanism for the catalytic oxidation of catechol by the di-copper complexes.

case. Indeed, the occurrence of a steric match is unlikely to be an important factor since other substrates such as hydroquinone, incapable of providing a steric match, are also catalytically oxidised at comparable rates.

An interesting reaction is the oxidation of acetonitrile to 3,5-dimethyl-1,2,4-triazole. This occurred when $[Cu_2L^2(MeCN)_2][ClO_4]_2$ was heated in MeCN/EtOH solvent mixture containing a little water in the presence of air yielding red crystals of the new complex $[Cu_5(L^2)_2(TAZ)_2][ClO_4]_3$·EtOH *11* (TAZ = the anion of 3,5-dimethyl-1,2,4-triazole) in ~ 60% yield. The structure of *11*, shown in Figure 7, was determined by X-ray diffraction (24). The cation comprises five Cu(1) atoms, two molecules of macrocycle and two triazole anions. Four of the Cu(I) atoms have a three-coordinate (distorted trigonal planar) geometry while the central Cu(I) atom, positioned at a centre of symmetry, is two-coordinate with a linear arrangement. This central Cu atom is linked to the two pairs of three-coordinate Cu atoms by the two co-planar bridging triazolyl anions. The macrocycle molecules have a non-planar, saddle-shaped conformation. This is reflected in the ^{1}H NMR spectrum (Figure 7) which shows the inequivalence of the CH_3 groups in each saturated segment of the macro-cycle (at δ 0.8 and δ 1.15) and also in the two protons of the adjacent methylene groups (at δ 3.5 and δ 4.4). The Cu...Cu distance within each 'Cu$_2$L^2' moiety is 3.34 Å. The complex may also be prepared by the 'spontaneous self-assembly' method in the absence of air and water starting from two equivalents of pre-prepared 3,5-dimethyl-1,2,4-triazole together two equivalents of *1* and one equivalent of $[Cu(MeCN)_4]ClO_4$. An analogous heterometallic complex $[AgCu_4(L^2)_2(TAZ)_2][ClO_4]_3$ containing Ag(I) as the central metal atom in place of Cu(I) has been synthesised by a similar method.

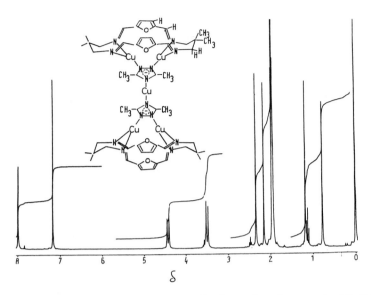

Figure 7. The structure and ^{1}H NMR spectrum in CD$_3$CN of the polynuclear complex [Cu$_5$(L^1)$_2$(TAZ)$_2$]$^{3+}$ cation.

A possible mechanism for the formation of the triazole from acetonitrile is indicated in Figure 8. In this scheme the first step is an aerobic oxidation of the di-Cu(I)

POSSIBLE   MECHANISM   FOR   ACETONITRILE   OXIDATION

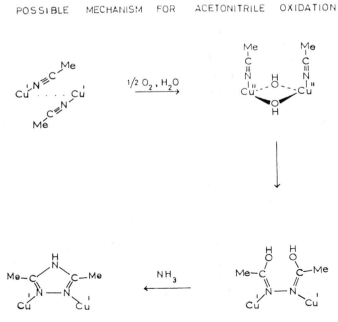

Figure 8. Possible mechanism for the copper-mediated hydrolysis/oxidation of acetonitrile to 3,5-dimethyl-1,2,4-triazole.

complex to the di-Cu(II) species. Nucleophilic attack, either intramolecular by the bridging OH$^-$ groups or intermolecular by H$_2$O, at the nitrile carbon atoms with concomitant nitrile-to-Cu(II) electron transfer and subsequent coupling of the adjacent radicals so formed could lead to the bridging diazo alcohol. The NH$_3$ needed for the final ring closure step could be generated separately in a metal-promoted hydrolysis of acetonitrile.

Reaction of the Di-Cu(I) Complex [Cu$_2$L^1(MeCN)$_2$]$^{2+}$ with Dioxygen in the absence of Substrate

It is implicit in the mechanism outlined in Figure 6 for the catalytic oxidation of catechol to *o*-quinone that if the oxidation were carried out under non-catalytic conditions, where substrate and di-Cu(I) complex are present in equivalent amounts, that one mol O$_2$ would be consumed for every mol [Cu(I)$_2$], rather than 0.5 mol O$_2$. This was observed. It might also be argued that the [Cu(I)$_2$] complex would consume one mol O$_2$ in the absence of substrate, as found for hemocyanin and tyrosinase (1,2) and certain synthetic systems (7,8,12), to generate a di-μ-peroxo-di-Cu(II) species. In fact, it was found (19) that complex *1* consumed only 0.5 mol O$_2$ per di-copper unit indicating that each O$_2$ molecule is associated in its reduction with four copper atoms rather than two i.e. that O$_2$ becomes fully reduced in an overall four-electron transfer to water. Such a situation could occur if the initial coordination of O$_2$ by *1*, generating the two-electron reduction product peroxide *12*, is followed by a fast bimolecular two-electron transfer with a second molecule of *1* to generate the μ-oxo species *13*, this possibly having a dimeric structure. Aggregate structures containing oxo-bridged

$$Cu^I...Cu^I + O_2 \rightleftharpoons Cu^{II} - (O_2)^{2-} - Cu^{II}$$
$$\qquad\quad 1 \qquad\qquad\qquad\qquad 12$$

$$Cu^{II} - (O_2)^{2-} - Cu^{II} + Cu^I...Cu^I \Rightarrow [Cu^{II} - O - Cu^{II}]_2$$
$$\qquad 12 \qquad\qquad\qquad 1 \qquad\qquad\qquad 13$$

Cu(II) ions are well established (25). Moreover, aggregate structures in copper complexes of macrocycle L^1 have already been shown to occur. Complex *11* has been referred to above. Another example is the tetranuclear cation [Cu$_4$(L^1)$_2$(C$\equiv$CPh)]$^{3+}$ (26). A particularly relevant example is the hexanuclear Cu(I) complex [Cu$_6$(L^1)$_3$-(SPh)$_2$]$^{4+}$ isolated as a by-product of the catalytic oxidation of PhSH to PhSSPh (19). As shown in Figure 9 this complex contains six three-coordinate Cu(I) ions linked via two thiolate groups each tetrahedrally bound to three Cu atoms and one phenyl carbon atom (23). These examples clearly demonstrate the ability of 'Cu$_2$L^1' units to associate through the agency of small coordinatively unsaturated bridging atoms or groups and thereby to provide a ready mechanism for electron transfer reactions.

An even more direct demonstration of molecular association of dinuclear 'Cu$_2$L^1' units involving μ-oxo bridges has been achieved by spectrophotometric monitoring

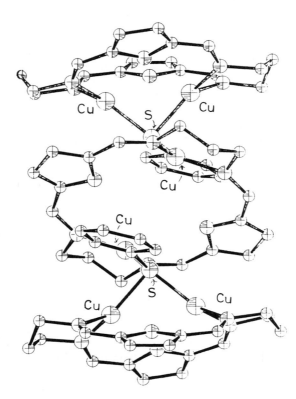

Figure 9. The structure of the hexanuclear cation]$Cu_6(L^1)_3(SPh)_2$]$^{4+}$.

of the reaction of the di-Cu(I) complex *1* with O_2 in DMA. Orange solutions of *1* on exposure to O_2 first become intensely brown in colour before finally becoming green suggesting the formation of an intermediate (27). Electronic spectra in the visible and near IR regions of the reactant complex *1*, the intermediate and the final oxidation product (believed to be the μ-oxo species *13*) are compared in Figure 10. It can be seen that the intermediate absorbs strongly at 11,600 cm^{-1}. By titration of the intensity of this absorption band as a function of the quantity of O_2 added it was established that the concentration of the intermediate is optimised when 0.25 mol O_2 per di-Cu(I) complex is comsumed i.e. the stoichiometry of the intermediate is 'Cu_4O'. It follows that 'Cu_4O' must have a mixed valence '$2Cu^I, 2Cu^{II}$' formalism. This is also evident in the consumption by 'Cu_4O' of a further 0.25 mol O_2. These conclusions were further confirmed in separate experiments which showed that the intermediate could also be generated at optimum concentration by mixing equimolar quantities of complexes *1* and *13* in solution. These experiments also revealed that the apparent molar extinction coefficient at 11,600 cm^{-1} of the mixed valence species is concentration dependent i.e. that it exists in equilibrium with its dissociation products *1* and *13* (Figure 11). On the basis of the relatively high intensity and low energy of the 11,600 cm^{-1} absorption it seems likely that it is due to an intervalence charge transfer transition. ESR spectra are complex and not yet fully understood

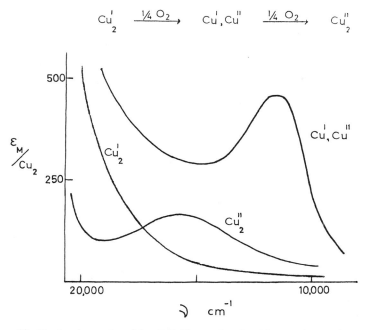

Figure 10. Electronic spectra of the di-Cu(I) complex *1* and its reaction products with O_2.

but preliminary experiments in which the integrated intensity of the ESR signal was monitored as a function of the amount of O_2 consumed by the di-Cu(I) complex *1* showed the signal to pass through a maximum intensity at 0.25 mol O_2 per mol Cu(I)$_2$. While the meaning of these results is not yet fully clear it seems that the fully oxidised product *13* may be strongly antiferromagnetically coupled.

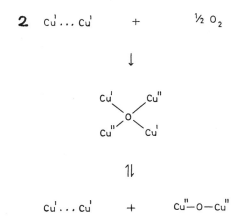

Figure 11. Formation of the mixed valence species [Cu$_4$O]$^{4+}$ via oxidation of [Cu(I)$_2$] and via association of [Cu(I)$_2$] with [Cu(II)$_2$O]$^{2+}$.

In conclusion, our results to date suggest that the di-Cu(I) complexes promote the four-electron reduction of O_2 passing through the μ-peroxo-di-Cu(II) (two-electron reduction) stage. In the presence of oxidisable substrate reduction beyond the peroxo stage is achieved via substrate dehydrogenation. In the absence of substrate it occurs via association with a second unit of di-Cu(I). No substrate hydroxylation or other form of direct oxygen insertion has yet been unequivocably established for these systems. It may be that for this to occur it is first necessary to prevent the $[Cu^{II}(O_2)Cu^{II}] + [Cu^{I}_2]$ association.

References and Footnotes

1. E.I. Solomon in *Copper Proteins*, Ed., T.G. Spiro, Wiley-Interscience, New York, (1981).
2. E.I. Solomon in *Copper Coordination Chemistry: Biochemical and Inorganic Perspectives*, Ed. K.D. Karlin and J. Zubieta, Adenine Press, New York, p. 1 (1983).
3. See, for example, several chapters of Ref. 2 and references cited therein.
4. J.E. Bulkowski, P.L. Burk, M.-F. Ludman and J.A. Osborn, *J. Chem. Soc., Chem. Comm.*, 498 (1977).
5. P.L. Burk, J.A. Osborn, M.-T. Youinou, Y. Agnus, R. Louis and R. Weiss, *J. Am. Chem. Soc., 99,* 4111 (1977).
6. R.R. Gagne, J.L. Allison, R.S. Gall and C.A. Koval, *J. Am. Chem. Soc., 99,* 7170 (1977).
7. M.G. Burnett, V. McKee and S.M. Nelson, *J. Chem. Soc., Chem. Comm.*, 829 (1980).
8. M.G. Simmons, C.L. Merrill, L.J. Wilson, L.A. Bottomley and K.M. Kadish, *J. Chem. Soc., Dalton Trans.*, 1827 (1980).
9. K.D. Karlin, P.L. Dahlstrom, S.N. Cozette, P.M. Scensny and J. Zubieta, *J. Chem. Soc., Chem. Comm.*, 881 (1981).
10. V. McKee, J.V. Dagdigian, R. Bau and C.A. Reed, *J. Am. Chem. Soc., 103,* 7000 (1981).
11. T.N. Sorrell, M.R. Malachowski and D.L. Jameson, *Inorg. Chem., 21,* 3252 (1982).
12. H.M. Hendriks, P.J.M.W.L. Birker, J. van Rihn, G.C. Verschoor and J. Reedijk, *J. Am. Chem. Soc., 104,* 3607 (1982).
13. Y. Nishida, N. Oishi, H. Kuramoto and S. Kida, *Inorg. Chim. Acta, 57,* 253 (1982).
14. K. Moore and G.S. Vigee, *Inorg. Chim. Acta, 66,* 125 (1982).
15. S.M. Nelson, *Pure Appl. Chem., 52,* 2461 (1980).
16. S.M. Nelson, p. 331 of Ref. 2.
17. M.G.B. Drew, F.S. Esho and S.M. Nelson, *J. Chem. Soc., Dalton Trans.*, 1653 (1983).
18. S.M. Nelson, F.S. Esho and M.G.B. Drew, *J. Chem. Soc., Chem. Comm.*, 388 (1981).
19. S.M. Nelson, F.S. Esho, A. Lavery and M.G.B. Drew, *J. Am. Chem. Soc., 105,* 5693 (1983).
20. B. Bleaney and K.D. Bowers, *Proc. Roy. Soc., Ser. A (London) 214,* 451 (1952).
21. J.R. Fritch, G.G. Christoph and W.P. Schaefer, *Inorg. Chem., 12,* 2170 (1973).
22. J.M. Brown, L. Powers, B. Kincaid, J.A. Larrahee and T.G. Spiro, *J. Am. Chem. Soc., 102,* 4210 (1980); M.S. Co and K.O. Hodgson, *J. Am. Chem. Soc., 103,* 3200 (1981).
23. M.G.B. Drew, unpublished results.
24. M.G.B. Drew, P. Yates, J. Trocha-Grimshaw, K.P. McKillop and S.M. Nelson, *J. Chem. Soc., Chem. Comm.*, 262 (1985).
25. G. Davies, M.F. El-Shazly, M.W. Rupick, M.R. Churchill and F.J. Rotella, *J. Chem. Soc., Chem. Comm.*, 1045 (1978); G. Davies, A. El-Toukhy, K.D. Onan and M. Veidis, *Inorg. Chim. Acta, 84,* 41 (1984).
26. M.G.B. Drew, F.S. Esho and S.M. Nelson, *J. Chem. Soc., Chem. Comm.*, 1347 (1982).
27. This is not a true intermediate in that it is not formed 'en route' from complex *1* to complex *13*. Rather, it is the reversible product of association of product *13* with unreacted *1* (see following text).

Biological & Inorganic Copper Chemistry,
ISBN 0-940030-11-X, Eds., K. D. Karlin & J. Zubieta, Adenine Press, ©Adenine Press, 1985

Binuclear Copper Complexes: Synthetic Models for the Active Site of Type III Copper Proteins

Thomas N. Sorrell
Department of Chemistry
The University of North Carolina at Chapel Hill
Chapel Hill, NC 27514

Abstract

We have prepared two ligands that approximate the copper-binding site in hemocyanin, a binuclear copper protein that functions as an oxygen carrier in many marine organisms. Both ligands provide one μ-phenolate and three nitrogen donors to each metal. For the copper(II) derivatives, one of those ligands (N_6O) holds the coppers ~3.1 Å apart and allows them to be spanned by an additional one-atom bridge such as OH. The other (bpeac) forces the coppers farther apart (> 3.5 Å) and requires a bridge having more than a single atom. The reduced [Cu(I)/Cu(I)] form of the N_6O ligand has not been prepared because of its propensity for disproportionation; however, $Cu_2(bpeac)^+$ is readily isolated and reacts with dioxygen to form what is most likely an oligomeric μ-oxo species. These results imply that isolation of the O_2-binding site may be necessary in order for the protein to function. The synthesis of a sterically hindered analog of $Cu_2(bpeac)^+$ has been prepared, and reaction with O_2 gives a different product which may be a dioxygen adduct.

Introduction

Hemocyanin (Hc) (1) is a copper-containing protein which functions to transport dioxygen in many species of arthropods and molluscs. Spectroscopic (2-5) and, more recently, crystallographic (6) characterization of its active site has been extensive, leading to the proposed active site structures illustrated in equation 1.

$$X = N,\ H_2O \qquad (1)$$

41

The salient features can be summarized as follows: 1) the deoxy [Cu(I)/Cu(I)] form of the protein is either two- or three-coordinate bound most likely by histidyl-imidazole groups; 2) reaction of the deoxy form with O_2 gives the oxy derivative (HcO$_2$) which contains two formally Cu(II) centers separated by 3.6 Å; 3) the oxygen molecule bridges the coppers in a 1,2-fashion, is bound as peroxide, and gives rise to intense LMCT bands in the absorption spectrum; and 4) a bridging ligand, endogenous to the protein, provides for strong antiferromagnetic coupling between the coppers in the oxidized form, and HcO$_2$ is diamagnetic.

Attempts to structurally model any of the derivatives of hemocyanin have been limited, mainly due to a lack of chelating ligands that can provide the appropriate donors. A tyrosinyl phenolate has been proposed as the endogenous bridge in Hc (4,5), but an alkoxide from serine or threonine cannot be ruled out (7). In fact, one of the best models for a hemocyanin derivative is one in which the copper ions are bridged by an alkoxide ion (7).

Our strategy for mimicking the structural aspects of the hemocyanin active site has been straightforward. First we undertook the preparation of binucleating ligands that would provide two or three nitrogen donors each to two copper ions. In addition the ligand had to incorporate a phenolate group positioned to bridge the metals. As a second consideration, we initially chose to concentrate on modelling the oxidized derivatives of the protein, the so-called "met" forms, because of the relatively greater knowledge about the structural and spectroscopic properties of copper(II) compared to copper(I). We further focussed our study of copper(II) complexes to the azide derivative for three reasons: 1) metHc-azide is diamagnetic, like HcO$_2$; 2) the coppers are separated by about the same distance in the two derivatives (3.6-3.7 Å); and 3) azide, like peroxide, gives rise to discernible LMCT bands in the UV/visible region.

Binuclear Copper (II) Complexes

The first binucleating ligand and its copper(II) complex were relatively simple (8). While several μ-phenolato copper complexes had been prepared previously (9-13), none met all of the structural criteria for the Hc active site that had been es-tablished by the spectroscopic studies. The most prominent shortcoming was that the copper ions were four-coordinate since the ligands had been made by Schiff-base condensations and could only incorporate a single "side-arm" donor. The scheme used to prepare our first system is illustrated in equation 2.

(2)

The resulting copper(II) complex of the ligand N_6O crystallized as the μ-hydroxy derivative, an extremely stable species (*1a*). Its structure, shown in Figure 1, is interesting because the coppers adopt different coordination geometries, a feature we have seen in other subsequently isolated complexes (vide infra). The geometry about Cu2 is square-pyramidal, but that for Cu1 is more trigonal bipyramidal. This may account for the striking difference in the Cu-O(phenolate) distances: Cu2-O2 [1.927(8) Å] is significantly shorter than Cu1-O2 [2.002(8) Å].

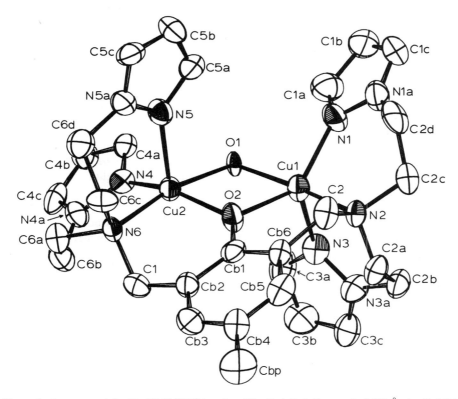

Figure 1. Structure of the $Cu_2(N_6O)(OH)^{2+}$ cation. The Cu1-Cu2 distance is 3.053 Å, the Cu1-O1-Cu2 angle is 103.6°, and the Cu1-O2-Cu2 angle is 101.9°. Other distances and angles are given in ref. 8.

The magnetic susceptibility of *1a* shows that the coppers are strongly antiferromagnetically coupled. The triplet state lies 420 cm^{-1} above the ground singlet state, in reasonable agreement with the data collected by Hodgson and Hatfield on bis (μ-hydroxy) copper(II) dimers (14). Whether each copper is tetragonal or not, the major exchange pathway should be the hydroxide bridge since that angle is larger; therefore the orbital overlap should be greater. This is not to say that the phenolate does not influence the antiferromagnetic coupling, however.

Recalling our strategy to examine azide derivatives of any model systems, we synthesized $Cu_2(N_6O)(N_3)^{2+}$ (**1b**) by the route shown in equation 3.

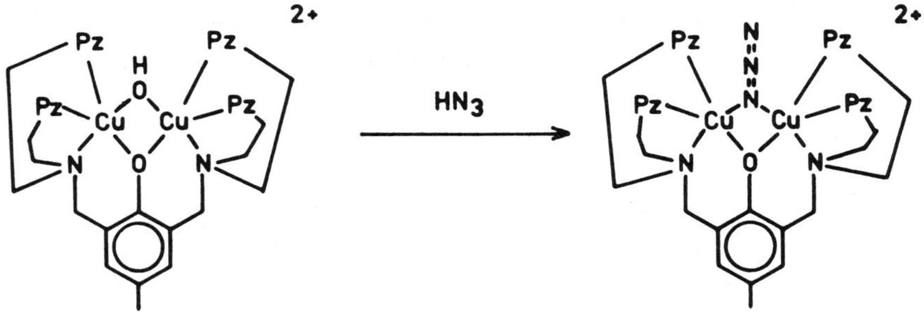

$$1a \qquad\qquad\qquad 1b \qquad\qquad (3)$$

This complex is not very stable and is readily converted back to **1a** in moist air and solvents. However, we were able to isolate single crystals, and a preliminary structure is shown in Figure 2.

This structure of **1b** is quite different from that of the corresponding μ-hydroxy complex **1a**. Most noticeable is that the coppers in **1b**, while their geometries are slightly different, are clearly tetragonal with long axial Cu-N bonds. Moreover, the Cu-O(phenolate) distances are nearly equal. Thus, we are confident is assigning a tetragonal geometry to each copper in **1b**.

The magnetic susceptibility of **1b** is very similar to that of **1a**. The coupling constant, $-2J$, of 450 cm^{-1} for **1b** is slightly larger than the 420 cm^{-1} splitting for **1a** in keeping with the larger Cu1-O-Cu2 angle in **1b** (106.8°) compared to **1a** (103.6° for the hydroxy bridge). However, Kahn has stated that a μ-1,1-azide will lead to a ferromagnetic interaction and has reported a μ-1,1-azido-μ-hydroxo copper dimer that is ferromagnetic even though the hydroxide bridge is in a position to promote antiferromagnetic coupling (15). This implies that for **1b**, either the antiferromagnetic coupling component mediated by the phenolate bridge must be larger than 450 cm^{-1} and is offset by the ferromagnetic influence of the azido bridge or a 1,1-azido bridge does not always have to lead to ferromagnetic exchange. Further studies of this system should prove interesting.

It began to become clear that further studies on the N_6O system would never lead to the preparation of a diamagnetic copper(II) dimer because the work of Reed (7), Lippard (16), and Osborn (17) showed that the Cu-O-Cu angle would have to be much greater than 105° before very strong magnetic coupling would result. Also the electronic spectrum for **1b** (vide infra) and the Cu-Cu distance were not like that

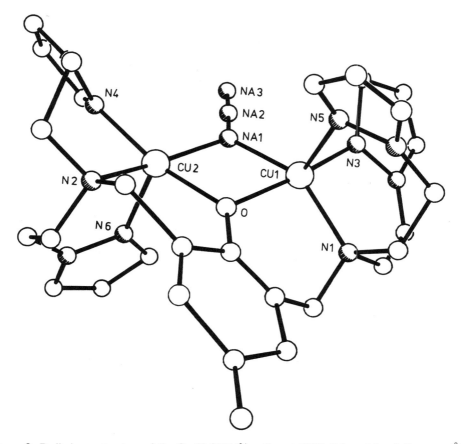

Figure 2. Preliminary structure of the $Cu_2(N_6O)(N_3)^{2+}$ cation at 133K. Selected bond distances (Å): Cu1-N1, 2.044; Cu1-N3, 1.985; Cu1-N5, 2.208; Cu1-NA1, 1.988; Cu1-O, 1.951; Cu2-N2, 2.063; Cu2-N4, 2.086; Cu2-N6, 2.238; Cu2-NA1, 1.993; Cu2-O, 1.940; NA1-NA2, 1.212; NA2-NA3, 1.056; Cu1-Cu2, 3.149. Selected angles (°): Cu1-O-Cu2, 106.8; Cu1-NA1-Cu2, 103.4; O-Cu1-NA1, 74.5; O-Cu1-N1, 90.0; O-Cu1-N3, 166.9; O-Cu1-N5, 94.8; N1-Cu1-N3, 96.8; N1-Cu1-N5, 96.1; N1-Cu1-NA1, 148.1; N3-Cu1-N5, 95.6; N3-Cu1-NA1, 94.1; N5-Cu1-NA1, 112.6; O-Cu2-NA1, 74.7; O-Cu2-N2, 94.1; O-Cu2-N4, 169.4; O-Cu2-N6, 97.7; N2-Cu2-N4, 91.8; N2-Cu2-N6, 97.0; N2-Cu2-NA1, 160.6; N4-Cu2-N6, 90.3; N4-Cu2-NA1, 97.1; N6-Cu2-NA1, 100.1; Cu1-NA1-NA2, 128.2; Cu2-NA1-NA2, 128.0; NA1-NA2-NA3, 176.3.

observed for metHc-azide; therefore, we began to examine related systems. We reasoned that if the size of the chelate rings in the ligand backbone could be decreased from six-membered rings (A) to five-membered rings (B), we would necessarily pull the coppers apart, increase the Cu-O-Cu angle, and initiate the alternate bridging mode for the azide ion (Figure 3).

However, such ligands were unknown and required a synthetic strategy which would permit ready derivatization in case the initial donors would not bind the coppers as we proposed. This was realized by the synthetic scheme illustrated in Figure 4.

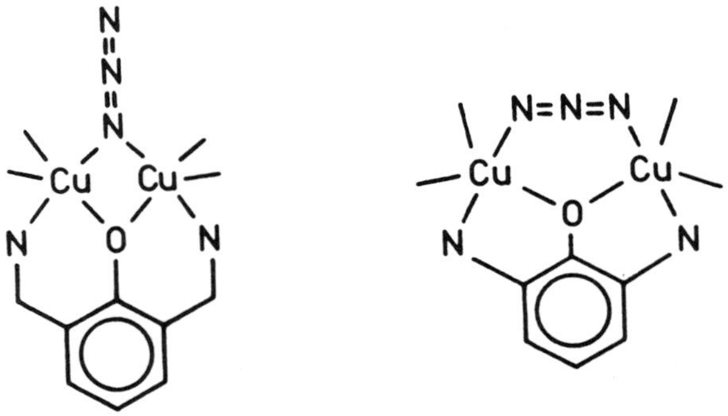

Figure 3. Possible bridging modes for azide ion showing accompanying chelation modes by the ligand.

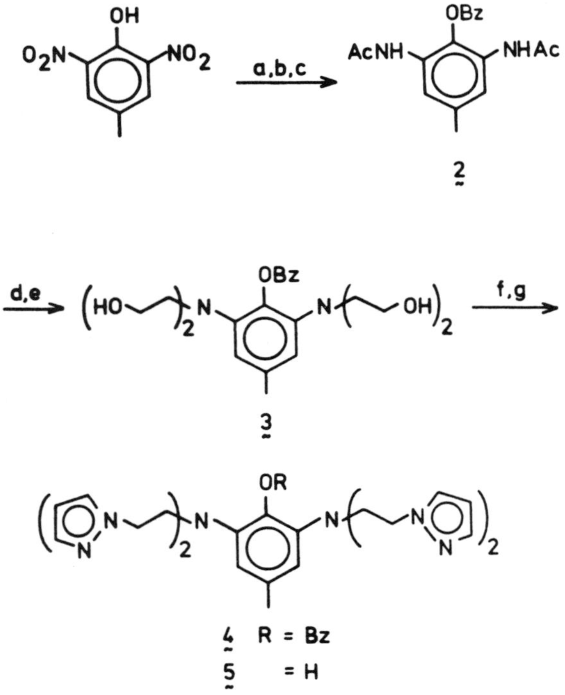

Figure 4. Scheme for the preparation of Hbpeac. Reagents: a, H_2, PtO_2, Ac_2O; b) dilute OH^-; c) OEt^-, $C_6H_5CH_2Cl$; d) OEt^-, reflux 4 d; e) ethylene oxide, HOAc, H_2O; f) $SOCl_2$; g) sodium pyrazolate, DMF, 25°, 4 d; 4⟹5, HBr, H_2O, reflux, 10 h.

The resulting ligand, bpeac, reacts with $Cu(ClO_4)_2$ and either acetate or azide ion to form cyrstalline compounds **6** and **7**, respectively (18). Both complexes were subsequently characterized and their structures are shown in Figures 5 and 6. The acetate derivative, like $Cu_2(N_6O)(OH)^{2+}$, has two copper ions with different co-ordination geometries. Also like *1a*, the Cu-O(phenolate) bond distances are unequal with the longer bond [Cu2-O1] being formed between the phenolate and the copper more distorted toward the trigonal-bipyramidal geometry. For this compound, however, we can make a strong case that Cu2 is trigonal bipyramidal because 1) the Cu-N4 bond, which would be expected to be the axial position of a tetragonal pyramid is shorter than Cu-N2 and 2) the copper(II) ions in **6** are not magnetically coupled at all (2J = 0). The latter evidence means that the phenolate cannot be overlapping with the $d_{x^2-y^2}$ orbitals of each copper since that should give rise to strong antiferromagnetic coupling. This complex is magnetically identical to Reed's μ-acetato dimer which has two trigonal-bipyramidal coppers (7).

The μ-1,3-azide is much different from all of the other Cu(II) dimers discussed above since it is diamagnetic, and $-2J$ is 1800 cm^{-1}. The structure shows two

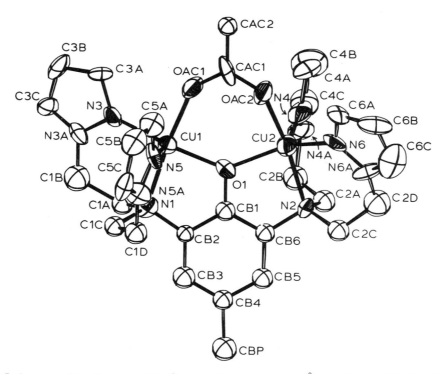

Figure 5. Structure of the Cu_2(bpeac)(OAc)$^{2+}$ cation. Selected distances (Å): Cu1-Cu2, 3.562(3); Cu1-O1, 1.905(12); Cu2-O1, 1.976(12); Cu1-N1, 2.046(16); Cu1-N3, 1.974(15); Cu1-N5, 2.209(16); Cu1-OAC1, 1.946(14); Cu2-N2, 2.120(14); Cu2-N4; 2.062(24); Cu2-N6, 2.004(19); Cu2-OAC2, 1.940(13). Selected angles (°): Cu1-O1-Cu2, 133.2(7), O1-Cu1-OAC1, 91.5(5); O1-Cu2-OAC2, 90.9(6).

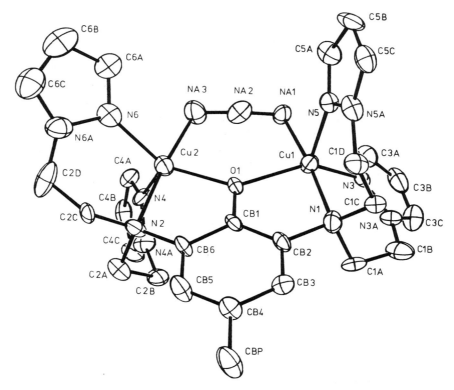

Figure 6. Structure of the $Cu_2(bpeac)(N_3)^{2+}$ cation determined at 133K. Selected distances (Å): Cu1-Cu2, 3.765(2); Cu1-O1, 2.017(5); Cu2-O1, 2.013(6); Cu1-N1, 2.036(8); Cu1-N3, 2.007(8); Cu1-N5; 2.142 (8); Cu1-NA1, 2.002(8); Cu2-N2, 2.097(8); Cu2-N4, 2.119(7); Cu2-N6, 2.004(9); Cu2-NA3, 2.011(9); NA1-NA2, 1.147(12); NA2-NA3, 1.205(13). Selected angles (°): Cu1-O1-Cu2, 138.2(3); O1-Cu1-NA1, 90.4(3); O1-Cu2-NA3, 89.8(3); Cu1-NA1-NA2, 114.2(7); Cu2-NA3-NA2, 114.6(7); NA1-NA2-NA3, 172.1(10).

apparently tetragonal copper ions that are separated by 3.765 Å. The Cu-O (phenolate) bond distances are equal, like *1b* and unlike *1a* and *6*, and one of the Cu-N(pyrazole) bonds on each copper is longer than all of the other Cu-N bonds. A tetragonal geometry puts the phenolate in a position to overlap with the $d_{x^2-y^2}$ orbital on each copper and leads to the observed antiferromagnetic coupling.

The electronic spectra for the binuclear copper(II) complexes are shown in Figures 7 and 8. Figure 7 compares the spectra for the 1,1- and 1,3-μ-azido complexes.

The occurrence of an azide $\Rightarrow$ copper CT band at 462 nm makes the 1,1-azide a deep brown color that contrasts with the emerald green appearance of the 1,3-azide complex. A summary comparison of the properties of the azido complexes is given in Table I along with data for metHc-azide. These data support the conclusion that the azide ligand binds in a 1,3-fashion at the protein active site. Figure 8 compares the spectra for the 1,3-azide and the μ-acetato complexes.

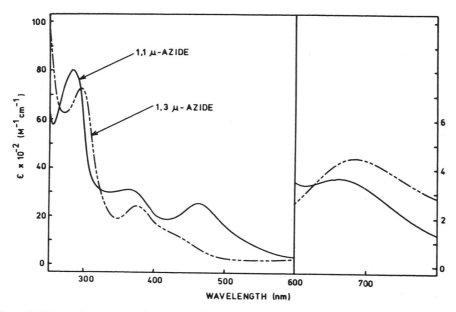

Figure 7. Electronic spectra of $Cu_2(N_6O)(N_3)^{2+}$ (1b) (——) and $Cu_2(bpeac)(N_3)^{2+}$ (7) (-·—·-)in CH_3CN.

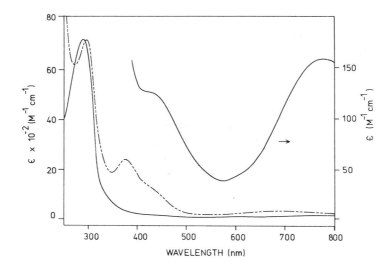

Figure 8. Electronic spectra of $Cu_2(bpeac)(OAc)^{2+}$ (6) (——) and $Cu_2(bpeac)(N_3)^{2+}$ (7) (-·—·-) in CH_3CN.

Because acetate does not influence the absorption spectrum by charge transfer to copper, the spectrum of *6* consists of the pyrazole $\Rightarrow$ copper CT band at about 300 nm, a phenolate $\Rightarrow$ copper CT band at 446 nm, and the d-d absorption of 778 nm. Noteworthy is the observation of the very low intensity phenolate $\Rightarrow$ copper CT band (confirmed by resonance Raman spectroscopy). This fact is interesting because previously reported five-coordinate μ-phenolato-copper(II) dimers generally show a stronger transition at higher energy (360-390 nm, $\epsilon \simeq 10^3$ M^{-1} cm^{-1}) (3,19,20). Furthermore, the weakness of this transition may explain why enhanced Cu-O-(phenolate) bands are not observed in the resonance Raman spectra of hemocyanin.

Table I
Summary of Data for Binuclear Azide Complexes

	λ_{max} (nm)	νN_3 (cm^{-1})	$-2J$ (cm^{-1})	Cu-Cu (Å)
Cu$_2$(N$_6$O)N$_3{}^{2+}$	364, 462	2065	450	3.149
Cu$_2$(bpeac)N$_3{}^{2+}$	376, 444(sh)	2032	1800	3.765
metHc-azide (Busycon)	380, 430(sh)	2042	>1000	3.66

Binuclear Copper(I) Complexes

Although we began this study by attempting to model the oxidized forms of hemocyanin, our ultimate goal was to mimic the oxygen-binding behavior of this and related proteins. Thus, while the work discussed above progressed, we prepared for this phase of the study by examining the chemistry of copper(I) complexes (21-24). It was clear from that investigation that the copper(I) ion could be stabilized with heterocyclic nitrogen donors, and that 2-, 3-, and 4-coordinate complexes could be prepared. However, some of those species were air sensitive and had a tendency toward disproportionation, while all lacked the typical spectroscopic handles available for studying many other transition metal ions. The latter problem was overcome by correlating the copper $\Rightarrow$ pyrazole CT transition with coordination number (25).

Our attempts to prepare the copper(I) derivative of the N$_6$O ligand resulted in failure. The desired complex disproportionated immediately upon its generation in solution, a stark contrast to the results obtained by Karlin on the same ligand system having pyridine instead of pyrazole donors (26). However, because the bpeac system had given us an excellent model for metHc-azide, we focussed on using it to prepare a copper(I) dimer.

The bimetallic complex **8** was prepared by stirring the potassium salt of bpeac with Cu(CH$_3$CN)$_4$BF$_4$ in methanol under an inert atmosphere (27). The resulting precipitate could be crystallized from acetonitrile-THF to give colorless crystals. The structure of **8** is shown in Figure 9.

Each copper ion resides in a distorted tetrahedral environment with normal Cu-N bond distances. The Cu-O bonds are much longer than those in the copper(II) dimers, reflecting the weaker interaction expected between the soft Cu(I) and hard phenolate ions. This results in a Cu-Cu separation much longer than that determined for deoxyhemocyanin from EXAFS studies (4) but about the same as that found for *P. interruptus* hemocyanin from X-ray crystallography (6). Cu$_2$(bpeac)$^+$ is one of only two copper(I) dimers that have a single phenolate bridge between the copper

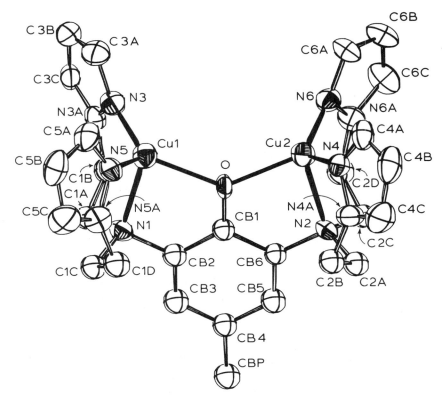

Figure 9. Structure of the $Cu_2(bpeac)^+$ cation. Selected distances (Å): Cu1-Cu2, 3.825(3); Cu1-O, 2.077(8); Cu2-O, 2.093(8). The Cu1-O-Cu2 angle is 133.0(4). Other distances and angles can be found in ref. 27.

ions. The other is the complex prepared by Karlin, mentioned above (26). Previous attempts to prepare such species have been unsuccessful, and other μ-phenolato copper(I) dimers have always had a second bridging group (11,28,29). While the X-ray structure shows no evidence for a bridging group (6) in deoxyHc, the isolation of **8** demonstrates the viability of phenolate bridging.

The cavity between the two coppers in **8** should provide an ideal environment for binding small molecules such as O_2. When **8** is treated with dioxygen in acetonitrile (or CH_2Cl_2) at 238K, the initially colorless solution turns dark green. The spectral changes for this reaction are shown in Figure 10.

The clean isosbestic behavior observed for this experiment coupled with manometric measurements that show uptake of only 0.5 equivalents of O_2 per dimer is consistent with the following reaction sequence:

$$Cu_2(bpeac)^+ + O_2 \Rightarrow Cu_2(bpeac)O_2^+ \qquad \text{(rds)} \qquad (4)$$

$$Cu_2(bpeac)O_2^+ + Cu_2(bpeac)^+ \Rightarrow \{[Cu_2(bpeac)O]_2\}_x \quad \text{(fast)} \qquad (5)$$

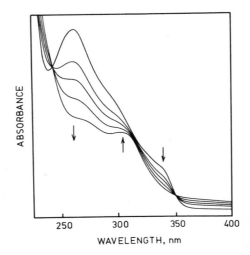

Figure 10. Spectra showing the reaction of $Cu_2(bpeac)^+$ with dioxygen at 238K in acetonitrile.

This result shows that site isolation might be important for hemocyanin to prevent the bimolecular, four-electron reduction of dioxygen as previously demonstrated in the case of hemoglobin (30).

Since a sterically-hindered analog of bpeac should inhibit the reaction shown in equation 5, we undertook the synthesis of (t-butyl)$_4$(bpeac). This was readily accomplished by the scheme shown in Figure 4, substituting 3-t-butylpyrazole for pyrazole in the pentultimate step (31). The copper(I) complex was prepared by the same method used previously, and the proposed structure of this complex (*9*) is shown in Figure 11.

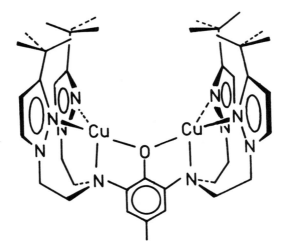

Figure 11. Proposed structure for the $Cu_2(t\text{-Bubpeac})^+$ cation showing the creation of a hydrophobic pocket for O_2 binding.

The reaction of *9* with dioxygen resulted in the formation of a species different from that generated with *8*, and the spectrum of this product is shown in Figure 12. The reaction with dioxygen occurs in methanol at room temperature but not in methylene chloride, THF, or acetonitrile and not at lower temperatures (32). The resulting red-orange solution slowly decomposes with dimunition of the band at 505 nm, possibly by oxidation of the solvent. We are currently trying to characterize this system further; unfortunately, the complex fluoresces so strongly that attempts to observe an O-O stretch by resonance Raman spectroscopy have so far been fruitless (33). The fact that methanol must be used to generate this species raises the possibility that it may be a hydroperoxide complex.

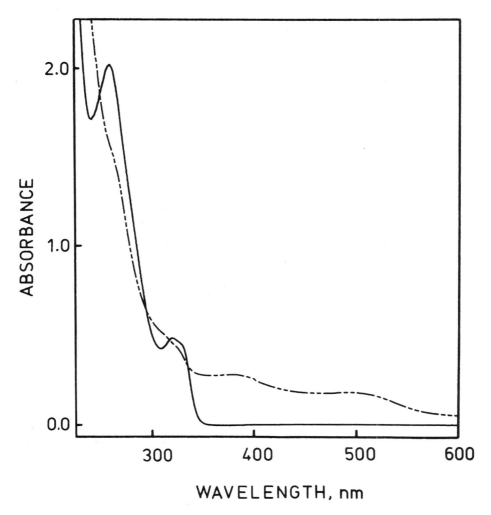

Figure 12. Spectra of $Cu_2(t\text{-Bubpeac})^+$ (9) in methanol under N_2 (——) and after addition of O_2 (–·–·–). The concentration of the solution is approximately 1×10^{-4} M.

The versatility of bpeac and its derivatives should prove useful in isolating a binuclear copper dioxygen adduct which structurally and spectroscopically mimicks HcO_2. Many factors still need to be examined including the size of the oxygen-binding pocket, its polarity (hydrogen-bonding may be important), and the nature of the donors. We envision the preparation of bpeac derivatives providing substituted-pyrazole, pyridine, and benzimidazole donors. The latter point is particularly important since the use of pyridine ligands has already led to the generation of a phenoxy-bridged copper-dioxygen complex (26).

Acknowledgments

I am indebted to my colleagues who have contributed to the work presented here: Andy Borovik, Debbie Ellis, Don Jameson, and Prof. Derek Hodgson (UNC); Prof. Charles O'Connor (University of New Orleans); and Joe Reibenspies and Prof. Oren Anderson (Colorado State University). We thankfully acknowledge financial support from the donors of the Petroleum Research Fund, administered by the American Chemical Society, and from the National Science Foundation.

References and Footnotes

1. Abbreviations used in this paper: Hc, hemocyanin; HcO_2, oxyhemocyanin; metHc, the oxidized forms of hemocyanin; N_6O, the anion of 2,6-bis{bis[2-(1-pyrazoyl)ethyl]aminomethyl}-p-cresol; bpeac, the anion of 2,6-bis{bis[2-(1-pyrazoyl)ethyl]amino}-p-cresol; OAc, acetate; THF, tetrahydrofuran.
2. E.I. Solomon in *Copper Proteins*, Ed., T.G. Spiro, John Wiley & Sons, New York, chapter 1, (1983).
3. E.I. Solomon, K.W. Penfield and D.E. Wilcox, *Struct. Bonding 53*, 1 (1983).
4. G.L. Woolery, L. Powers, M. Winkler, E.I. Solomon, and T.G. Spiro, *J. Am. Chem. Soc. 106*, 86 (1984).
5. D.E. Wilcox, J.R. Long, and E.I. Solomon, *J. Am. Chem. Soc. 106* 2186 (1984).
6. W.P.J. Gaykema, W.G.J. Hol, J.M. Vereijken, N.M. Soeter, H.J. Bak and J.J. Beintema, *Nature, 309*, 23 (1984).
7. V. McKee, J.V. Dadgegian, R. Bau and C.A. Reed, *J. Am. Chem. Soc. 103*, 7000 (1981).
8. T.N. Sorrell, D.L. Jameson and C.J. O'Connor, *Inorg. Chem. 23*, 190 (1984).
9. R. Robson, *Inorg. Nucl. Chem. Lett. 6*, 125 (1970).
10. W.D. McFayden and R. Robson, *J. Coord. Chem. 5*, 49 (1976).
11. R.R. Gagné, R.P. Kreh and J.A. Dodge, *J. Am. Chem. Soc. 101*, 6917 (1979).
12. J.J. Grzybowski, P.H. Merrel and F.L. Urbach, *Inorg. Chem. 17*, 3078 (1978).
13. H. Okawa, T. Tokii, Y. Nonaka, Y. Muto and S. Kida, *Bull. Chem. Soc. Jpn. 46*, 1462 (1973).
14. D.J. Hodgson, *Prog. Inorg. Chem. 19*, 173 (1975) and references therein.
15. O. Kahn, S. Sikorav, J. Gouteron, S. Jeannin and Y. Jeannin, *Inorg. Chem. 22*, 2877 (1983).
16. P.K. Coughlin and S.J. Lippard, *J. Am. Chem. Soc. 106*, 2328 (1984).
17. P.L. Burk, J.A. Osborn, M.-T. Youinou, Y. Agnus, R. Louis and R. Weiss, *J. Am. Chem. Soc. 103*, 1273 (1981).
18. T.N. Sorrell, C.J. O'Connor, O.P. Anderson and J.H. Reibenspies, *J. Am. Chem. Soc.*, in press.
19. K.D. Karlin, J.C. Hayes, Y. Gultneh, R.W. Cruse, J.W. McKown, J.P. Hutchinson, and J. Zubieta, *J. Am. Chem. Soc. 106*, 2121 (1984).
20. K.D. Karlin, J.C. Hayes, J.P. Hutchinson, and J. Zubieta, *J. Chem. Soc., Chem. Commun.* 376 (1983).
21. T.N. Sorrell and D.L. Jameson, *Inorg. Chem. 21*, 1014 (1982).
22. T.N.Sorrell, M.R. Malachowski, and D.L. Jameson, *Inorg. Chem. 21*, 3250 (1982).
23. T.N. Sorrell and M.R. Malachowski, *Inorg. Chem. 22*, 1883 (1983).
24. T.N. Sorrell and D.L. Jameson, *J. Am. Chem. Soc. 105*, 6013 (1983).
25. T.N. Sorrell and A.S. Borovik, unpublished results.
26. K.D. Karlin, R.W. Cruse, Y. Gultneh, J.C. Hayes and J. Zubieta, *J. Am. Chem. Soc. 106*, 3372 (1984).

27. T.N. Sorrell and A.S. Borovik, *J. Chem. Soc., Chem. Commun.,* 1489 (1984).

28. R.R. Gagné, C.A. Koval, T.J. Smith and M.C. Cimolino, *J. Am. Chem. Soc. 101,* 4571 (1979).

29. J.J. Grzybowski and F.L. Urbach, *Inorg. Chem. 19,* 2604 (1980).

30. J.P. Collman, T.R. Halbert and K.S. Suslick in *Metal Ion Activation of Dioxygen,* Ed. T.G. Spiro, Wiley-Interscience, New York, p 1 (1980).

31. T. N. Sorrell, D.J. Ellis and A.S. Borovik, unpublished results.

32. In other solvents, different spectra are obtained but none are as clean as the one obtained in methanol. Complex 9 reacts very slowly with dioxygen in methanol at 273K, but no reaction is seen at lower temperatures.

33. We thank Jim Pate in Prof. Ed Solomon's lab for attempting the resonance Raman spectrum of this complex.

Biological & Inorganic Copper Chemistry,
ISBN 0-940030-11-X, Eds., K. D. Karlin & J. Zubieta, Adenine Press, ©Adenine Press, 1985

Copper Catalyzed Oxidation of Phenol.
An Alternative Method for the Industrial
Production of Hydroquinone

James E. Lyons and Chao-Yang Hsu
Applied Research and Development Department
Sun Company
Marcus Hook, Pennsylvania 19061

Abstract

Hydroquinone, an important commodity chemical used in antioxidant and photographic chemistry is currently manufactured by three rather difficult and costly series of reactions. The direct air oxidation of phenol to *p*-benzoquinone followed by catalytic reduction as a simple, straightforward means of producing hydroquinone has been investigated in our laboratories.

Both Cu(I) and Cu(II) in polar aprotic solvents are effective catalysts for the oxidation of phenol. Selectivity to *p*-benzoquinone is a function of solvents, promoters, inhibitors, the ligand system and reaction conditions. Bases such as hydroxide, alkoxide and amines promote the Cu(II)-catalyzed oxidation of phenol to *p*-benzoquinone. Group VIII metals also aid this reaction. Our catalyst systems achieve selectivities to the *para* quinone of over 90%. By-products include diphenoquinone, muconic acids and polymers. It is interesting to contrast catalysts having binucleating ligand systems with those that do not. The former catalysts model tryosinase and produce *o*-benzoquinone; the latter can catalyze *p*-benzoquinone formation selectivity. A mechanism is proposed to rationalize our results.

The copper catalyst which is used to oxidize phenol is also effective in catalyzing its subsequent hydrogenation to hydroquinone, thus affording a convenient one-pot preparation of hydroquinone using a single catalyst.

Introduction

Hydroquinone, an important commodity chemical used in antioxidant and photographic chemistry is currently manufactured by three rather difficult and costly series of reactions, Figure 1. Routes from aniline and cumene are multi-step processes which produce lower value co-products in addition to the desired hydroquinone. The direct route from phenol uses costly hydrogen peroxide and is unselective, giving hydroquinone in less than 60% yield.

A more practical route to hydroquinone, if it could be achieved in a selective manner under mild conditions of temperature and pressure, would be the oxidation

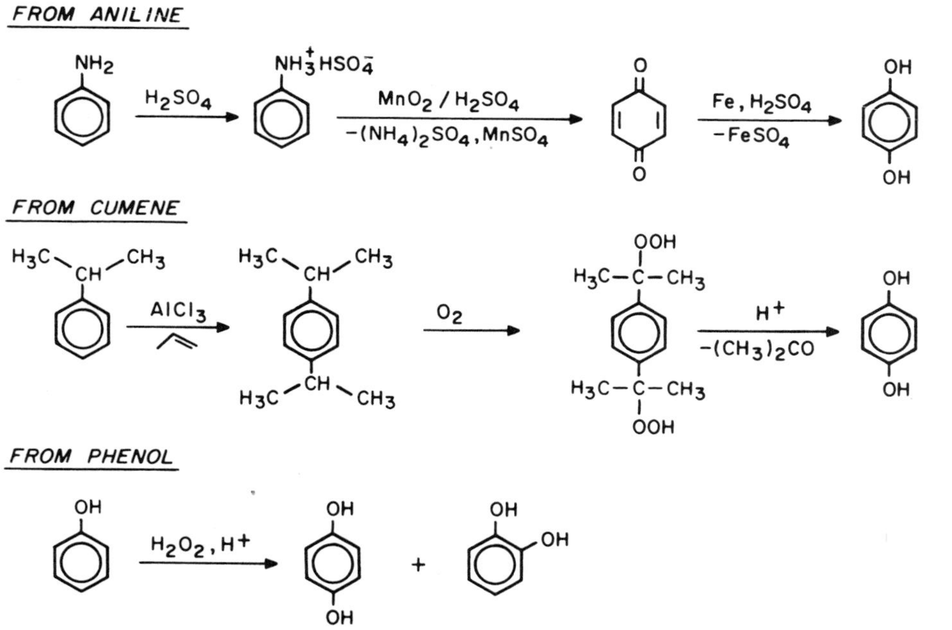

FROM ANILINE

FROM CUMENE

FROM PHENOL

Figure 1. Industrial production of hydroquinone.

of phenol to *p*-benzoquinone, PBQ, followed by catalytic reduction of PBQ to hydroquinone, Figure 2. Reports from both the journal and patent literature (1-10) indicate that the oxidation of phenol to PBQ is catalyzed by salts and complexes of manganese, cobalt and copper. The catalytic hydrogenation of PBQ to hydroquinone is readily accomplished in the presence of a variety of catalysts, (11,12) including Cu(I) in homogeneous solution (13,14).

Copper halides in acetonitrile were found to be particularly effective catalyst systems for carrying out the oxidation of phenol to PBQ (4,5). PBQ could be produced in greater than 85% yield but only at pressures in excess of 100 atmospheres of pure oxygen (5). Figure 3 shows the effect of oxygen partial pressure on PBQ yield when cuprous bromide was used as the catalyst in acetonitrile (5).

Because of the commercial implications of a selective, low pressure oxidation of phenol to PBQ we have carried out a study of the effect of copper catalysts in this reaction. In this paper, we report preliminary results obtained for phenol oxidations catalyzed by simple copper compounds in solution.

Copper Catalyzed Phenol Oxidations

We began our studies on copper catalysts for phenol oxidation by employing acetonitrile as the solvent and carrying out reactions in magnetically stirred mini-

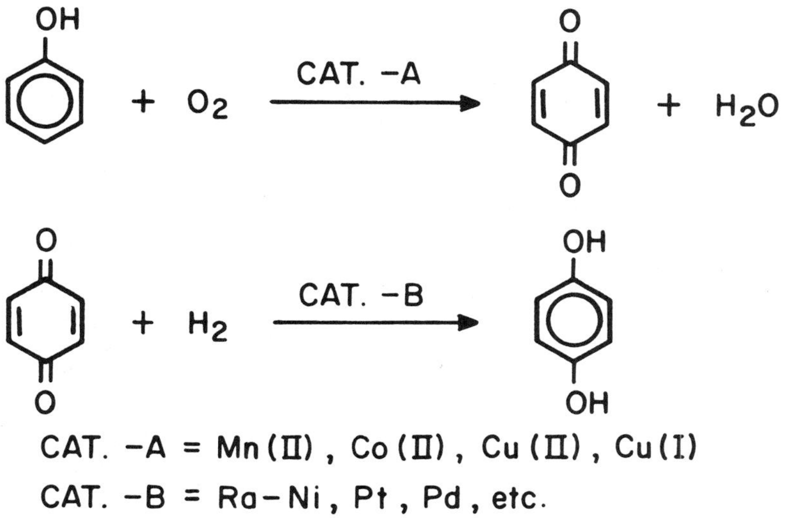

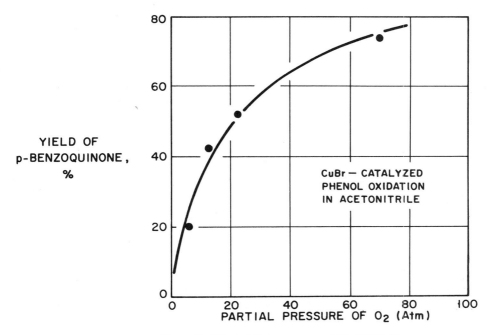

Figure 2. A two-step synthesis of hydroquinone from phenol.

Figure 3. Effect of O_2 pressure on yield of PBQ (5).

autoclaves under 750 psi of a gas mixture which was 40% oxygen and 60% nitrogen, Figure 4. When either cuprous chloride or cupric chloride was used as the catalyst, PBQ was produced as the major product; however, large amounts of muconic acids,

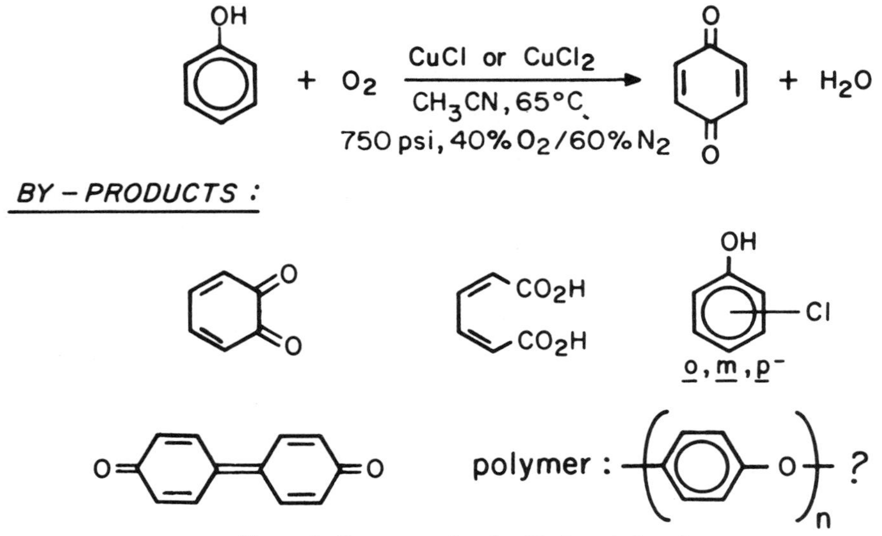

Figure 4. Copper catalyzed oxidation of phenol.

diphenoquinone and polymers were also formed. Small amounts of the chlorophenols and traces of *o*-benzoquinone, OBQ, were also found among the reaction products. Product analyses were performed by combining standardized gas chromatography with high pressure liquid chromatography of reaction mixtures.

At this point, a rough reaction scheme, Figure 5, was formulated in an attempt to rationalize what was known about this reaction. We postulated that an active Cu(II) species formed *in situ* might oxidize phenol to produce Cu(I) and an associated phenoxy radical in acetonitrile. The phenoxy radical (either free or in the copper coordination sphere) might couple by known reactions to give either diphenoquinone or polymers (15,16). Coupling products are known to predominate when reactions are carried out at low oxygen pressure. At high oxygen concentrations however, the dioxygen molecule might preferentially attack a phenoxy radical ring producing an intermediate which could give rise to PBQ. Products of *ortho*-oxidation: OBQ and the muconic acids might arise either from the same phenoxy radical or *via* catalytic pathways similar to those proposed for binuclear copper complexes which model tyrosinase (17,18).

Investigations of a large number of copper compounds showed that in acetonitrile cuprous and cupric chlorides were the superior catalysts. Results of some of the better reactions are given in Table I. Less effective were $Cu(NO_3)_2$, CuBr, Cu(OH)Cl, $NaCuCl_3$ and CuOCl. Nearly all other simple compounds were ineffective. Little or no catalytic reaction occurred when cupric carboxylates, hydroxide, oxide, carbonate, sulfate, phosphate, chlorate, or fluoride were used. Cuprous carboxylates, fluoroborate, triflate, oxide, thiophenoxide, isocyanate, cyanide and iodide were also ineffective in our hands even though the latter two compounds were reported to catalyze the oxidation of phenol (5).

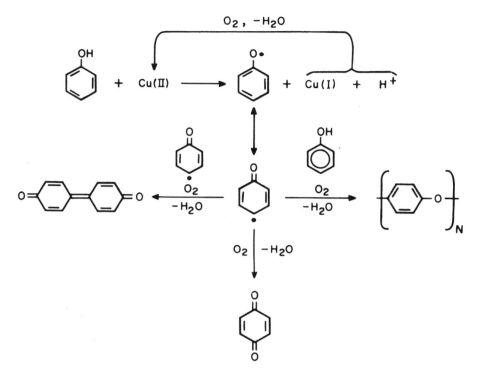

Figure 5. Copper catalyzed phenol oxidation.

Table I

CATALYTIC OXIDATION OF
PHENOL TO p-BENZOQUINONE (PBQ) IN ACETONITRILE
EFFECT OF THE COPPER COMPOUND USED AS CATALYST

CATALYST [b]	REACTION TEMP., °C	PHENOL CONV., %	PBQ SEL., %	PBQ YIELD, %	MOLES PBQ/ G.- ATOM Cu
CuCl₂	65	73	49	36	5.2
CuCl₂	40	54	47	25	3.4
Cu(NO₃)₂	65	58	36	21	1.5
CuCl	65	90	54	49	7.0
CuCl	40	59	75	44	5.9
CuCl	25	35	76	27	3.7
CuBr	65	43	32	26	3.5
CuBr	40	34	46	16	2.1

a) PHENOL , 7.5 mmoles ; ACETONITRILE , 5 ml ; CATALYST , 0.55 mmole ;
   OXIDANT, 40% O₂ /60% N₂ at 750 psig initial ; t = 3 hrs .

b) NaCuCl₃ , Cu(OH)Cl AND CuOCl ALSO CATALYZED REACTION POORLY.

As had been noted in earlier work (6), the metallic materials from which the autoclave was constructed affected the course of the catalytic reactions. For this reason, all of our runs were made in glass lined reactors using a teflon-coated magnetic stirrer. An early patent (6) showed that metal powders could beneficially affect the PBQ yield. We found this to be particularly true of the $CuCl_2$-catalyzed oxidation of phenol, Table II. If the presence of a substantial amount of Cu(I) in these reactions is essential for high reaction rate and selectivity, the added metal could enhance the rate of formation of Cu(I) from Cu(II), (Eq. 1).

$$xCuCl_2 + M \Rightarrow xCuCl + MCl_x \qquad (1)$$

Table II

TALYTIC OXIDATION OF PHENOL TO PBQ IN ACETONITRILE

EFFECT OF ADDED METALS ON $CuCl_2$ – CATALYZED REACTIONS [a]

ADDED METAL	CONVERSION OF PHENOL	SELECTIVITY TO PBQ, %	PBQ YIELD, %
COBALT	∼99	60	59
IRON	>99	58	58
ALUMINUM	>99	50	50
MAGNESIUM	>99	50	50
PLATINUM	>99	48	48
CHROMIUM	∼99	46	46
PALLADIUM	∼99	36	36
NONE [b]	80	42	34
ZINC	51	44	22

a) PHENOL , 3.8 mmoles ; ACETONITRILE , 5ml ; $CuCl_2$, 1.1 mmole ; OXIDANT 40 % O_2/60 % N_2 at 750 psig ; 2 hrs .

b) 3 hrs .

The Effect of Base on the Copper-Catalyzed Oxidation of Phenol

The phenoxide anion should be a better reducing agent towards Cu(II) than phenol itself. If the generation of a sizeable standing concentration of Cu(I) is beneficial, strong bases such as hydroxide ion might be expected to aid the reaction, (Eqs. 2, 3). Table III shows that added LiOH significantly enhances the $CuCl_2$-catalyzed oxidation of phenol to PBQ but inhibits the CuCl-catalyzed reaction. In addition, while base concentrations up to 1 mole LiOH per gram·atom of Cu are beneficial in the $CuCl_2$-catalyzed oxidation, more than one mole of base per g·atom of Cu is harmful.

$$LiOH + PhOH \Rightarrow PhOLi + H_2O \qquad (2)$$

$$PhOLi + CuCl_2 \Rightarrow PhO\cdot + CuCl + LiCl \qquad (3)$$

An additional benefit of adding base to the $CuCl_2$-catalyzed oxidations is the reduction of unwanted chlorophenol by-products, Figure 4. Chlorophenols may be

Table III

OXIDATION OF PHENOL TO PBQ CATALYZED BY CuCl$_2$ AND CuCl

EFFECT OF ADDED LiOH [a]

CATALYST	BASE	BASE, mmoles	H$_2$O, mmoles	PHENOL CONV., %	PBQ SEL., %	PBQ YIELD, %	MOLES PBQ/ G.-ATOM Cu
CuCl$_2$	NONE	—	—	73	49	36	5.2
	NONE	—	14	35	48	17	2.3
	LiOH	0.55	—	98	48	47	6.4
	LiOH	0.55	14	60	68	41	5.6
	LiOH	1.10	14	46	74	34	4.6
	LiOH	1.65	14	13	27	3.5	0.5
CuCl	NONE	—	—	90	54	49	7.0
	NONE	—	14	61	78	48	7.0
	LiOH	0.55	—	79	47	37	5.0
	LiOH	0.55	14	45	38	17	2.3

a) PHENOL , 7.5 mmoles ; ACETONITRILE + H$_2$O , 5 ml ; CATALYST , 0.55 mmoles ;
OXIDANT 40% O$_2$/60% N$_2$ at 750 psig initial ; T = 65°C ; t = 3 hrs .

formed in up to 4% yield in some instances but their concentrations may be reduced to a negligible quantity by introduction of strong base. When cuprous chloride is used as the catalyst for phenol oxidation in acetonitrile, the chlorophenols are not formed in appreciable amounts even without added base.

Table IV shows the effects of phenoxide, alkoxide and Group IIA oxides and hydroxide on the course of copper catalyzed oxidation of phenol in acetonitrile.

Table IV

OXIDATION OF PHENOL TO PBQ CATALYZED BY CuCl$_2$ AND CuCl

EFFECT OF ADDED BASE [a]

CATALYST	BASE	BASE mmoles	PHENOL CONV., %	PBQ SEL., %	PBQ YIELD, %	MOLES PBQ/ G.-ATOM Cu
CuCl$_2$	NONE	—	73	49	36	5.2
	NaOPh	0.55	98	55	54	7.4
	NaOPh	1.10	68	57	39	5.3
	NaOMe	0.55	95	52	49	6.7
	NaOMe	1.10	79	37	29	4.0
	CaO	0.55	95	47	45	6.1
	Ca(OH)$_2$	0.55	94	44	41	5.6
CuCl	NONE	—	90	54	49	7.0
	NaOPh	0.55	45	27	12	—
	NaOPh	1.10	NR	—	—	—
	BeO	0.55	93	60	56	7.6
	CaO	0.55	94	56	53	7.2

a) PHENOL , 7.5 mmoles , ACETONITRILE , 5 ml ; CATALYST , 0.55 mmole ;
40% O$_2$/60% N$_2$ at 750 psig ; T = 65°C ; t = 3 hrs .

Again, up to one mole of base per gram·atom of copper proved beneficial to the $CuCl_2$-catalyzed reaction whereas excess base was damaging. Addition of phenoxide in any substantial amount was detrimental to the CuCl-catalyzed reaction. The presence of Group IIA oxides did not seem to affect the CuCl-catalyzed phenol oxidation in a negative way.

Recent work by Floriani and co-workers (19) has shown that stable crystalline solids could be formed by reaction of cuprous chloride with PhONa followed by the addition of alkyl isocyanides (4). The formation of stable bridged copper(I) phenoxides may be a catalyst deactivation pathway in our reactions.

$$2CuCl + 2PhONa \xrightarrow[RNC]{-2NaCl}
\begin{array}{c}
\text{Ph} \\
| \\
RNC \quad O \quad CNR \\
\diagdown \quad \diagup \quad \diagdown \quad \diagup \\
Cu \quad \quad Cu \\
\diagup \quad \diagdown \quad \diagup \quad \diagdown \\
RNC \quad O \quad CNR \\
| \\
\text{Ph}
\end{array} \quad (4)$$

It is of interest to note that small amounts of group IA acetates and carbonates also appear to have a beneficial effect on the $CuCl_2$-catalyzed oxidations of phenol as shown in Table V.

Table V

OXIDATION OF PHENOL TO PBQ CATALYZED BY CuCl₂ AND CuCl

EFFECT OF METAL SALTS[a]

CATALYST	SALT	SALT mmoles	PHENOL CONV., %	PBQ SEL.,%	PBQ YIELD,%	MOLES PBQ/ G.- ATOM Cu
$CuCl_2$	NONE	—	73	49	36	5.2
	LiOAc	0.55	94	59	55	7.6
	NaOAc	0.55	92	58	53	7.3
	KOAc	0.55	83	51	42	5.8
	Na_2CO_3	0.55	97	55	53	7.3
CuCl	NONE	—	90	54	49	7.0
	LiOAc	0.55	93	59	55	7.5
	Li_2CO_3	0.55	91	54	46	6.3
	Na_2CO_3	0.55	97	52	50	6.9

a) PHENOL , 7.5 mmoles ; ACETONITRILE , 5 ml ; CATALYST , 0.55 mmole ;
40% O_2/60% N_2 at 750 psig initial ; T = 65°C ; t = 3 hrs .

The Effect of Water on Copper-Catalyzed Oxidations in Acetonitrile

As can be seen in Table III, the addition of water to both $CuCl_2$- and CuCl-catalyzed oxidations of phenol causes a large decrease in phenol conversion after

Table VI

CATALYTIC OXIDATION OF PHENOL TO PBQ IN ACETONITRILE

EFFECT OF WATER ON THE CuCl CATALYZED REACTION [a]

H_2O, ml	H_2O, moles per mole PhOH	CONVERSION OF PHENOL, mole %	SELECTIVITY TO p–BENZO–QUINONE, %
NONE	—	90	54
0.125	0.88	78	71
0.250	1.75	61	78
0.375	2.63	51	81
0.500	3.50	46	85

a) PHENOL, 8 mmoles ; CuCl, 0.55 mmole ;(ACETONITRILE + H_2O)–5ml ;
40% O_2/60% N_2 at 750 psig , 65°C , 3 hrs.

three hours reaction time. Furthermore, this decrease in conversion is accompanied by a marked increase in selectivity to PBQ when cuprous chloride is the catalyst.

Table VI shows that as water is incrementally added to the reaction mixture, the selectivity to PBQ steadily rises but the phenol conversion with time steadily drops. Under certain conditions, Figure 6, with addition of sufficient water, the selectivity

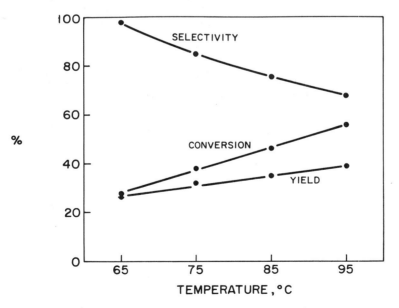

a) PHENOL, 16 mmole ; ACETONITRILE , 4.5 ml ; H_2O, 0.5 ml ; CuCl,
0.55 mmole ; 40% O_2/60% N_2 at 750 psig , 3 hrs.

Figure 6. Effect of temperature on PBQ yeild.

to PBQ exceeds 95% but phenol conversion in this case is only 28% after 3 hours. In an attempt to increase the rate of the H_2O-modified oxidation of phenol to PBQ the reaction temperature was increased from 65°C to 95°C, Figure 6. However, as reaction temperature increases, selectivity to PBQ diminishes and little practical increase in product yield is realized.

Water exhibits a pronounced effect on both reaction rate and selectivity. Water, however, is a product of the oxidation of phenol to PBQ. Thus, we have noticed that over very long reaction times the rate of reaction slows but selectivity increases slightly. This behavior is unavoidable in our batch mini-autoclaves. In continuous commercial operation, however, water build-up could be a serious problem. This problem may be conveniently avoided, however, by continuously adding acetonitrile while continuously removing the low-boiling (87/13) acetonitrile/water azeotrope (20) by distillation during reaction. This procedure serves to remove the water of reaction while running at constant solvent composition. Constant feeding of acetonitrile and simultaneous azeotropic distillation can conveniently provide any desired acetonitrile/water ratio as a reaction medium.

The Effect of Organic Solvents on Phenol Oxidations

We have studied the copper-catalyzed oxidation of phenol in a variety of organic solvents and found that acetonitrile is superior. Table VII compares results of reactions in acetonitrile with those run in nitromethane. It is interesting to note that the base effects noticed for reactions run in acetonitrile are different in nitromethane. In acetonitrile bases such as phenoxide and trialkylamine enhance product yields

Table VII

EFFECT OF BASES ON THE RATE AND SELECTIVITY OF THE COPPER-CATALYZED OXIDATION OF PHENOL [a]

CATALYST	BASE	SOLVENT	PHENOL CONV., %	PBQ SEL., %	MOLES PBQ/ G.-ATOM Cu
$CuCl_2$	—	CH_3CN	32	55	5.1
$CuCl_2$	LiOPh	CH_3CN	62	90	16.2
$CuCl_2$	Et_3N	CH_3CN	63	70	12.8
CuCl	—	CH_3CN	47	61	8.3
CuCl	LiOPh	CH_3CN	44	45	5.8
CuCl	Et_3N	CH_3CN	50	21	3.1
$CuCl_2$	—	CH_3NO_2	28	43	3.5
$CuCl_2$	LiOPh	CH_3NO_2	31	62	5.6
$CuCl_2$	Et_3N	CH_3NO_2	82	43	10.3
CuCl	—	CH_3NO_2	17	28	1.4
CuCl	LiOPh	CH_3NO_2	42	56	6.8
CuCl	Et_3N	CH_3NO_2	57	40	6.6

a) PHENOL , 16 mmoles ; SOLVENT , 5 ml ; CATALYST , 0.55 mmole ;
40% O_2/60% N_2 at 750 psig initial ; T= 65°C ; t = 3 hrs .

of CuCl$_2$-catalyzed oxidations but give poor results in CuCl-catalyzed reactions. On the other hand, added base enhances product yields in both CuCl$_2$- and CuCl-catalyzed reactions in nitromethane.

We were not able to observe truly catalytic reactions in solvents other than nitromethane and acetonitrile, Table VIII. No reaction occurred in methylene chloride, sulfolane and water under mild conditions. Cuprous chloride promoted slow reaction in methanol, dimethylformamide, dimethylacetamide and dimethyl-sulfoxide but CuCl$_2$ was inactive in these solvents.

Table VIII
EFFECT OF SOLVENT ON
THE COPPER–CATALYZED OXIDATION OF PHENOL [1]

SOLVENT	COPPER SALT	p-BENZOQUINONE YIELD, mmole	PHENOL CONV., %	PBQ SEL., %
WATER	CuCl	0	—	—
WATER	CuCl$_2$	0	—	—
METHANOL	CuCl	0.25	16	21
METHANOL	CuCl$_2$	0	—	—
CH$_2$Cl$_2$	CuCl	0	—	—
CH$_2$Cl$_2$	CuCl$_2$	0	—	—
SULFOLANE	CuCl	0	—	—
SULFOLANE	CuCl$_2$	0	—	—
DMA [2]	CuCl	1.08	na	na
DMA	CuCl$_2$	0	—	—
DMF	CuCl	0.32	12	36
DMF	CuCl$_2$	0	—	—
DMSO	CuCl	1.37	29	63
DMSO	CuCl$_2$	na	na	na
ACETONITRILE	CuCl	3.65	90	54
ACETONITRILE	CuCl$_2$	2.43	73	49
ACETONITRILE	CuCl / LiOH aq.	—	—	—
ACETONITRILE	CuCl$_2$ / LiOH aq.	3.06	46	74

1) PHENOL , 7.4 mmoles ; SOLVENT , 5 ml ; COPPER SALT , 0.55 mmole ; 40% O$_2$/60% N$_2$ at 750 psig initial ; T = 65°C ; t = 3hrs .
2) PHENOL CONCENTRATION was 14.5 mmoles and CuCl , 0.50 mmole .

An interesting relationship between CuCl concentration and PBQ yield was noticed in runs carried out in dimethylacetamide. In this solvent, regardless of temperature and reaction time, it was not possible to exceed 2 mmoles PBQ per mmole CuCl employed Table IX. It appears as though in dimethylacetamide there is a stoichio-metric reaction which involves one cuprous chloride in the production of two moles of PBQ but no more.

Some Kinetic Features of Phenol Oxidations

The data reported in previous sections of this paper was obtained in mini-autoclaves by carrying out reactions for a certain period of time and then cooling the reactor, opening it and analyzing products. Because these reactions involved oxidations under pressure it was somewhat cumbersome to conduct kinetic measurements; however, some kinetic data was obtained for a number of runs in a Teflon-lined, stirred 300 ml autoclave through which mixtures of oxygen and nitrogen were rapidly sparged under pressure. This method provided a constant oxygen partial pressure and enabled us to make several interesting kinetic observations concerning these reactions.

Table IX
EFFECT OF CATALYST CONCENTRATION ON THE CuCl-CATALYZED OXIDATION OF PHENOL IN DMA[a]

[CuCl] mmoles	REACTION TIME, min.	REACTION TEMP., °C	PHENOL CONV., %	p-BENZOQUINONE YIELD, mmole
0.25	180	65	5.4	0.61
0.50	180	65	9.5	0.93
0.75	180	65	10.9	1.53
1.00	180	65	18.4	1.82
0.25	300	65	3.9	0.51
0.50	300	65	11.1	0.95
0.75	300	65	16.9	1.38
1.00	300	65	20.8	2.03
0.25	180	85	5.1	0.73
0.50	180	85	17.3	1.21
0.75	180	85	18.0	1.50
1.00	180	85	32.3	1.84

a) PHENOL, 16 mmole ; 5ml of DMA ; CuCl ; 40% O_2/60% N_2 initially at 750 psig.

When a mixture of 40% O_2 and 60% N_2 was sparged at 250 mls/min through an acetonitrile solution which was 3.2 M in phenol and 0.1 M in $CuCl_2$ at 65°C, there was an induction period of nearly 90 minutes, Figure 7, after which phenol disappeared in a second order manner, Figure 8. Identical experiments carried out using CuCl as the catalyst, Figures 9, 10 showed no induction period but smooth second order disappearance of phenol from the outset. From the slopes of the second order plots, Figures 8, 10, it is apparent that the rate of the $CuCl_2$-catalyzed reaction is essentially the same as the CuCl-catalyzed run after the induction period is complete.

When under these conditions in aqueous acetonitrile, using CuCl as the catalyst, the oxygen content in the oxidizing gas was halved, the rate of phenol oxidation was also halved, indicating that over this concentration range the reaction behaves as if it is first order in molecular oxygen, Figure 11.

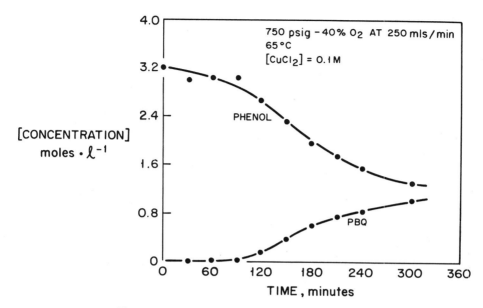

Figure 7. CuCl₂-catalyzed oxidation of phenol in acetonitrile.

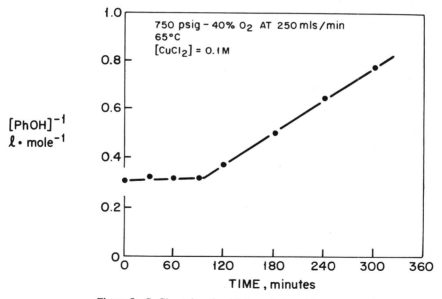

Figure 8. CuCl-catalyzed oxidation of phenol in acetonitrile.

Reaction Pathways

It would seem that an important criterion for the copper-catalyzed PBQ-forming reaction is the ability to continually regenerate an active Cu(I) species. The ev-

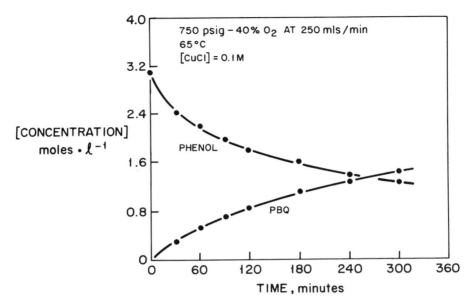

Figure 9. CuCl-catalyzed oxidation of phenol in acetonitrile.

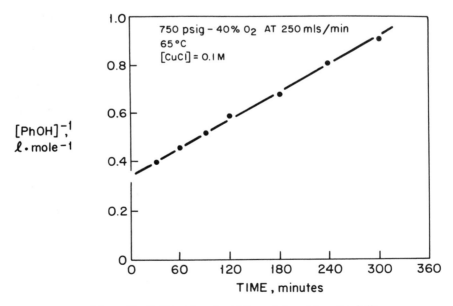

Figure 10, CuCl-catalyzed oxidation of phenol in acetonitrile.

idence that suggests this is: a) the absence of an induction period when CuCl is the catalyst, b) an induction period with $CuCl_2$, c) promotion of $CuCl_2$ with zero-valent transition metals, d) promotion of $CuCl_2$ with added base and e) the relative ease of reaction in acetonitrile—a solvent in which Cu(I) is stable (21).

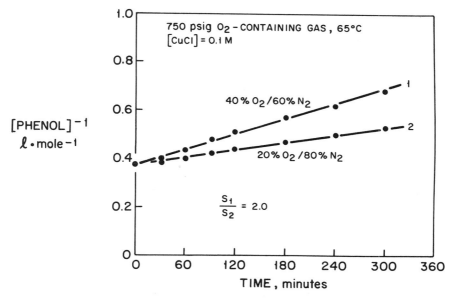

Figure 11. CuCl-catalyzed oxidation of phenol in aqueous acetonitrile (V/V:CH$_3$CN/H$_2$O = 90/10).

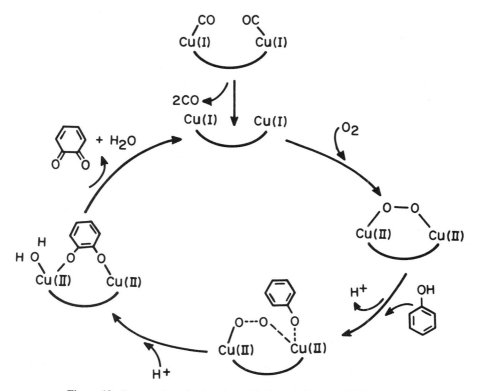

Figure 12. Proposed mechanism for oxidation of phenol to OBQ (17).

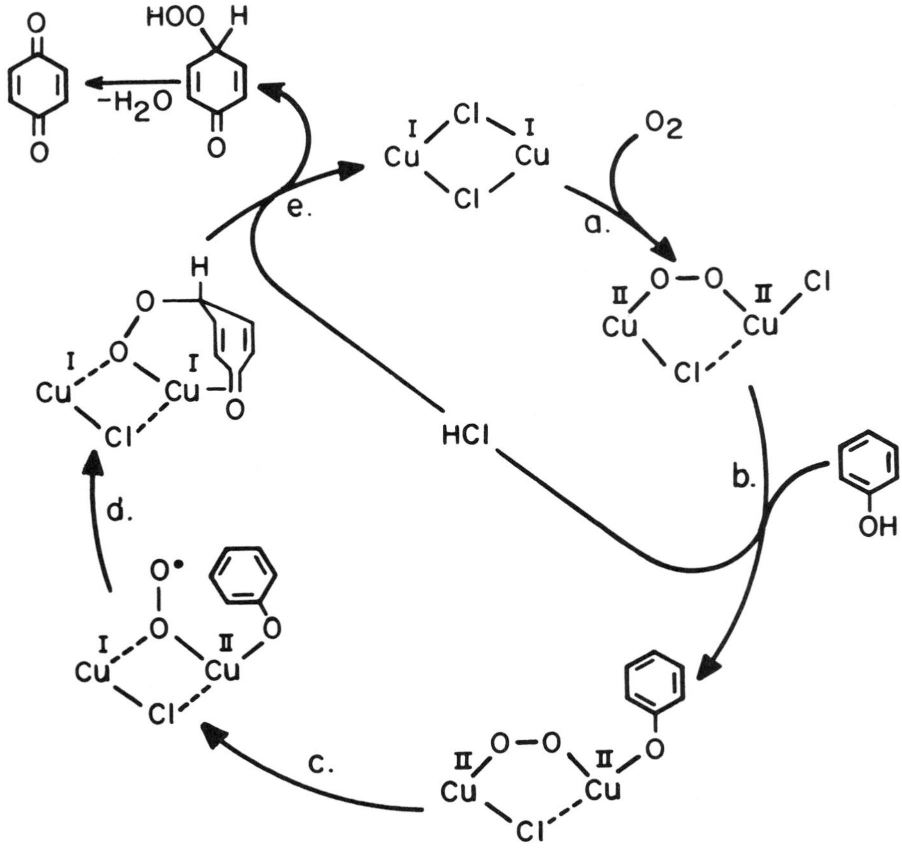

Figure 13. Schematic representation of phenol oxidation by CuCl in acetonitrile.

A mechanism has been proposed, Figure 12, for the catalytic conversion of phenol to OBQ when the catalyst used is a complex of dicopper(I) and a binucleating macrocycle (17). It is likely that, a certain amount of catalytically active chloro bridged species are present in acetonitrile solution. If one attempts to draw a pathway having intermediates similar to those in Figure 12 for the oxidation of phenol to PBQ catalyzed by CuCl in acetonitrile, Figure 13, one is hard pressed to explain the high *para*-selectivity which is observed.

An alternative scheme, Figure 14, may be proposed for this reaction. In such a scheme, an active catalyst may be formed in solution which interacts with dioxygen in a rapid reversible reaction to form a chlorobridged copper(II) complex. The bridged peroxo complex might then react step-wise with two equivalents of phenol to form a copper(II) phenoxide. Copper(II) phenoxides are unstable relative to copper(I) in acetonitrile (2) so Cu(II) is reduced to Cu(I) while phenoxide is oxidized

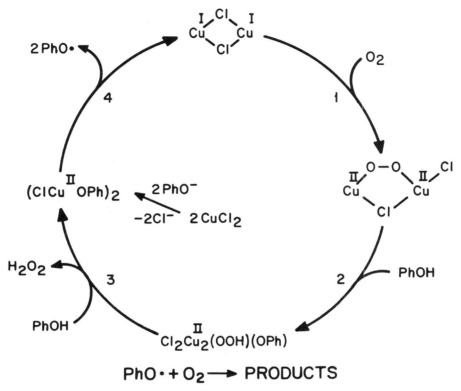

Figure 14. Schematic representation of phenol oxidation catalyzed by a bridged copper(I) dimer in acetonitrile.

to phenoxy radical. Phenoxy radical, either free or in the coordination sphere could then couple with dioxygen to produce PBQ.

The series of reactions shown in Figure 14 is consistent with a reaction which is first order in oxygen and second order in phenol as long as Step 3 is rate determining. In this scheme, base promotes the CuCl$_2$-catalyzed pathway by providing rapid entry into the catalytic cycle *via* the copper(II) phenoxide.

Another reaction scheme, Figure 15, should also be considered. In this scheme a monomeric copper(I) complex could react reversibly with dioxygen to form a superoxo complex. The superoxo complex could abstract hydrogen from phenol to produce a phenoxy radical. The resulting cupric hydroperoxide might react with another molecule of phenol to produce a copper(II) phenoxide which would decompose to phenoxy radical and copper(I). It should be noted, however, that the mononuclear complex: (CH$_3$CN)$_4$Cu$^+$BF$_4^-$ was *not* an active catalyst for phenol oxidation in acetonitrile. On the other hand, Bulkowski and Summers found that when the catalyst was changed from dicopper(I) in a binucleating macrocycle to an analogous mononuclear copper(I) complex, *ortho* selectivity was lost and PBQ was

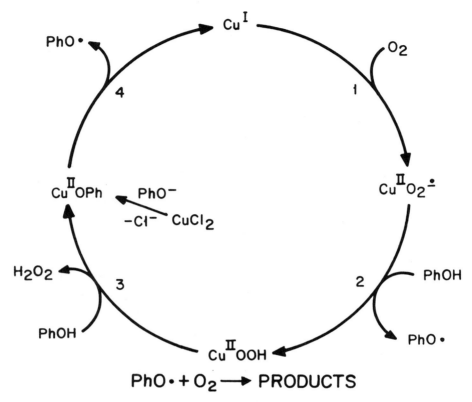

Figure 15. Schematic representation of phenol oxidation catlyzed by monomeric copper(I) in acetonitrile.

formed, albeit unselectively (17). These authors, however worked at low oxygen partial pressure where selective formation of PBQ might not be expected. In any case, it would seem that chloro bridged copper species may not be essential for forming PBQ from phenol.

As shown in Figure 5, the phenoxy radical has a number of reaction pathways open to it. Only two incorporate oxygen into the molecule by coupling the phenoxy radical with dioxygen. The products of direct ring oxygenation are PBQ and OBQ (and/or muconic acids). Thus, if a pathway similar to the one shown in Figure 14 represents the reaction mechanism, high oxygen partial pressure will promote coupling of the phenoxy radical with O_2 to give the quinones which are observed. The regioselectivity of attack of dioxygen on the phenoxy radical seems highly dependent on the nature of the catalyst and hence, perhaps coupling may occur before a fully free phenoxy radical is produced.

Copper-Catalyzed Hydrogenation of PBQ and Other Applications of Phenol Oxidations

As was mentioned, in the Introduction, a potential commercial application of the selective copper catalyzed oxidation of phenol to PBQ would lie in the production of its hydrogenation product—hydroquinone. In this regard, we have found that it is possible to hydrogenate PBQ to hydroquinone using the same catalyst which was used to oxidize phenol. Such a one-pot synthesis can be conveniently carried out by simply purging the reaction mixture from a typical phenol oxidation free of oxygen and then admitting hydrogen to 1500 psig. At 175°C nearly complete hydrogenation of the available PBQ occurs to give the desired hydroquinone.

It should also be mentioned that alkyl substituted phenols are oxidized in the presence of copper halides to give the corresponding paraquinones. Alkyl group substitution appears to enhance the reactivity of the aromatic ring toward oxidation. A number of important antioxidants can be synthesized in this way. In fact, the commercial production of trimethylhydroquinone, a Vitamin E precursor, is accomplished by copper-catalyzed oxidation of 2,3,5-trimethylphenol (7) followed by hydrogenation over a nickel catalyst.

Copper Catalyzed Oxidation of Aromatics—Industrial Perspective

The catalytic oxidation of phenols using copper complexes as catalysts is a rich and diverse area of reaction chemistry leading to numerous products of industrial importance. Commodity chemical monomers such as hydroquinone and polymers like the polyphenylene oxides are important large scale derivatives of phenols but substituted diphenols are useful specialty chemicals with uses as radical inhibitors, and as precursors for other valuable synthetic products such as Vitamin E. We are learning how to control reaction pathways which enable us to produce these important products selectively. The potential now exists for converting a particular phenol to either a polyphenylene oxide (15), a diphenoquinone (15), a quinone, (1-10), a muconic acid derivative (23), or a dyhydroxy aromatic (24) using the proper copper complex under appropriate conditions. As mechanistic understanding of reaction pathways matures, the industrial chemist will be able to fine tune the catalytic chemistry to provide efficient and competitive commercial processes.

Acknowledgements

The authors wish to acknowledge Joyce R. Fistere, and Robert A. Ledley for technical support, Robert W. Shinn for reactor design and construction, and Yana L. Hofman and Robert W. Warren for product separations, identification and analyses.

References and Footnotes

1. Zombeck, A., Drago, R. S., Corden, B. B., and Gaul, J. H., *J. Am. Chem. Soc., 103,* 7580 (1981).
2. Nishinaga, A., Nishizawa, K., Tomita, H. and Matsuura, T., *J. Am. Chem. Soc., 99,* 1287 (1977).
3. Beltrame, P., Beltrame, P. L., and Carniti, P., *Ind. Eng. Chem. Prod. Res. Dev., 18,* 208, (1979).
4. Reilly, E. L., U. S. Patent 4,257,968 (1981).
5. Reilly, E. L., U. S. Patent 3,987,068 (1976).
6. Constantini, M., and Jouffret, F., U. S. Patent 4,208,339 (1980).

7. Brenner, W., U. S. Patent 3,796,732 (1974).
8. Dietle, H. K. and Young, H. S., U. S. Patent 4,360,469 (1982).
9. Hutchings, D. A., U. S. Patent 3,859,317 (1975).
10. Hsu, C.-Y. and Lyons, J. E., U. S. Patent 4,442,036 (1984).
11. Cornubert, R. and Phelisse, J., *Compt. Rend.,* 229, 460 (1949).
12. Popova, N. M. and Sokolskii, D. V., *Trudy Inst. Khim. Nauk, Akad. Nauk Kasakh, S.S.R.,* 2, 84 (1958); *Chem. Abstr., 53,* 275b (1959).
13. Calvin, M., *J. Am. Chem. Soc., 61,* 2230 (1939).
14. Weller, S. and Mills, G. A., *J. Am. Chem. Soc., 75,* 769 (1953).
15. Hay, A. S., U. S. Patent 3,210,384 (1963).
16. Davies, G. and El-Sayed, M., *Inorg. Chem., 22,* 1257 (1982).
17. Bulkowski, J. E. and Summers, W. E. III, Copper Coordination Chemistry: Biochemical and Inorganic Perspectives, Ed., K. D. Karlin and J. Zubieta, Adenine Press, New York, pp.457-472 (1983).
18. Solomon, E. I., Copper Coordination Chemistry: Biochemical and Inorganic Perspectives, Ed., K. D. Karlin and J. Zubieta, Adenine Press, New York, pp. 1-22 (1983).
19. Pasquali, M., Fiaschi, P., Floriani, C., and Gaetani-Manfredotti, A., *J. Chem Soc., Chem. Commun., 197,* (1983).
20. Othmer, D. F. and Josefowitz, S., *Ind. Eng. Chem., 39,* 1176, (1947).
21. Munakata, M. and Kitagawa, S., Copper Coordination Chemistry: Biochemical and Inorganic Perspectives, Ed., K. D. Karlin and J. Zubieta, Adenine Press, New York, pp. 473-493 (1983).
22. Calderazzo, F. and Dell'Amico, G., *J.C.S., Dalton,* 1238, (1979).
23. Rogic, M. M., Swerdloff, M. D., and Demmin, T. R., Copper Coordination Chemistry: Biochemical and Inorganic Perspectives, Ed., K. D. Karlin and J. Zubieta, Adenine Press, New York, pp. 259-279 (1983).
24. Jallabert, C. Lapinte, C., and Reviere, H., *J. Molec. Catal., 14,* 75, (1982).

Biological & Inorganic Copper Chemistry,
ISBN 0-940030-11-X, Eds., K. D. Karlin & J. Zubieta, Adenine Press, ©Adenine Press, 1985

The Synthesis and Structure of Halo(diamine)copper(I) Complexes and a Phenoxide Derivative

Deborah A. Haitko* and Mary F. Garbauskas

General Electric Corporate Research and Development
Schenectady, New York 12301

Introduction

In 1959 A.S. Hay at General Electric Corporate Research and Development first reported the following copper catalyzed reaction (Scheme I) in which 2,6-disubstituted phenols in the presence of copper and pyridine with oxygen yields the carbon-oxygen coupled product, 2,6-disubstituted-1,4-polyphenylene oxide, the carbon-carbon coupled product, 3,3',5,5'-tetrasubstituted diphenylquinone, and the byproduct, water (1). The ratio of II versus III depends upon the steric bulk of substituents R and R' as well as the copper/pyridine ratio (2). Isolation of copper(II) species which are likely intermediates within the above catalytic scheme have been

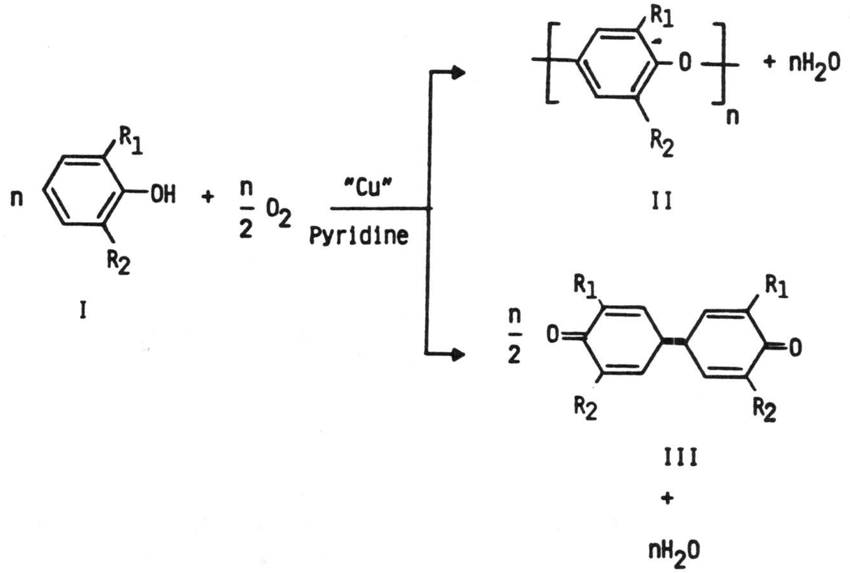

Scheme I

performed by several groups (3). Structural characterization of the dimeric [Cu(py)(OMe)Cl] complex first reported by Finkbeiner, et al. (4) was performed by Willett and Breneman (5). The role of the dimeric [Cu(py)(OMe)Cl] species, a known initiator of oxidative-coupling of 2,6-disubstituted phenols toward oxidative carbon-carbon bond cleavage of certain catechols to yield cis, cis muconic acid monomethylester, has also been extensively studied (6). The synthesis of stabilized copper(II) phenoxide species was performed by Harrod (7) in order to determine the overall thermal stability when complexed with various amine ligands. A direct analogy between copper complexes containing halogen-substituted phenoxide ligands that are stabilized toward oxidative-coupling and copper complexes containing reactive unsubstituted phenoxide ligands may not be valid. We sought, therefore, to explore the reaction chemistry of copper complexes possessing an unsubstituted phenoxide moiety. Since the oxidative-coupling of 2,6-xylenol involves a "copper/amine" catalyst we also wished to consider amine-containing copper complexes containing a copper-aryloxide fragment. The synthesis and structural analysis of halo(diamine)copper(I) complexes provided the synthetic route desired to form phenoxo(diamine)copper(I) complexes.

Halo(diamine)copper(I) Complexes

Synthesis of halo(diamine)copper(I) complexes can be accomplished using the straightforward synthesis shown in the scheme below:

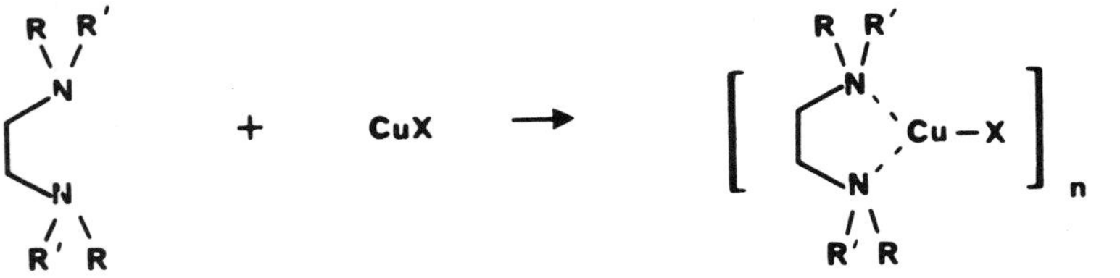

$$n = 1$$

$$
\begin{cases}
R' = H \\
R = CH_3CH_2, \; CH(CH_3)_2, \; C(CH_3)_3 \\
R' = R = CH_3, \; CH_3CH_2 \\
X = CL, \; BR, \; I
\end{cases}
$$

Solvent = CH_3CN

in which an equivalent of an alkyl substituted diamine chosen is added to an acetonitrile solution containing the appropriate cuprous halide. The diamines considered and their abbreviations are given in Figure 1. Structural characterization of a series of halo(diamine)copper(I) complexes was performed yielding essentially

Figure 1. List of abbreviations used throughout text.

N,N'-di-tert-butylethylenediamine	=	DBEDA
N,N'-di-isopropylethylenediamine	=	DIED
N,N'-diethylethylenediamine	=	DEED
N,N,N',N'-tetraethylethylenediamine	=	TEED
N,N,N',N'-tetramethylethylenediamine	=	TMED

Figure 1. List of abbreviations used throughout test. N,N'-di-tert-butylethylenediamine = DBEDA; N,N'-di-isopropylethylenediamine = DIED; N,N'-diethylethylenediamine = DEED; N,N,N',N'-tetra-ethylethylenediamine = TEED; N,N,N',N'-tetramethylethylenediamine = TMED

four different coordination geometries surrounding the copper(I) atom. The inherent restriction imposed through complexation of a chelating diamine limits the co-ordination geometries possible in contrast with the variety of coordination geometries found in copper(I) halide complexes ligated by monodentate Group 5 donor ligands (8). All of the halo(diamine)copper(I) complexes studied are extremely air and moisture sensitive, particularly in solution.

Allan S. Hay at the General Electric Corporation Research and Development Center was the first to report the synthesis of DBEDACuBr which was presumed to

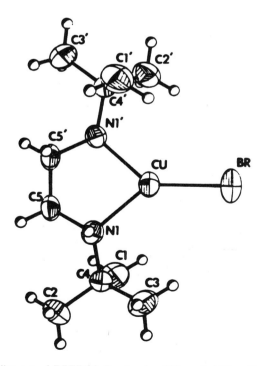

Figure 2. An ORTEP diagram of DBEDACuBr showing 50% probability ellipsoids. Pertinent bond lengths (Å): Cu-Br, 2.285(1); Cu-N, 2.098(5); N1-C-5, 1.487(8); C5-C5, 1.487(13). Pertinent bond angles (°): Br-Cu-N1, 136.8(1); N1-Cu-N1, 86.4(3).

exist as a dimer with bridging bromine atoms (9). An ORTEP diagram of the molecule is shown in Figure 2. DBEDACuBr exists as a monomer in solid form with pseudo-trigonal planar geometry surrounding the copper(I) atom. The crystallographically imposed C_2 axis of symmetry within the molecule leads to equivalence of the copper-nitrogen bond lengths and nitrogen-copper-bromine bond angles. The copper atom lies exactly within the plane formed by the two nitrogen and bromine atoms. The t-butyl groups bound to nitrogen, lie trans with respect to the plane formed by the heavy atoms. The molecular structures of the DBEDACuCl

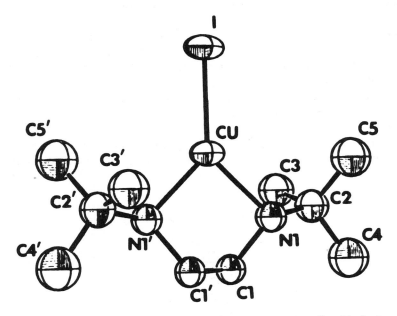

Figure 3. An ORTEP diagram of DBEDACuI showing 50% probability ellipsoids (hydrogen atoms omitted). Pertinent bond lengths (Å): Cu-I, 2.450(2); Cu-N, 2.072(10). Pertinent bond angles (°): I-Cu-N, 136.6(3); N-Cu-N, 86.9(5).

and DBEDACuI complexes is shown in Figure 3. Decreasing the alkyl substitution of the N,N'-dialkylethylenediamine from tert-butyl to iso-propyl we find that like the halo(DBEDA)copper(I) complexes, DIEDCuBr (10) is monomeric in the solid state with pseudo-trigonal planar geometry surrounding the copper(I) atom as is shown in Figure 4. The copper-nitrogen bond lengths of 2.062(6)Å and copper-bromine bond length of 2.263(2)Å are similar to those found in the DBEDACuBr complex. A comparison of the proton nuclear magnetic resonance spectrum of the free DIED ligand versus that of the DIEDCuBr complex shows the hydrogens bound to nitrogen experience the greatest chemical shift difference upon coordination to copper(I) with a difference in the order of 1.5 parts per million. The molecular structure of the u-iodo(DIED)copper(I) dimer is shown in Figure 5 illustrating the overall pseudo-tetrahedral geometry surrounding the copper(I) atom. The increase in coordination number to four in the u-iodo(DIED)copper(I) dimer

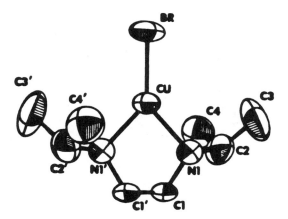

Figure 4. An ORTEP diagram of the nonhydrogen atoms of the DIEDCuBr molecule showing thermal ellipsoid probability of 50%, ref. 10. Pertinent bond lengths (Å): Cu-Br, 2.263(2); Cu-N1, 2.062(6). Pertinent bond angles (°): Br-Cu-N1, 137.5(2); N1-Cu-N1, 85.0(4).

leads to an increase in the copper-nitrogen bond lengths (~0.1Å) versus the copper-nitrogen bond lengths found for the previously described three-coordinate copper(I) complexes. Deviation from tetrahedral geometry is revealed through the dihedral angles between the planes formed by atoms Cu1, N2, N1 and I2, Cu1, I1 with a dihedral angle of 97.9° and I2, Cu2, I1 and N4, Cu2, N3 with a dihedral angle of 85.9°. An intriguing feature of the dimeric u-iodo(DIED)copper(I) complex is the

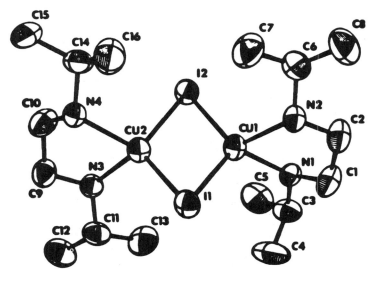

Figure 5. An ORTEP diagram of the nonhydrogen atoms of the [DIEDCuI]$_2$ dimer showing 40% probability ellipsoids. Pertinent bond lengths (Å): I1-Cu1, 2.661(1); I1-Cu2, 2.579(1); I2-Cu1, 2.581(1); I2-Cu2, 2.666(1); Cu1-Cu2, 2.733(1); Cu-N$_{avg}$, 2.17. Pertinent bond angles (°): Cu1-I1-Cu2, 62.8(6), Cu1-I2-Cu2, 62.7(7), I1-Cu1-I2, 116.9(4), I1-Cu2-I2, 116.8(4).

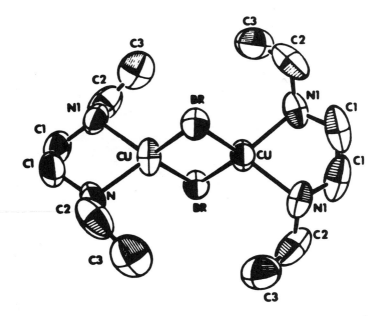

Figure 6. The molecular structure of the u-bromo(DEED) copper(I) dimer (omitting hydrogen atoms). Selected bond lengths (Å): Cu-Br, 2.463(1); Cu-N, 2.148(5), Cu-Cu, 2.740(2). Selected bond angles (°): N-Cu-N, 83.8(3); Cu-Br-Cu, 67.61(4).

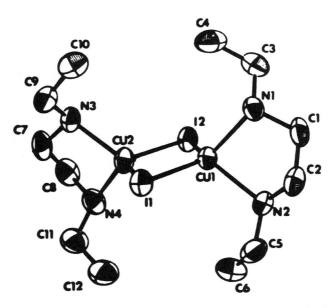

Figure 7. The molecular structure of the u-iodo (DEED) copper(I) dimer (omitting hydrogen atoms). Selected bond lengths (Å): Cu-N$_{avg}$, 2.15; Cu-I$_{avg}$, 2.62; Cu1-Cu2, 2.600(1); and angles (°): Cu-1-I1-Cu2, 60.25(2); Cu1-I2-Cu2, 58.76(2).

distance between the two copper(I) atoms with an intramolecular separation of 2.733(1)Å. Significant intramolecular copper(I)-copper(I) interactions have been observed in complexes containing both sigma and pi-donating amines (11). The reaction of N,N'-diethylethylenediamine with either cuprous bromide or cuprous iodide leads to the formation of u-halogen bridged dimers as shown in Figures 6 and 7, respectively (12). The u-bromo(DEED)copper(I) dimer crystallizes in the Fddd space group and is the only u-halogen bridged dimer of the series that possesses equivalent copper-halogen and copper-nitrogen bond lengths. The copper(I)-copper(I) separation in the u-bromo(DEED)copper(I) dimer is similar to that of the u-iodo (DIED)copper(I) dimer with a separation of 2.740(2)Å. The deviation from tetrahedral geometry is reflected by the dihedral angle of 83.2(2)° formed by the planes containing the copper and two bromine atoms and the copper and two nitrogen atoms. The u-iodo(DEED)copper(I) dimer crystallizes such that three of the alkyl substituents bound to nitrogen are oriented in the same direction in space with respect to the plane roughly formed by the four nitrogen atoms leading to inequivalence of the two monomeric units within the dimer. Dissociation of the dimer to two monomers

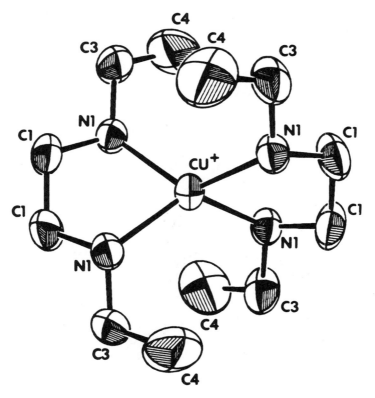

Figure 8. The molecular structure of the (DEED)$_2$Cu$^+$ cation (hydrogen atoms omitted). Selected bond lengths (Å): Cu1-N1, 2.117(5); Cu2-C1, 2.069(4). Selected bond angles (°): N1-Cu1-N1, 120.67(33); N1-Cu1-N1, 125.75(29); C1-Cu2-C1, 180.00(0).

occurs in acetonitrile based on vapor phase osmometry results. Nuclear magnetic resonance studies indicate exchange between free and complexed diamine for the halo(diamine)copper(I) complexes is rapid at room temperature. The rapid exchange of diamine ligands is supported by the observation of a single isomer in the proton nuclear magnetic resonance spectrum of the dissociated u-iodo(DEED)copper(I) dimer in acetonitrile.

Interestingly we find that the reaction of N,N'-diethylethylenediamine with cuprous chloride forms the products of a ligand disproportionation reaction yielding the bis(DEED)copper(I) cation and the dichlorocuprate. The molecular structure of the cation is shown in Figure 8. An analogy can be made to a reaction recently reported by Pasquali and Ghilardi in which addition of 1,2-bisdiphenylphosphino-ethane to a solution containing mesitylcopper(I) led to formation of (disphos)$_2$Cu$^+$ cation and dimesitylcuprate (13). Similar ligand disproportionation reactions involving arsenic donor ligands and various copper(I) halides have been reported (14).

Tetraethylethylenediamine forms u-halogen bridged dimers with each of the copper(I) halides and each dimer has a copper(I)-copper(I) interaction on the order of 2.60Å (15). Recently, the structure and reactivity toward oxygen was reported for the u-bromo(TEED)copper(I) dimer (15).

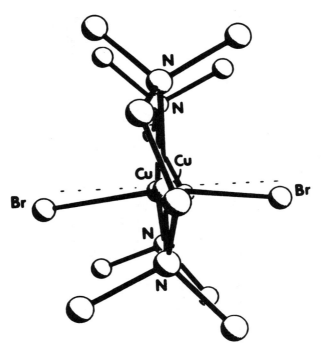

Figure 9. An ORTEP diagram of the u-bromo(TMED)copper(I) dimer (nonhydrogen atoms only). Pertinent bond lengths (Å): Cu-Br$_{avg}$, 2.47; Cu-N$_{avg}$, 2.17; Cu1-Cu2, 2.563(2).

The shortest distances between the copper(I) atoms of the u-halogen bridged dimers are found with the u-iodo and u-bromo (TMED)copper(I) complexes. The molecular structure of the u-bromo (TMED)copper(I) dimer is shown in Figure 9. The u-bromo (TMED)copper(I) dimer exhibits the shortest copper(I)-copper(I) interaction of the series with a distance of 2.563(2)Å. The copper atoms and halogen atoms of the u-iodo or u-bromo (TMED)copper(I) dimers do not form a plane as is observed in the previously discussed u-halogen bridged dimers. The deviation from planarity can be seen in Figure 9 viewing the u-bromo(TMED)copper(I) dimer through the plane roughly formed by the four nitrogen atoms.

The angle formed by the bromine atoms subtended by the mid-point between the copper-copper vector is 163° so that the deviation from planarity is approximately 17° (17). The reaction between tetramethylethylenediamine and cuprous chloride leads to a ligand disproportionation to form the $(TMED)_2Cu^+$ cation and dichloro-cuprate (18). The cation bistetramethylethylenediamine copper(I) was first observed

Table I.   Structural Summary of Diamine Copper(I) Halide Complexes

Diamine	CuCl	CuBr	CuI
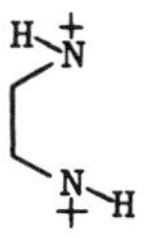 (structure)	Monomer	Monomer	Monomer
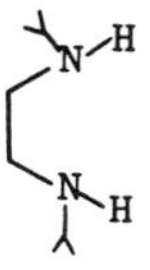 (structure)		Monomer	Dimer* 2.73Å
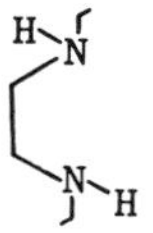 (structure)	Ligand Disproportionation	Dimer 2.74Å	Dimer 2.60Å
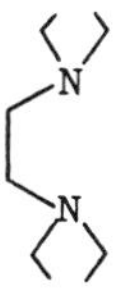 (structure)	Dimer 2.60Å	Dimer 2.60Å	Dimer 2.66Å
(structure)	Ligand Disproportionation	Dimer 2.56Å	Dimer 2.58Å

* Cu-Cu Distance

by C. Floriani (19) that formed upon warming excess tetramethylethylenediamine in the presence of a methanol adduct of $(TMED)Cu(CO)^+B\phi_4^-$ to room temperature.

A summary of the copper(I) complexes discussed is shown in Table I. Factors that govern monomer versus dimer formation are mainly intrinsic such as the inductive effect of the alkyl substituent bound to nitrogen, electronegativity of the halide, and steric interactions of all ligands. Extrinsic factors such as the solvent used for crystallization and crystal packing forces must also be considered.

Phenoxo(diamine)copper(I) Complexes

The characterization of the halo(diamine)copper(I) complexes led to a synthetic route for the phenoxocopper(I) derivatives desired. Addition of potassium phenoxide to a solution of chloro(DBEDA)copper(I) led to precipitation of potassium chloride and formation of phenoxo(DBEDA)copper(I) (18). Proton nuclear magnetic resonance spectra indicate that the chemical shifts of the t-butyl methyl protons and methylene protons of the DBEDA portion of the phenoxo(DBEDA)copper(I) complex differ little from the starting material, chloro(DBEDA)copper(I). The chemical shifts of the para and ortho protons of the phenoxide moiety shift nearly 0.3 and 0.2 ppm downfield, respectively, from tetramethylsilane upon coordination to the (DBEDA) copper(I) fragment as compared to the shifts found for potassium phenoxide. The results of the three-dimensional x-ray crystallographic analysis of phenoxo(DBEDA) copper(I) dimer are shown in Figures 10 and 11. There are remarkable structural

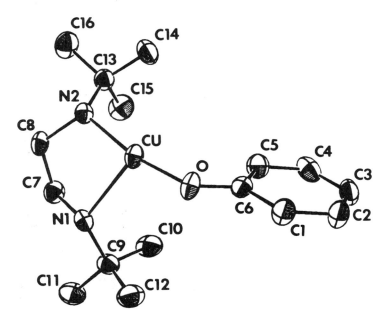

Figure 10. The molecular structure of half of the phenoxo-(DBEDA) copper(I) dimer. Hydrogen atoms omitted for clarity.

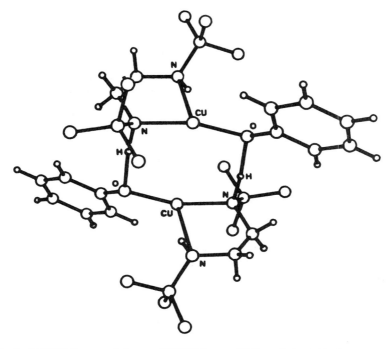

Figure 11. An ORTEP diagram of phenoxo(DBEDA)copper(I) dimer (selected hydrogen atoms shown).

features within the phenoxo(DBEDA)copper(I) dimer. The overall geometry surrounding copper(I) is a distorted three-coordinate geometry approximating a T-shaped orientation of ligands about the metal atom. the molecule exists in solid form as a dimer with association occuring through hydrogen-bonding of the hydrogen bound to nitrogen and the oxygen of a neighboring phenoxide group. The distortions from a trigonal planar geometry surrounding the copper(I) atom are reflected in the grossly inequivalent copper-nitrogen bond lengths for Cu-N1 and Cu-N2 of 2.346(3)Å and 1.969(3)Å, respectively. The Cu-N1 bond length is quite long by comparison to other copper(I) complexes containing saturated nitrogen donor ligands (19). The copper-oxygen bond length of 1.879(2)Å is slightly shorter than the copper-oxygen bond in $[p\text{-MeC}_6H_4NC]_2Cu(2,6\text{-Bu}_2{}^+C_6H_3O]$ (20). The angles subtended at the copper atom reflect the T-shape geometry with the angle about N2-Cu-O approaching linearity at 165.9(1)° and the angle about N1-Cu-O of 108.6(1)°. The Cu-O-C6 angle is 128.5(2)° and the oxygen atom lies 0.133Å from the plane formed by Cu, N1, and N2. Unlike the halo (DBEDA)copper(I) complexes, the t-butyl groups in phenoxo(DBEDA)copper(I) are oriented cis with respect to the plane formed by Cu, N1, and N2. There is no bonding between the copper atoms in the phenoxo(DBEDA)copper(I) dimer with an inter-molecular separation of 3.17Å. Phenoxo (DBEDA)copper(I) is reactive toward carbon monoxide yielding an adduct with a Cu-CO infrared stretch at 2050cm^{-1}. Work is currently in progress to characterize the carbonyl adducts.

Conclusion

The synthetic and structural characterization of a series of halo(diamine)copper(I) complexes has been described. A delicate balance between intrinsic and extrinsic factors described governs the formation of monomer, dimer, or products of ligand disproportionation. The characterization of the halo(diamine)copper(I) adducts has led to a synthetic route toward phenoxo(diamine)copper(I). Phenoxo(DBEDA) copper(I) represents the first structurally characterized phenoxocopper(I) complex involving coordination of a sigma-donating amine such as N,N'-di-tert-butylethylene-diamine. A study of the reaction chemistry of novel phenoxo-copper(I) complexes is currently underway.

Acknowledgement

We wish to thank the General Electric Company for support of the work presented. We are also indebted to Dr. Michael Extine and Dr. Jan Troup of the Molecular Structure Corporation who performed several of the crystal structure determinations. Discussions with Dr. Allan S. Hay and Dr. D.M. White of General Electric are also gratefully acknowledged.

References and Footnotes

1. a. A.S. Hay, H.S. Blanchard, C.F. Endres, and J.W. Eustance, *J. Amer. Chem. Soc. 81,* 6335 (1959). b. A.S. Hay, *J. Polymer Sci. 58,* 581 (1962).
2. a. A.S. Hay, *SPE Trans. 2,* 108 (1962). b. G.F. Endres, A.S. Hay, J.W. Eustance, and J. Kwiatek, *SPE Trans. 2,* 109 (1962). c. G.F. Endres, A.S. Hay, and J.W. Eustance, *J. Org. Chem. 28,* 1300 (1963). d. H. Finkbeiner, A.S. Hay, H.S. Blanchard, and G.F. Endres, *J. Org. Chem. 31,* 549 (1966).
3. a. G.F. Endres, A.S. Hay, and J.W. Eustance, *J. Org. Chem. 28,* 1300 (1963). b. H.S. Blanchard, H.L. Finkbeiner, and G.F. Endres, *Polymer Preprints, Am. Chem. Soc. 2,* 331 (1961). c. I. Bodek and G. Davies, *Inorg. Chem. 17,* 1814 (1978). d. I. Bodek and G. Davies, *Inorg. Chim. Acta 27,* 213 (1978).
4. See reference 3b.
5. R.D. Willett and G.L. Breneman, *Inorg. Chem. 22,* 326 (1983).
6. a. J. Tsuji and H. Takayanagi, *J. Amer. Chem. Soc. 96,* 7349 (1974). b. M.M. Rojic in *"Aspects of Mechanism and Organometallic Chemistry",* Ed., J.H. Brewster, Plenum Press, New York, p. 141 (1978). c. M.M. Rojic and T.R. Demmin, *J. Amer. Chem. Soc. 100,* 5472 (1978). d. T.R. Demmin, M.D. Swerdloff, and M.M. Rojic, *J. Amer. Chem. Soc. 103,* 5796 (1981). e. M.M. Rojic, T.R. Demmin, and W.B. Hammond, *J. Amer. Chem. Soc. 98,* 7441 (1976).
7. J.F. Harrod, *Can. J. Chem. 47,* 442 (1969).
8. See for example: a. S.J. Lippard and J.J. Mayerle, *Inorg. Chem. 11,* 753 (1972) and references cited therein. b. J.T. Gill, J.J. Magerle, P.S. Welcker, D.F. Lewis, D.A. Ucko, D.J. Barton, D. Stowens, and S.J. Lippard, *Inorg. Chem. 15,* 111 (1976). c. M.R. Churchill and K.L. Kalra, *Inorg. Chem. 13,* 1065 (1974). d. M.R. Churchill and K.L. Kalra, *ibid. 13,* 1427 (1974). e. M.R. Churchill and K.L. Kalra, *ibid. 13,* 1899 (1974). f. M.R. Churchill and F.J. Rotella, *ibid. 18,* 116 (1979). g. P.G. Eller, G.J. Kubas and R.R. Ryan, *Inorg. Chem. 16,* 2454 (1977). h. A. Kabesh and R.S. Nyholm, *J. Chem. Soc. 38* (1951). i. N. Marsich, G. Nardin, and L. Randaccio, *J. Am. Chem. Soc. 95,* 4053 (1973). j. N. Bresciani, N. Marsich, G. Nardin, and L. Randaccio, *Inorg. Chim. Acta 10,* L5 (1974). k. A. Camus, G. Nardin, and L. Randaccio, *Inorg. Chim. Acta 12,* 23 (1975). l. V.G. Albano, P.L. Bellon, and G. Ciani, *J. Chem. Soc. Dalton,* 1938 (1972).
9. A.S. Hay, U.S. Patent 3,914,266 (1975).
10. D.A. Haitko, *J. of Coord. Chem. 13,* 119 (1984).

11. See for example: a. M. Pasquali, C. Floriani, A. Gaetani-Manfredotti, and C. Guastini, *J. Amer. Chem. Soc.* 185, *103* (1981). b. M. Pasquali, C. Floriani, G. Venturi, A. Gaetani-Manfredotti, and A. Chiesi-Villa, *ibid. 104,* 4092 (1982). c. V. Schramm, *Inorg. Chem. 17,* 714 (1978). d. R.R. Gagne, R.P. Kreh, J.A. Dodge, R.E. Marsh, and M. McCool, *Inorg. Chem. 21,* 254 (1982). e. M.R. Churchill, G. Davies, M.A. El-Sayed, J.A. Fournier, J.P. Hutchinson, and J.A. Zubieta, *Inorg. Chem. 23,* 783 (1984).

12. D.A. Haitko, to be published.

13. P. Leoni, M. Pasquali, and C.A. Ghilardi, *J. Chem. Soc. Chem. Commun.* 240 (1983).

14. R.S. Nyholm, *J. Chem. Soc.* 38 (1951).

15. D.A. Haitko and M.F. Garbauskas, submitted to *Acta Crystallographica.*

16. M.R. Churchill, G. Davies, M.A. El-Sayed, J.A. Fournier, J.P. Hutchinson, and J.A. Zubieta, *Inorg. Chem. 23,* 783 (1984).

17. D.A. Haitko and M.F. Garbauskas, submitted to *Acta Crystallographica.*

18. D.A. Haitko and M.F. Garbauskas, submitted to *Inorg. Chem.*

19. See for example: a. M. Pasquali, C. Floriani, G. Venturi, A. Gaetani-Manfredotti and A. Chiese-Villa, *J. Amer. Chem. Soc. 104,* 4092 (1982). b. M. Pasquali, C. Floriani, and A. Gaetani-Manfredotti, *Inorg. Chem. 20,* 3382 (1981).

20. P. Fiashi, C. Floriani, M. Pasquali, A. Chiesi-Villa, and Carlo Guastini, *J. Chem. Soc., Chem. Commun.* 888 (1984).

Biological & Inorganic Copper Chemistry,
ISBN 0-940030-11-X, Eds., K. D. Karlin & J. Zubieta, Adenine Press, ©Adenine Press, 1985

Reactions of α-Diketones and o-Quinones with Metallic Copper and Dioxygen

Gábor Speier and Zoltán Tyeklár

Institute of Organic Chemistry,
Veszprém University of Chemical Engineering,
8201 Veszprém, Hungary

Abstract

Metallic copper reacts under argon in the presence of pyridine (py), 2,2'-bipyridine (bpy), or tetramethylethylenediamine (tmen) with 2,2'-furil, benzil or di-2-pyridyl diketone to the corresponding semidione anions and consecutively to ene-diolate dianions. With 3,5-di-t-butyl-o-benzoquinone catecholato copper(II) complexes, with 9,10-phenanthrenequinone bis(semiquinone) copper(II) and catecholato copper(II) complexes are formed. 1,2-Dicarbonyls give with copper (ratio 1:1) and dioxygen in pyridine dicarboxylato copper(II) complexes of the type $(ArCOO)_2Cupy_n$. 1,2-Dicarbonyls react with metallic copper in the ratio 1:2 and dioxygen to give carboxylate copper oxygen complexes of the formulae $(ArCOOCu)_4O_2py_n$. In cases of 3,5-di-t-butyl-o-benzoquonone and 9,10-phenanthrenequinone with copper powder and dioxygen oxidative $C-C$ bond cleavage can be achieved using py and bpy as ligands. In case of the catecholato copper(II) complex of 9,10-phenanthrenequinone with tmen as ligand in acetonitrile only the quinone but in pyridine also diphenic acid could be isolated after oxygenation and hydrolysis.

Introduction

The reversible binding and activation of dioxygen is the most interesting aspect of Cu(I) chemistry (1). The Cu(I)/Cu(II) redox couple shows some similarities with that of Fe(II)/Fe(III) in biological systems. Copper ions form the prosthetic group of the oxygen transport protein hemocyanin (2) and of several important oxidases (3,4), and oxygenases (5). Model studies of biological oxidations of simple copper(I) complexes seem to be of particular importance (1,6). Cuprous chloride in pyridine affords an active catalyst for the oxidative cleavage of catechol with molecular oxygen to produce *cis,cis*-muconic acid monomethyl ester in the presence of methanol (7). This is analogous to the oxidative cleavage of catechol to *cis,cis*-muconic acid by the enzyme pyrocatechase (8). It was further demonstrated, that the oxidizing agent is a dimeric cupric methoxy hydroxide, formed by addition of water to $Cu(OCH_3)Cl$, and it also converts phenol to catechol and o-benzoquinone, followed by scission to *cis-cis*-muconic acid methyl ester (9). 9,10-Phenanthrenequinone undergoes oxygenolysis by copper(I) chloride and bromide to diphenato copper(II) halide pyridine complexes (10), and 3,5-di-t-butyl-o-benzoquinone is transformed to *cis,cis*-2,4-di-t-butyl-muconic acid dimethyl ester by $Cu(OCH_3)Cl$ in pyridine (11).

Since the Cu(O)/Cu(I) redox couple (E_{ox}^{o} = −0.521 V) is more negative than Cu(I)/Cu(II) (E_{ox}^{o} = −0.153 V) (12), the use of copper(O) in pyrocatechase model reactions seemed promising. Copper(I) chloride and bromide form only olefinic complexes with quinones (13,14), although they are good electron acceptors but metallic copper is able to transfer electrons to π-acids such as nitrobenzenes, *p*-benzoquinone (15), and tetracyanoethylene (16) forming radical anions. These considerations and an early report of Mohler (17) on the oxygenation of benzoin to benzoic acid by copper in pyridine prompted us to investigate the reactions of metallic copper with α-diketones and *o*-quinones and their oxygenolysis in the presence of copper.

Materials and Methods

Pyridine was purified by distillation over KOH and CaH_2, acetonitrile over P_2O_5 and K_2CO_3 and dichloromethane over P_2O_5. Tetramethylethylenediamine was dried over CaH_2 and distilled. 2,2'-Bipyridine and copper powder were commercial products and used as supplied. Benzil (18), 2,2'-furil (19), di-2-pyridyl diketone (20), 3,5-di-*t*-butyl-*o*-benzoquinone (21), and 9,10-phenanthrenequinone (22) were prepared according to the literature. The solvents were stored under argon and standard inert gas technique was used. EPR spectra were run on a JEOL JES-FE3X instrument in sealed tubes. Magnetic susceptibilities were measured on a Bruker B-E 10B8 magnetic balance and UV-VIS spectra taken on a Specord 75 IR (Carl Zeiss) spectrophotometer. All isolated compounds gave satisfactory elemental analyses.

Results and Discussion

The experimental results are treated in three sections a) the reactions of metallic copper with α-diketones and *o*-quinones under argon; b) the oxygenolysis of α-diketones and *o*-quinones in the presence of metallic copper, and c) the reaction of species formed under argon with dioxygen.

a) 2,2'-Furil reacts with copper in pyridine to give an EPR spectrum as shown in Figure 1. On adding bpy to the solution the spectrum does not change. In the presence of tmen in pyridine only a poorly resolved spectrum could be obtained,

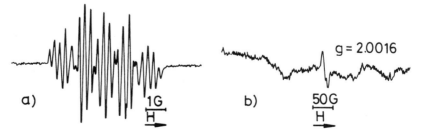

Figure 1. The EPR spectra of a) 2,2'-furil and Cu in pyridine and b) benzil and Cu in pyridine at room temperature.

however. The semidione anion so formed is usually a mixture of *cis* and *trans* species. The two forms give rise to different EPR spectra, because the coupling constants of the ring protons are greater in the *cis-* than in the *trans*-isomer (23). The calculated coupling constants $a_H3=1.25$; $a_H4=0.25$; $a_H5=1.17$ for the *cis-* and $a_H3=0.98$; $a_H4=0.28$; $a_H5=0.90$ G for the *trans*-isomer with a concentration ratio of 50:50% could be obtained by simulation, suggesting a somewhat greater deviation of coplanarity in the *cis*-isomer.

In the reaction of benzil with metallic copper in pyridine under Ar the semidione anion is formed only temporarily and is poorly resolved as shown in Figure 1. The EPR signal vanishes relatively fast but the yellow color of the solution persists. In the UV-VIS spectrum of the solution a new band at $\lambda_{max}=362$ nm may be assigned to the metal-to-ligand CT band of an enediolate dicopper(I) pyridine complex. Several copper(I) complexes with π-binding ligands show MLCT bands in the visible region (24).

In the case of di-2-pyridyl diketone no EPR signal could be detected in the reaction with copper with py, bpy or tmen ligands. A MLCT transition in the UV-VIS spectrum of the pyridine solution at $\lambda_{max}=349$ nm, however, suggests the presence of a diamagnetic ene-diolate dicopper(I) complex. In the case of the two latter diketones the lifetimes of the semidione anions are small and they are easily reduced further by copper to the EPR-silent and ene-diolate dicopper(I) complexes. In these cases no solid products could be isolated. Probably, equilibria are operating with small concentrations on the product side.

With 3,5-di-*t*-butyl-*o*-benzoquinone and metallic copper in acetonitrile catecholato copper(II) complexes as shown on Figure 2 could be isolated. The catecholato

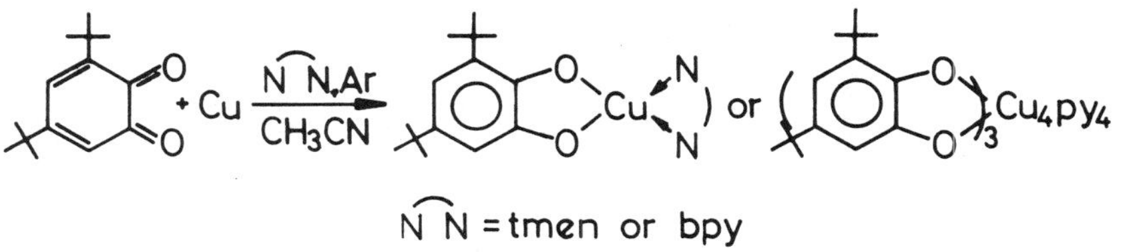

$$\widehat{N\ N} = tmen\ or\ bpy$$

Figure 2. The reaction of 3,5-di-*t*-butyl-*o*-benzoquinone with copper in the presence of py, bpy, or tmen ligands.

complex with bpy has been obtained in 85% yield and was shown to be identical with that described by Brown *et al.* (25). The paramagnetic (1.99 BM) tmen complex has been isolated in 92% yield as bright brown crystals. With py as ligand fine brown needles of probably tetranuclear catecholato copper complex with a magnetic moment of 2.77 BM/4Cu have been obtained. The EPR spectra of these complexes reveal, that these are true catecholato copper(II) complexes; even in solution no signals of semiquinone species could be found. With the bpy complex in pyridine the hyperfine coupling of copper(II) $a_{Cu}=87.8$ G at $g=2.124$ and the fourth band

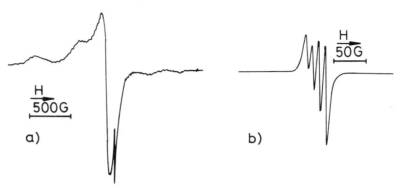

Figure 3. The EPR spectrum of 3,5-di-*t*-butyl-catecholato(2,2′-bipyridine)copper(II) in methanol at room temperature.

splitted by two equivalent nitrogens (a_N=10.9 G), as shown in Figure 3, support this statement. The catecholato copper(II) complex with tmen shows a similar but less resolved spectrum (g=2.120; a_{Cu}=93.4; a_N~6.5 G). The pyridine complex exhibits a more complicated picture indicating the presence of a mixture of several species. The reaction of 9,10-phenanthrenequinone with metallic copper in pyridine leads in 96% yield to the bis(semiquinone)copper(II) complex as shown in Figure 4. The

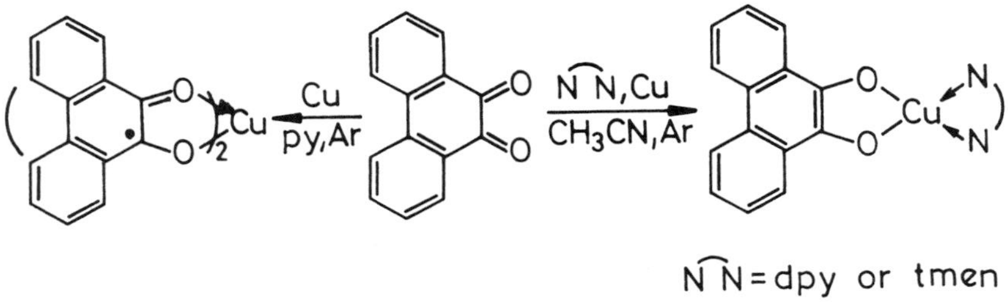

N N = dpy or tmen

Figure 4. The reaction of 9,10-phenanthrenequinone with copper in the presence of by, bpy, and tmen ligands.

compound exhibits a room temperature magnetic moment of only 1.73 BM, probably due to strong antiferromagnetic interaction between the three paramagnetic centers. Its EPR spectrum taken on a solid sample shows qualitative the existence of Cu(II) and the semiquinone ligand (Figure 5). In acetonitrile solution the d-d transition of

a)

b)

Figure 5. The EPR spectra of bis(9,10-phenanthrenesemiquinone)copper(II) a) in solid form at room temperature b) in pyridine solution at 58°C.

Cu(II) at λ_{max}=742 nm could also be observed, which was absent in pyridine. In pyridine solution only the signal of the semiquinone ligand at g=2.0098 with hyperfine coupling of a_{Cu}=10.1 G, as shown in Figure 5, could be seen. The EPR spectra reveal that the bis(semiquinone)copper(II) complex is transformed in pyridine to the semiquinone copper(I) complex and the free quinone.

With tmen and bpy, as shown in Figure 4, catecholato copper(II) complexes are formed in 92 and 96% yields, respectively. The bpy complex is paramagnetic with 1.82 BM at room temperature and can be prepared also from the bis(semiquinone)-copper(II) complex by adding bpy (yield 98%). The ochre coloured tmen complex with a magnetic moment of 1.77 BM is a true catecholato complex apparent from its solid state EPR spectrum. In acetonitrile, however, a weak signal at g=2.0066 without hyperfine structure and a hyperfine coupled signal at the g value of 2.111 with a_{Cu}=90.6 due to copper(II) can be seen, as shown in Figure 6. There is an

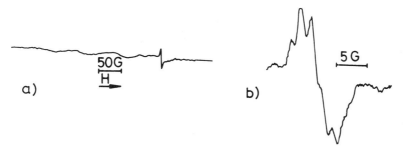

Figure 6. The EPR spectrum of the catecholato copper (II) complex from 9,10-phenanthrenequinone with tmen ligand in acetonitrile at room temperature (a); The signal at g=2.0042 enlarged (b).

equilibrium between catecholato copper(II) and semiquinone copper(I) complexes. In pyridine, which stabilizes Cu(I) considerably, only semiquinone copper(I) species are present giving an EPR signal identical to that shown in Figure 5b.

A general scheme for the reactions of α-diketones and o-quinones with metallic copper is proposed in Figure 7. It can be seen, that in the reaction of copper with α-diketones semidione anions (I) and ene-diolate complexes (II) are present in solutions, while with 3,5-di-t-butyl-o-benzoquinone catecholato copper(II) complexes are formed and are present in solution. 9,10-Phenanthrenequinone give bis(semi-quinone) and catecholato copper(II) complexes, which on dissolution result in semiquinone copper(I) complexes (III) in concentrations depending on the solvent.

b) In the reactions of 2,2'-furil, benzil, and bi-2-pyridyl diketone and metallic copper (stoichiometry 1:1) in pyridine (or in acetonitrile with py) with dioxygen, after a short induction period O_2-uptake ensues and then ceases at a 1:1 ratio of O_2 to diketones (Figure 8.) After hydrolysis and extraction furan-2-carboxylic acid (95%),

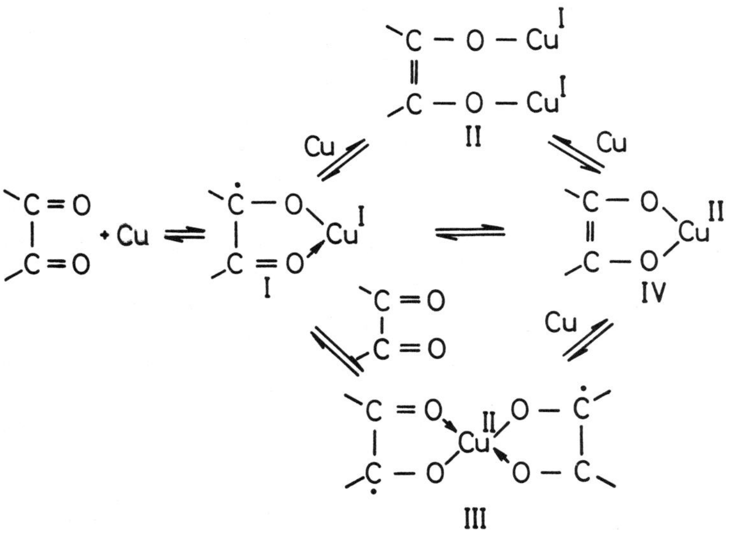

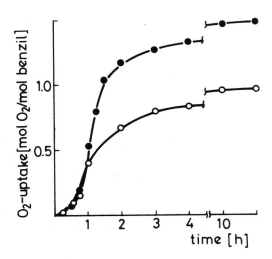

Figure 7. General scheme for the formation of species in the reaction of α-diketones and o-quinones with copper.

Figure 8. The dioxygen-uptake of benzil and copper in pyridine. ○ Copper to benzil ratio 1:1, ● Copper to benzil ratio 2:1.

benzoic acid (98%), and picolinic acid (85%) have been isolated. Oxidizing benzil in acetonitrile with tmen as ligand benzoic acid was isolated after the usual work-up in 90% yield. The primarily formed carboxylato complexes could be also isolated and characterized as summarized in Table I.

Table I
Characterization of carboxylato copper(II) complexes (26)

Complex	Color	Yield (%)	$\nu_{CO_2}(cm^{-1})$	$\mu_{eff}(BM)$
$(C_6H_5COO)_2Cupy_2$	blue	92	1601; 1379	1.79
$(C_4H_3OCOO)_2Cupy_2$	violet	97	1600; 1352	1.69
$(C_5H_4NCOO)_2Cu$	violet	~100	1628; 1340	1.84
$(C_6H_5COO)_2Cu(tmen)$	blue	93	1551; 1379	1.83

Reacting the diketones mentioned before with copper in the stoichiometry 1:2 in pyridine or in acetonitrile containing py as ligand the O_2-uptake increases to 1.5:1 with respect to the diketones, as shown in Figure 8. From the solutions carboxylato copper oxygen complexes could be isolated and characterized as summarized in Table II.

Table II
Characterization of carboxylato copper oxygen complexes

Complex	Color	Yield (%)	$\nu_{CO_2}(cm^{-1})$	$\mu_{eff}(BM)$
$(C_6H_5COOCu)_4O_2py_2$	green	90	1624; 1401	2.27
$(C_4H_3OCOOCu)_4O_2py_4$	brown	~100	1650; 1365	2.73
$(C_5H_4NCOOCu)_4O_2py$	bright blue	46	1650; 1344	2.84

From the magnetic moments it can be concluded, that either not all Cu atoms are in the oxidation state +2 or that a strong antiferromagnetic interaction is responsible for their small susceptibility. No O,O stretching frequences could be found in the IR spectra. In solutoin (CH_2Cl_2,py) they showed typical four-line EPR spectra centered at about g=2.15 with copper hyperfine coupling constants of ~70 G. The complexes are very sensitive towards moisture, therefore no reliable molecular weight determinations could be carried out. They may have a polinuclear structure similar to those proposed for oxygen complexes prepared from copper halides with nitrogen containing ligands (27).

The $(C_6H_5COOCu)_4O_2py_2$ complex reacts with benzil under argon in pyridine according to eq. 1, where benzil is oxygenolyzed

$$(C_6H_5COOCu)_4O_2py_2 + C_6H_5COCOC_6H_5 \overset{py}{\Rightarrow} 2(C_6H_5COO)_2Cupy_2 + (C_6H_5COOCu)_2py$$

(1)

to benzoate by the oxygen complex in 73% yield. Reacting benzil with copper (stoichiometry 1:2) in acetonitrile in the presence of tmen as the ligand no oxygen complex is formed. A different reaction, as shown in eq. 2, takes place resulting

$$C_6H_5COCOC_6H_5 + 2Cu + tmen + 1.5\ O_2 = (C_6H_5COO)_2Cu(tmen) + \text{``CuO''} \quad (2)$$

in the copper(II) carboxylate complex (yield 96%) and copper(II) oxide. It is interesting to note, however, that the reaction mixture formed in eq. 2 is still able to split one mol benzil in acetonitrile under dioxygen to the benzoate copper(II) complex.

3,5-Di-*t*-butil-*o*-benzoquinone and metallic copper in pyridine or acetonitrile with py or bpy as ligands react with dioxygen (O_2-uptake varies from 2.5 to 3.0 mol per

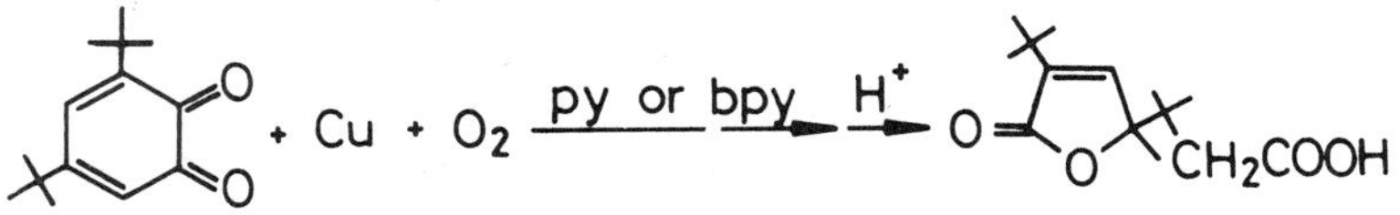

Figure 9. The reaction of 3,5-di-*t*-butyl-*o*-benzoquinone with dioxygen and copper in the presence of py, bpy, or tmen ligands followed by acidic hydrolysis.

quinone), according to Figure 9, producing 5-(carboxymethyl)-3,5-di-*t*-butylfuran-2-one in yields between 5 and 23%. In different amounts other products derived from 2,4-di-*t*-butyl-*cis,cis*-muconic acids could be detected by GC-MS as found earlier by us in the reaction of the quinone with hydrogen peroxide (28). The 3,5-di-*t*-butyl-catecholatocopper(II) complexes reacted with dioxygen (2.5-3.0 mol O_2 per complex) giving 5-(carboxymethyl)-3,5-di-*t*-butylfuran-2-one in yields as given above. Identical results were found by Brown *et al.* with bpy and 1,10-phenanthroline ligands in DMSO (29).

9,10-Phenanthrenequinone and metallic copper react with dioxygen in pyridine or acetonitrile with ligands such as py or bpy to cause oxidative ring cleavage. Upon acidic hydrolysis diphenic acid could be isolated in yields 90-96%. In acetonitrile with tmen as the ligand no ring scisson occurred and only the starting quinone could be isolated.

c) The bis(9,10-phenanthrenesemiquinone)copper(II) complex picks up one mol dioxygen in pyridine with respect to the starting complex. On acidic hydrolysis and work-up one mol diphenic acid (yield 92%), and one mol quinone (yield 99%), could be isolated. The catecholate copper(II) complex with bpy ligand consumes one mol dioxygen in pyridine and after the usual work-up gives again one mol diphenic acid (yield 95%). It is rather interesting, that the similar catecholato copper(II) complex with tmen as the ligand takes up one mol dioxygen too, but on hydrolysis only the starting 9,10-phenanthrenequinone could be isolated in 93% yield.

On the basis of the results outlined above we conclude, that in the oxygenolysis of α-diketones and *o*-quinones with metallic copper semidione and semiquinone copper(I) complexes are formed in solution or are present eventually in small concentrations. These react then with dioxygen to a trioxametallocycle, as shown

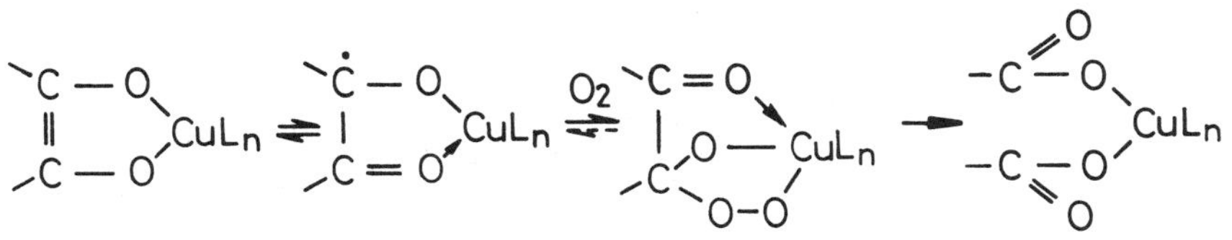

Figure 10. Proposed mechanism for the oxidative C—C bond cleavage in α-diketones and o-quinones.

in Figure 10, which decomposes *via* a dioxetane or Baeyer-Villiger route to the ring cleavage products. The trioxametallocycle has close relevance to the intermediate proposed by Hamilton for the mechanism of dioxygenase action (30). In the case of α-diketones and 3,5-di-t-butil-o-benzoquinone a mechanism *via* dicopper(I) enediolate and catecholate complexes with direct attack of dioxygen on the co-ordinated ligand can not be excluded.

Acknowledgements

The authors thank Professor L. Markó for stimulating discussions and A. Rockenbauer (Budapest) for running and interpreting the EPR spectra.

References and Footnotes

1. H. Gampp and A.D. Zuberbühler in *Metal Ions in Biological Systems,* Ed., H. Sigel, Marcel Dekker, Inc., New York and Basel, *Vol. 12,* p. 133 (1981).
2. J. V. Bannister, Ed., *Structure and Function of Hemocyanin,* Springer Verlag, New York (1977).
3. B.G. Malmström in *Oxidases and Related Redox Systems,* Eds., T.E. King, H.S. Mason, and M. Morrison, Wiley, New York, *Vol. 1,* p. 207 (1965).
4. E. Frieden, J.A. McDermott, and S. Osaki, in *Oxidases and Related Redox Systems,* Eds., T.E. King, H.S. Mason, and M. Morrison, Wiley, New York, *Vol. 1,* 240 (1965).
5. W.H. Vanneste and A. Zuberbühler in *Molecular Mechanism of Oxygen Activation,* Ed., O. Hayaishi, Academic Press, New York, p. 371 (1974).
6. R.A. Sheldon and J.K. Kochi, *Metal Catalyzed Oxidations of Organic Compounds,* Academic Press, New York (1981).
7. J. Tsuji and H. Takayanagi, *J. Am. Chem. Soc., 96,* 7349 (1974).
8. O. Hayaishi, M. Katagiri and S. Rothberg, *J. Am. Chem. Soc., 77,* 5450 (1966).
9. M.M. Rogic and T.R. Demmin, *J. Am. Chem. Soc., 100,* 5472 (1978).
10. G. Speier and Z. Tyeklár, *J. Chem. Soc. Dalton Trans.,* 1995 (1983)
11. G. Speier and Z. Tyeklár, *J. Mol. Catal., 9,* 233 (1980).
12. *Handbook of Chemistry and Physics,* Eds., C.D. Hodgman, R.C. Weast, and S.M. Selby, Chemical Rubber Publishing Co., Cleveland, 40th Edition, p. 1733 (1958).
13. F. Calderazzo and G. Dell'Amico, *J. Chem. Soc. Dalton Trans.,* 1238 (1979).
14. É. Balogh-Hergovich and G. Speier, *Inorg. Chim. Acta, 74,* 61 (1983).
15. Y. Ito, T. Konoike and T. Saegusa, *Tetrahedron Lett.,* 1287 (1974).
16. L.R. Melby, R.J. Harder, W.R. Hertler, R.E. Benson and W.E. Mochel, *J. Am. Chem. Soc., 84,* 3374 (1962).
17. H. Mohler, *Helv. Chim. Acta, 8,* 740 (1925).
18. H.T. Clarke and E.E. Dreger, *Org. Syn. Coll. Vol.1,* 87 (1941).
19. A.I. Vogel, *A Text Book of Practical Organic Chemistry,* Longmans, London, p. 835 (1961).
20. W. Mathes, W. Sauermilch and T. Klein, *Chem. Ber., 84,* 452 (1951).

21. H. Schulze and W. Flaig, *Liebigs Ann. Chem., 575,* 231 (1952).
22. *Organikum,* Eds., K. Schwetlick and Associates, VEB Deutscher Verlag der Wissenschaften, Berlin, p. 329 (1964).
23. F. Gerson, *High Resolution ESR Spectroscopy,* Wiley, New York p. 128 (1970).
24. M. Munakata and S. Kitagawa in *Copper Coordination Chemistry: Biochemical and Inorganic Perspectives,* Eds., K.D. Karlin and J. Zubieta, Adenine Press, New York, p. 473 (1983).
25. D.G. Brown, J.T. Reinprecht and G.C. Vogel, *Inorg. Nucl. Chem. Lett., 12,* 399 (1976).
26. M. Kato, H.B. Jonassen and J.C. Fanning, *Chem. Rev., 64,* 99 (1966).
27. G. Davies and M.A. El-Sayed, *Inorg. Chem., 22,* 1257 (1983).
28. G. Speier and Z. Tyeklár, *J. Chem. Soc. Perkin Trans. 2,* 1176 (1981).
29. D.G. Brown, L. Beckmann, C.H. Ashby, G.C. Vogel, and J.T. Reinprecht, *Tetrahedron Lett.,* 1363 (1977).
30. G.A. Hamilton in *Molecular Mechanism of Oxygen Activation,* Ed., O. Hayaishi, Academic Press, New York, p. 405 (1974).

Biological & Inorganic Copper Chemistry,
ISBN 0-940030-11-X, Eds., K. D. Karlin & J. Zubieta, Adenine Press, ©Adenine Press, 1985

The Reversible Binding and Activation of Dioxygen with Dinuclear Copper Complex Systems

Kenneth D. Karlin*, Richard W. Cruse, Yilma Gultneh, Jon C. Hayes, Jeffrey W. McKown and Jon Zubieta*
Department of Chemistry
State University of New York (SUNY) at Albany
Albany, New York 12222

Abstract

Recent studies involving the reactions of dioxygen and Cu(I) and Cu(II) complexes of a dinucleating ligand, *1*, and its derivatives and analogs are presented. A dinuclear copper(I) complex of *1(2)* reacts with dioxygen resulting in the hydroxylation of an aromatic ring contained in *1* to produce a dinuclear phenoxo- and hydroxo- bridged Cu(II) compound *3*. Isotopic labeling studies and the stoichiometry of reaction indicate that this reaction is a good model system for the action of the copper monoxygenases. The reaction of O_2 with a Cu(I) compound containing a mononuclear analog of *1* does not result in the hydroxylation of the ligand, but results in the irreversible four-electron reduction of dioxygen to give oxo- and hyroxo- Cu(II) species. The observation that dinuclear Cu(II) derivatives of *1* react with hydrogen peroxide to give the hyroxylated product *3* suggests that bridged dinuclear Cu(II)-peroxo intermediates are important in the reaction *2⇒3*. The phenol (*4*) which is produced by the reaction of *2⇒3* can be used to synthesize a novel phenoxo-bridged dinuclear Cu(I) complex *5*; this reacts *reversibly* with dioxygen at low temperature to produce a peroxo-bridged dinuclear Cu(II) complex, *6*, having a strong absorption band at 505 nm and exhibiting an O-O stretching vibration at 803 cm^{-1}.

Introduction

Recent interest in studies relating to the reactivity of dioxygen with copper ion complexes derives from the fact that copper compounds have been established to be useful catalysts in oxidation and oxygenation reactions both in biological and nonbiological systems. One area of major focus has been the development of chemical model systems which mimic the functional properties of the biological oxygenases. This approach can and has contributed to our understanding of the oxygenase catalyzed reactions (1-4). Just as important is to use concepts derived from the highly efficient enzymes to develop synthetic systems capable of effecting mild and selective oxidation or oxygenation of organic substrates by O_2 (4).

Our investigations have focused on mimicking the copper metalloproteins hemocyanin (Hc) and tyrosinase (Tyr) which contain dinuclear copper active sites in which the

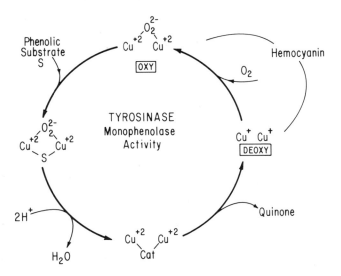

Cu(II) centers are electronically coupled. Hemocyanins (1-3,5) function as dioxygen carriers in the hemolymph of arthropods and molluscs whereas tyrosinase (1-3,5) is a monooxygenase utilizing O_2 in the hydroxylation of monophenols (i.e. monophenol to *o*-diphenol) and furthur acts as a two-electron oxidase (i.e. *o*-catechol to *o*-quinone). Spectroscopic and chemical evidence suggest that, in the deoxy form of Hc, two or three imidazole ligands from histidine coordinate to each cuprous ion. A recent x-ray structural investigation (3.2 A resolution) of *Panulirus interruptus* deoxy hemocyanin strongly suggests that *three* imidazoles are coordinated to each copper center with a Cu(I)...Cu(I) distance of 3.8 ± 0.4 A (6). Upon reaction of deoxy-Hc with O_2, significant coordination changes take place giving rise to tetragonally coordinated Cu(II) ions separated by 3.6 A and bridged by the O_2^{2-} ligand (that is derived from O_2) and an endogenous oxygen-containing group. There are parallels between the structures and reactivities of the Hc and Tyr active sites; for instance, Tyr forms an O_2 containing species (oxy-Tyr) which has spectral features similar to oxy-Hc. Thus, the binding of dioxygen by Hc and the O_2 "activation" (leading to facile & selective oxygen incorporation into a substrate) by Tyr appear to be related processes (Figure 1) (1-3,7).

Figure 1. Possible working mechanism of tyrosinase and the relationship between hemocyanin and tyrosinase (Adapted in part from reference 7).

Features of the activity of these copper proteins which are important in chemical investigations and modeling are that a) it is the Cu(I) (deoxy) form which interacts/reacts with O_2, b) dioxygen binding is necessary for "activation" and c) the copper ions are found in a coordination environment favorable to the reduced state of copper (three-coordination, unsaturated nitrogen ligands (6), positive formal reduction potential for tyrosinase (8)), and d) the occurrence of dinuclear centers which may favor 2-electron processes. In part, it is these considerations that prompted our use of the dinucleating ligand *m*-XYLpy2, *1*, in which two tridentate groups (py2) with an amino and two pyridine donors are bridged by a *m*-xylyl connecting unit. Here, we will discuss some of our recent findings on the reactivity of O_2 with Cu(I) and Cu(II) complexes of this ligand and its analogs and derivatives. These include the development of systems which mimic the action of both Hc (reversible binding of O_2) and tyrosinase (mono-oxygenase activity).

m−XYLpy2

Hydroxylation of an Arene in a Dinuclear Copper Complex System

The general scarcity of information available on copper(I) complexes containing nitrogenous ligands initially prompted us to synthesize a Cu(I) derivative of the ligand *1*. This resulted in the synthesis and crystallographic characterization of *2* (Figure 2), a complex mimicking some of the suggested structural and coordination properties of deoxy-Hc (9). Compound *2* is a dinuclear Cu(I) complex where each cuprous ion is three-coordinate with bonding to an amino and two pyridyl nitrogen donors of the tridentate (py2) arm of *m*-XYLpy2 (*1*). The coordination about each Cu(I) ion is nearly planar and T-shaped with N_{py}-Cu-N_{py} close to 153°. The two Cu(I) coordination spheres in each dinuclear unit are well separated with Cu...Cu = 8.94 A in the solid state.

Upon reaction of *2* with dioxygen in DMF or CH_2Cl_2, hydroxylation of the *m*-xylyl connecting unit of *1* occurs, resulting in the formation of the phenoxo- and hydroxo-doubly bridged dinuclear complex *3* (Figure 3). The incorporation of oxygen atoms into *3* during this reaction was shown by the x-ray crystallographic study of *3* (Figure 4). Each Cu(II) ion is pentacoordinate and in a nearly square based pyramidal geometry. The phenoxo- oxygen atom from the hydroxylated (and deprotonated) ligand and a hydroxo- oxygen atom bridge the two Cu(II) ions (Cu...Cu = 3.1 A) (10).

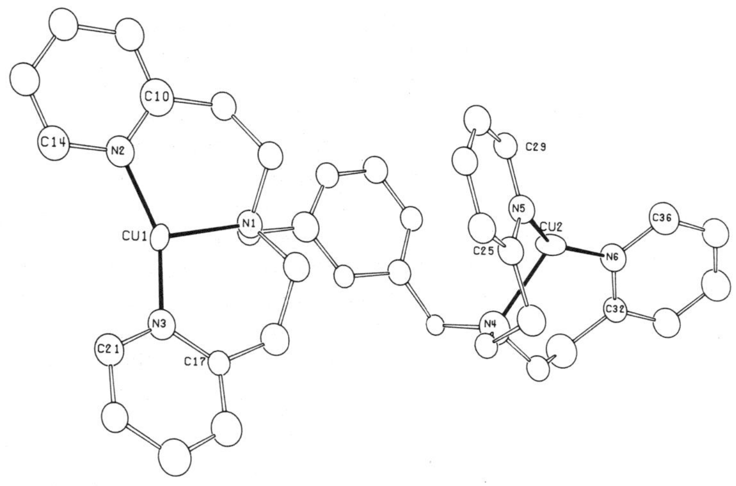

Figure 2. Structure of [Cu$_2$(*m*-XYLpy2]$^{+2}$, ref. 9.

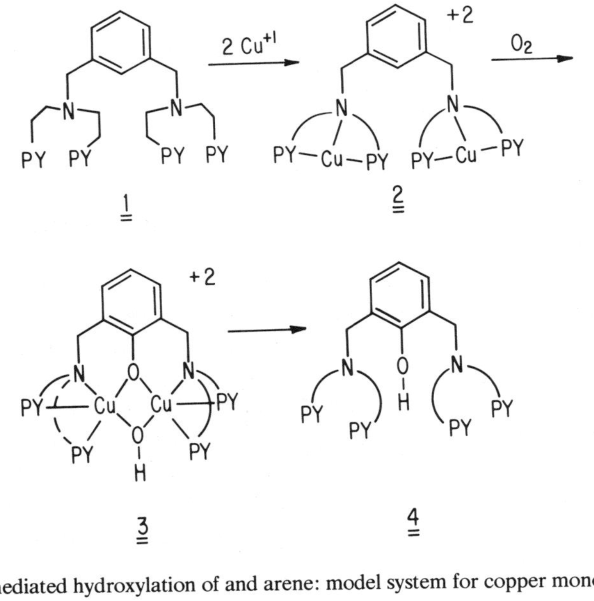

Figure 3. Copper-mediated hydroxylation of and arene: model system for copper monooxygenases, ref. 10.

The observed oxygen atom insertion into an arene and the stoichiometry of the reaction $2 + O_2 \Rightarrow 3$ is reminiscent of the action of the copper monooxygenases. The stoichiometry has been established by carrying out manometric measurements of O_2 uptake by **2** in DMF or CH_2Cl_2 (Cu:O_2 = 2:1). Mass spectrometric analyses (Field Desorption) of the product **3** prepared by using isotopically pure $^{18}O_2$ show unambiguously that both atoms of dioxygen are incorporated into the oxygenation

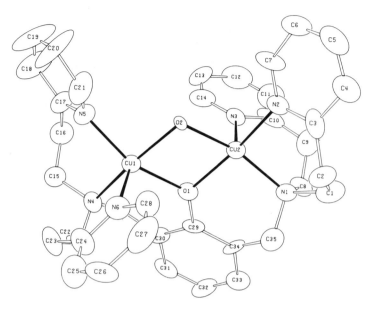

Figure 4. Structure of the oxygenated product, *3*, containing phenoxo- and hydroxo- bridged Cu(II) ions, ref. 10.

product. One atom of O is a phenoxo- oxygen, which bridges the two Cu(II) ions in *3*. The aromatic ring connecting the py2 units in *1* has been hydroxylated, formally an insertion of an O atom into the aromatic C-H bond. The other O atom in the product is part of a hydroxide bridging ligand, where the formal oxidation state of the oxygen atom is -2. Thus, the overall net reaction is a two-electron reduction of O$_2$ by two Cu(I) ions and can be described as

$$\text{XYL-H} + 2\text{Cu}^{+} + \text{O}_2 \Rightarrow 2\text{Cu}^{+2} + \text{OH}^{-} + \text{XYL-O}^{-}$$

where XYL-H is the dinucleating ligand *1* and -H is the site of hydroxylation. The Cu(II) ions can be leached out of complex *3* to produce the free phenol *4* (Figure 3), completing the sequence involving the copper mediated hydroxylation of an arene, *1*⇒*2*⇒*3*⇒*4*. The phenol, *4*, is shown to retain the ^{18}O label (by mass spectrometry) as further proof that the source of oxygen in the hydroxylation reaction is O$_2$ (10).

Reactivity of a Mononuclear Analog

In an effort to help identify the nature of the intermediates in the course of "activation" of O$_2$ in the oxygenation reaction described above, studies on the effects of synthetic ligand modification and variations are being pursued. One such case is a recent study of the reaction of dioxygen with a Cu(I) complex of ligand *A* (Figure 5) (11), which possesses the same tridentate chelating group as is found in *1*, and

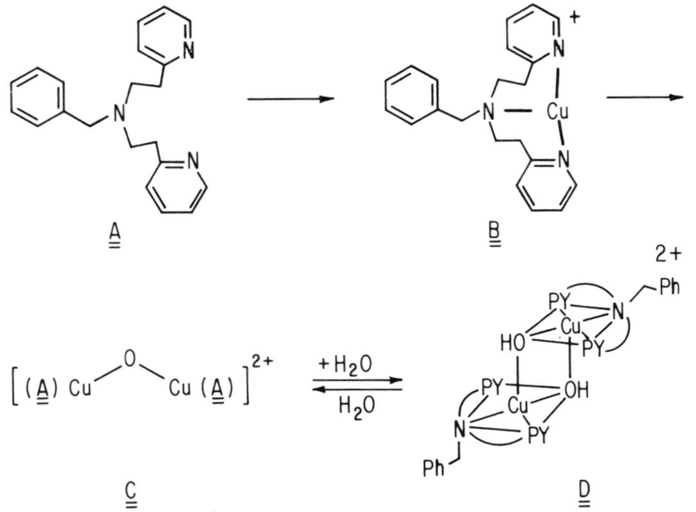

Figure 5. Four-electron reduction of Cu(*A*)$^+$ (*B*) giving oxo- and hydroxo- bridged products, ref. 11.

forms a three-coordinate Cu(I) mononuclear complex *B* (Figure 6). It also contains the potential aromatic substrate as the xylyl group that is found in *1*, which is potentially in the same proximity to the copper ion. Unlike the reaction of *2* with O$_2$, we find that, in the reaction of [Cu(*A*)]$^+$ with O$_2$ in CH$_2$Cl$_2$, hydroxylation of the phenyl group does not occur; instead, a compound formulated as a dinuclear oxo-bridged Cu(II) complex *C* forms (Figure 5). This furthur reacts reversibly with water to give the dihydroxo-bridged dinuclear Cu(II) complex *D*, which we have characterized crystallographically (Figure 7) (11).

The finding that the reaction of O$_2$ with [Cu(*A*)]$^+$ does not result in the hydroxylation of the benzyl group in ligand *A* is in sharp contrast to the reaction of O$_2$ with *2*. However, it is consistent with the notion that two Cu(I) ions in the appropriate proximity is a requirement for substrate oxygenation reaction as occurs in the two-electron transformation *2*⟹*3*. It seems likely that in this mononuclear system, *B* + O$_2$, a kinetic pathway leading to a reduction of dioxygen beyond the peroxy stage (i.e., beyond two electron reduction) is preferred. This would then detract from a pathway where oxygenation of a "substrate" may occur and leads to the irreversible four-electron reduction to oxo- (*C*) or hydroxo- (*D*) containing complexes (11-13).

Peroxo-Cu(II) Dinuclear Intermediates in the Hydroxylation Reaction, 2⟹3

Based on the known reduction of dioxygen to a peroxo- species in Hc, and the possible similarity and/or relationship to the monooxygenase Tyr, it seems reasonable to assume that reduction of O$_2$ by the dinuclear Cu(I) complex *2* proceeds to the peroxo- oxidation level in the hydroxylation reaction *2*⟹*3*, (Figure 3). Thus, if

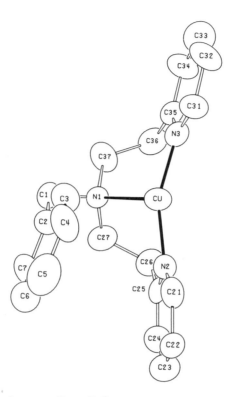

Figure 6. Structure of the three-coordinate Cu(I) complex, **B**, references 11 & 14.

in fact $Cu(II)_2(O_2^{2-})$ is an intermediate in this process, the oxygenation reaction should be observed in the reaction of a $Cu(II)_2$ derivative of *1* with hydrogen peroxide. This reaction indeed results in hydroxylation; this finding supports the notion that a peroxo-Cu(II) species (i.e. $Cu(II)_2(O_2^{2-})$ is a common intermediate in pathways developing either from $Cu(I)$-O_2 or $Cu(II)$-H_2O_2 (Figure 8) (14).

Dinuclear Cu(II) complexes of *1* were prepared by the reaction of the ligand with two equivalents of either $Cu(BF_4)_2$ or $Cu(NO_3)_2$ in aqueous DMF. These react with hydrogen peroxide to give >90% yields of hydroxylated product *3* which is confirmed by IR, UV-VIS spectroscopy and thin-layer chromatographic identification of the free phenol (*4*) obtained from these products. No hydroxylation is observed in the reaction of the free ligand *1* with hydrogen peroxide or when the dinuclear Cu(II) complexes of *2* are first treated with EDTA, then followed by hydrogen peroxide.

To confirm that *two* Cu ions are required for efficient hydroxylation, analogous reactions were carried out on a Cu(II) derivative of ligand *A*, the mononucleating analog of *1*. Here, no hydroxylation occurs in the reaction of $[Cu(A)]^{+2}$ with H_2O_2. Thus, we conclude that under these conditions it is not sufficient to just have a peroxo- species in the presence of *one* Cu ion, but that a peroxo- intermediate

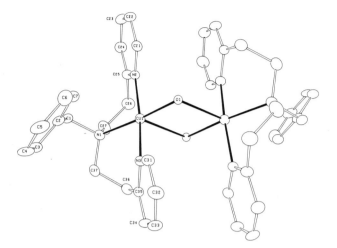

Figure 7. Structure of the dihyroxo- bridged Cu(II) dinuclear complex **D**, formed by reaction of **B** with dioxygen. Cu...Cu = 3.271 A, Cu-O$_{axial}$ = 2.30 A, Cu-O$_{equitorial}$ 1.93 A, ref. 11.

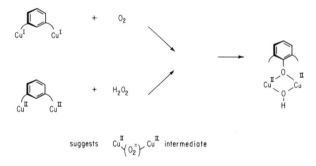

Figure 8. Common peroxo-Cu(II)$_2$ intermediates in the hydroxylation reaction proceeding either from Cu(I)$_2$- and O$_2$ or Cu(II)$_2$- and hydrogen peroxide, ref.

involving two Cu ions must be the precursor to oxygen atom transfer in the reaction of **2**⟹**3** (Figure 8). To speculate, it may be that the substrate juxtaposition with the copper ion(s) at the point of O$_2$ binding is one critical factor in determining whether hydroxylation could occur. The mode of peroxo- binding (i.e., μ-1,1-, μ-1,2- bridging, hydroperoxo-, etc.) probably will affect the reactivity; thus, the role of the copper ion(s) in influencing electronic and coordination properties of the bound peroxo-group will be very important. Furthur structural and mechanistic investigations are clearly necessary.

Reversible Binding of Dioxygen in a Dinuclear System via Peroxide Coordination

The occurrence of reversible copper-dioxygen binding in natural systems has inspired considerable efforts over the years to mimic the process in synthetic systems (15).

We have also sought to do this, especially since we had discovered evidence for peroxo-Cu intermediates in the monooxygenase model system described above. The evidence for an endogenous bridge in oxy- and met-Hc has resulted in the considerable use of phenol containing dinucleating ligands to model the copper active site in Hc (1). However, very little work has been carried out with Cu(I) derivatives of such ligands (12c,16). The facile production of the potential dinucleating ligand *4* via the hydroxylation reaction *2*⇒*3*⇒*4* (Figure 3) gave us an entry to such a ligand system. Indeed, the phenol *4* forms a phenoxo-bridged dinuclear Cu(I) complex *5*, which has been structurally characterized. Compound *5* reacts with O₂ resulting in the formation of a dinuclear Cu(II)-peroxide complex, *6*, that is stable at low temperature (17).

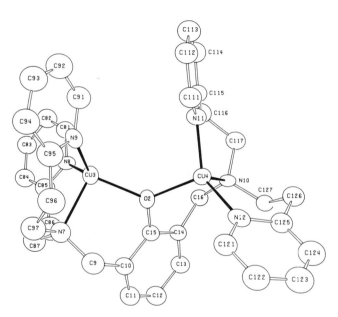

Figure 9. Structure of the phenoxo-bridged dinuclear Cu(I) complex *5*, ref. 17.

The structure of the monocation, *5*, is shown in Figure 9 (17). It consists of two tetra-coordinate Cu(I) ions ligated to the amino nitrogen and two pyridine donors of the py2 tridentate group. The fourth donor is the bridging phenoxo oxygen atom. The striking feature of the structure is that the Cu...Cu distance is between 3.6 and 3.7 A (in the two crystallographically independent molecules per asymetric unit) which is known to be the Cu...Cu distance in oxy-Hc (1-3). As can be seen in Figure 9, there is an empty "pocket" in the area where a second bridging ligand is coordinated in a number of doubly bridged Cu(II) binuclear compounds of this same ligand (10,18). Thus, this geometry may be expected to make the dinuclear Cu(I) center in *5* suitable for binding dioxygen by means of a two-electron redox process and bridging by the resulting peroxo- moiety.

When an orange (λ_{max} = 380 nm) dichloromethane solution of *5* is exposed to O_2 below $-50°C$, an intense violet color develops due to the formation of the peroxo-$Cu(II)_2$ complex, *6*. Manometric measurements at $-78°C$ indicate that 1 mol of O_2 is taken up per mole of *5*. The visible absorption spectrum (in Figure 10) of the violet solution exhibits a new strong transition at 505 nm (ϵ = 6300 $(M\text{-}Cm)^{-1}$) associated with the formation of *6*. In addition, a band at 385 nm is observed along with an absorption in the d-d region near 610 nm.

Confirming evidence for the formulation of *6* as a peroxo-Cu(II) species comes from resonance Raman spectroscopy. Here, a peak at 803 cm^{-1} is assigned to the O-O stretching vibration of a coordinated peroxo- group. This conclusion is based on (a) the perturbation in the O-O stretch observed upon isotopic substitution of $^{18}O_2$ (19) and (b) a comparison to the O-O stretch values observed for oxyhemocyanins, oxytyrosinase and ionic peroxides (17,19).

The results described here demonstrate that a dinuclear Cu(I) center can react with dioxygen to give a stable peroxo- binding Cu(II) compound in a synthetic system. This appears to be the first example of O_2 binding to Cu(I) where a distinct and strong visible absorption band (505 nm) is observed and where the oxidation state of the coordinated dioxygen ligand (as O_2^{2-}) has been confirmed by vibrational spectroscopy. A number of Cu(I) complexes appear to bind dioxygen reversibly or quasireversibly with the stoichiometry Cu:O_2 = 2:1 (20), but to our knowledge this was the first vibrational spectral evidence for a coordinated dioxygen moiety in copper model complexes.

The binding of dioxygen to *5* to form *6* is reversible, and cycling between *5* and *6* can be followed spectrophotometrically (Figure 10). The spectrum of the pure dinuclear phenoxo-bridged deoxy form *5* is labeled 0 (dotted curve). Oxygenation at $-78°$ gives the spectrum of the oxy form *6* which is the solid curve labeled 0 in Figure 10. Rapid warming to room temperature under vacuum removes the bound dioxygen regenerating the deoxy complex *5* (dotted curve 1). Lowering the temperature again to $-78°C$, and bubbling with O_2 regenerates the oxy compound *6* (solid curve 1) with a small amount (ca. 10%) of decomposition. The cycles can be repeated several times, as shown (Figure 10). If a solution of *6* is allowed to warm up slowly to room temperature, spectrum G is produced. This corresponds to the spectrum of the irreversibly oxidized hydroxo- bridged Cu(II) complex *3*, and is probably produced by copper catalyzed disporportionation of the peroxo- complex *6*.

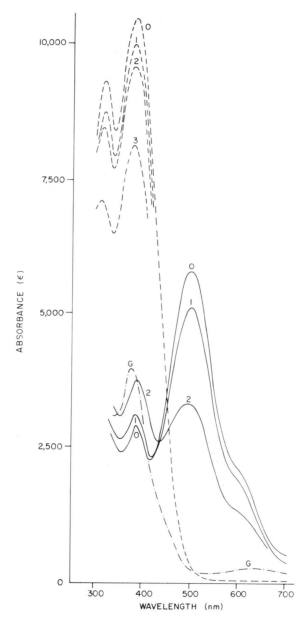

Figure 10. Visible absorption spectrum of the dioxygen (peroxo) complex **6** (solid curve 0), and cycling experiments between **5** and **6** demonstrating the reversible binding nature of dioxygen in this system. See text for explanation.

Another line of evidence demonstrating the reversibility of dioxygen binding by **5** comes from the observation that the same product is obtained in the reaction of either *5* or *6* with triphenylphosphine (PPh₃) (Figure 11). Compound *5* reacts with two mole equivalents of PPh₃, the same triphenylphosphine-Cu(I) adduct is obtained. with additional coordination from the amino nitrogen, *one* of the pyridyl nitrogens of the py2 units and a PPh₃ ligand (21). When the peroxo complex *6* is reacted with two mole equivalents of PPh₃, the same triphenylphosphine-Cu(I) adduct is obtained. One mole of dioxygen is liberated as demonstrated by manometric experiments and O_2 identification using alkaline pyrogallol (21). These results furthur substantiate that the reaction of *5* with O_2 is an equilibrium process (i.e. reversible); reaction of *6* with PPh₃ shifts the equilibrium back towards *5*, liberating O_2 and producing the triphenylphosphine-Cu(I) adduct.

Conclusions

We are finding that the dinucleating ligand *m*-XYLpy2 (*1*) and its analogs and derivatives produce a variety of interesting Cu(I) and Cu(II) complexes; the chemistry

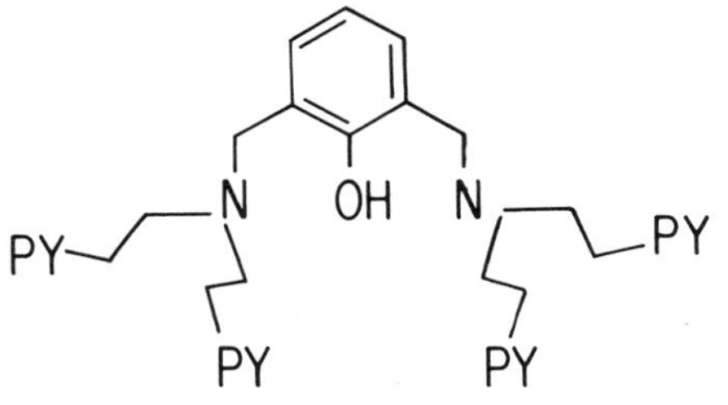

$$O_2 + \left[Cu_2^I (L\text{-}O^-) \right]^+ \rightleftharpoons \left[Cu_2^{II}(L\text{-}O^-)(O_2^=) \right]^+$$

$$\downarrow 2P\phi_3 \qquad\qquad \downarrow 2P\phi_3$$

$$\left[Cu_2^I (L\text{-}O^-)(P\phi_3)_2 \right]^+ \qquad \left[Cu_2^I (L\text{-}O)(P\phi_3)_2 \right]^+$$
$$+$$
$$O_2$$

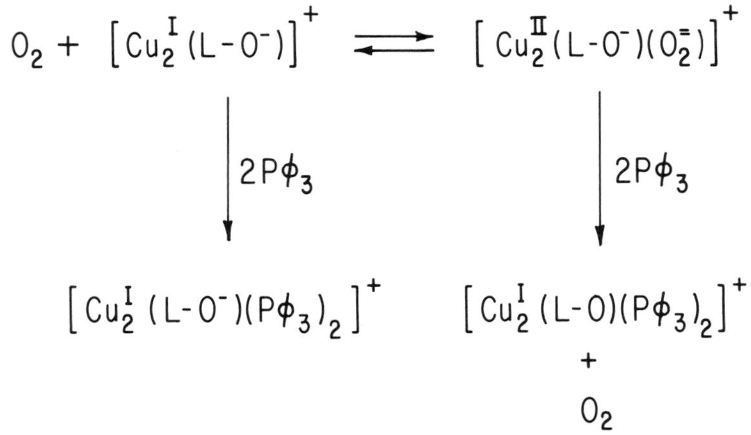

Figure 11. Reaction of *5* and/or *6* with triphenylphosphine to give a PPh₃ adduct, also substantiating the equilibria involved in the dioxygen binding reaction.

of these compounds show some capability to mimic certain structural and reactivity features observed in the oxygen carrier Hc and the monooxygenase Tyr. The results presented here demonstrate the validity of the model approach in studying the biochemistry of copper and the field of biomimetic chemistry in general (1-4,22).

A considerable number of questions remain concerning the systems presented here. At this point, little is understood about the details of the mechanism or the nature of the intermediates which are involved in the hydroxylation reaction, $2 \Rightarrow 3$. It is also puzzling that this reaction is so specific to the particular ligand system described here (*m*-XYLpy2). Any modification of the ligand such as a change in the donor group or chelate ring size shuts down the ligand hydroxylation reaction (21,23).

The absorption spectrum of the dioxygen complex *6* is significantly different from that of oxy-Hc (1-3,5), suggesting that the mode of coordination of the peroxo-group may be different. Possible binding modes include μ-1,1-, μ-1,2- or terminally bound peroxide (17). The fact that the reaction of *6* with PPh₃ does not give O=PPh₃ is somewhat surprising, but suggests that, at least in this system, it is not a bound peroxo- species which is an active oxygenation reagent. Furthur studies of the physical and chemical characteristics of *6* and related compounds are in progress.

Acknowledgements

We are grateful to the National Institutes of Health (KDK GM 28962, JZ GM27459) for support of the research described here. We also thank Professor E.I. Solomon, Jim Pate and Rich Reem for obtaining the resonance Raman data.

References and Footnotes

1. *"Copper Coordination Chemistry: Biochemical and Inorganic Perspectives"*, Eds., K.D. Karlin & J. Zubieta, Adenine Press, New York (1983).
2. E.I. Solomon, K.W. Penfield and D.E. Wilcox, *Structure & Bonding (Berlin), 53,* 1-57 (1983).
3. E.I. Solomon in reference 1, pp. 1-22.
4. R.A. Sheldon, J.K. Kochi, *"Metal-Catalyzed Oxidations of Organic Compounds"*, Academic Press, New York (1981).
5. E.I. Solomon in *"Metal Ions in Biology"*, Vol. 3, Ed., T.G. Spiro, Wiley-Interscience, New York, pp 41-108 (1981).
6. W.P.J. Gaykema, W.G.J. Hol, J.M. Vereijken, N.M. Soeter, H.J. Bak and J. J. Beintema, *Nature, 309,* 23-29 (1984).
7. M.E. Winkler, K. Lerch and E.I. Solomon, *J. Amer. Chem. Soc., 103,* 7001-7003 (1981).
8. K. Lerch in *"Metal Ions in Biological Systems"*, Vol. 13, Ed., H. Sigel, Marcel Dekker, New York, pp 143-186 (1981).
9. K.D. Karlin, Y. Gultneh, J.P. Hutchinson and J. Zubieta, *J. Amer. Chem. Soc., 104,* 5240-5242 (1982).
10. K.D. Karlin, J.C. Hayes, Y. Gultneh, R.W. Cruse, J.W. McKown, J.P. Hutchinson and J. Zubieta, *J. Amer. Chem. Soc., 106,* 2121-2128 (1984).
11. K.D. Karlin, Y. Gultneh, J.C. Hayes and J. Zubieta, *Inorg. Chem., 23,* 519-521 (1984).
12. a) G. Davies in reference 1, pp. 281-310. b) See chapter by S.M. Nelson in this volume. c) See chapter by T.N. Sorrell in this volume.
13. K.D. Karlin, J. Shi, J.C. Hayes, J.W. McKown, J.P. Hutchinson and J. Zubieta, *Inorg. Chim. Acta, 91,* L3-L7 (1984).

14. N.J. Blackburn, K.D. Karlin, M. Concannon, J.C. Hayes, Y. Gultneh and J. Zubieta, *J.C.S. Chem. Commun.*, 939-940 (1984).

15. A.D. Zuberbuhler, *Met. Ions Biol. Syst., 5,* 325-367 (1976).

16. R.R. Gagne, R.P. Kreh, J.A. Dodge, *J. Amer. Chem. Soc., 101,* 6917-6927 (1979).

17. K.D. Karlin, R.W. Cruse, Y. Gultneh, J.C. Hayes and J. Zubieta, *J. Amer. Chem. Soc., 106,* 3372-3374 (1984).

18. K.D. Karlin, J.C. Hayes, J.P. Hutchinson and J. Zubieta, *J.C.S. Chem. Commun.,* 376-378 (1983).

19. J. Pate, E.I. Solomon, R.W. Cruse and K.D. Karlin, to be published.

20. a) C.L. Merrill, L.J. Wilson, T.J. Thamann, T.M. Loehr, N.S. Ferris and W.H. Woodruff, *J. Chem. Soc. Dalton Trans.,* 2207-2221 (1984). b) see reference 20 in reference 17. c) see also chapter by L.J. Wilson in this volume. c) see also chapter by J.S. Thompson in this volume.

21. K.D. Karlin et. al, work in progress and to be published.

22. a) J.A. Ibers and R.H. Holm, *Science, 209,* 223-235 (1980). b) *"Biomimetic Chemistry",* Eds., D. Dolphin, C. McKenna, Y. Murakami, I. Tabushi, American Chemical Society, Washington, D.C., 1980, *Adv. Chem. Ser., No. 191.*

23. T.N. Sorrell, M.R. Malachowski and D.L. Jameson, *Inorg. Chem., 21,* 3250-3252 (1982).

Biological & Inorganic Copper Chemistry,
ISBN 0-940030-11-X, Eds., K. D. Karlin & J. Zubieta, Adenine Press, ©Adenine Press, 1985

Aprotic Reduction of Dioxygen by L_4Cu_4 and Transmetalation of L_4Cu_4 and $L_4Cu_4Y_2$ Complexes (Y = O or CO_3) by $M(NS)_2$ Reagents

by G.-Z. Cai, G. Davies, M.A. El-Sayed*
A. El-Toukhy* and T.R. Gilbert
Department of Chemistry
Northeastern University
Boston, MA 02115

Abstract

The neutral, tetranuclear complex L_4Cu_4 (*1*, L = 6-methyl-2-oxopyridinate), completely reduces dioxygen in aprotic solvents to give tetranuclear $L_4Cu_4O_2$, *2*. This product reacts rapidly with excess CO_2 to give $L_4Cu_4(CO_3)_2$, *3*, indicating that *2* has two μ_2-oxo groups outside the L_4Cu_4 core. Oxidation of excess *1* by O_2 is first-order in [*1*] and first-order in [O_2], with no detectable intermediates. The kinetic parameters are similar to those for aprotic oxidation of tetranuclear halo(pyridine)copper(I) complexes, indicating that insertion of O_2 into the Cu_4 core is also rate-determining. Complex *1* can be partially and completely transmetalated with $M(NS)_2$ reagents (M = Ni, Cu, Zn; NS is a nitrogen-sulfur ligand) in aprotic solvents to give trimeric $L_4Cu_2^IM$ and dimeric L_4M_2 species and Cu(NS) coproducts. The series of complexes $L_4Cu_{4-x}M_xY_2$ (x = 0-4; M = Ni or Zn; Y = O or CO_3) and the complexes $L_4CuNiZnCoY_2$ have been obtained by direct transmetalation of *2* and *3*. Some properties of these new transmetalation products are discussed.

*On leave of absence from the Department of Chemistry, Faculty of Science, Alexandria University, Egypt.

Introduction

Aprotic halo(pyridine)copper(I) complexes completely reduce dioxygen in aprotic solvents. The oxocopper(II) products have ligand-dependent, tetranuclear structures *I* and *II* (1-3) and the rate laws for oxidation are a direct reflection of the copper(I) reactant molecularity (1-4). The rate-determining step for oxidation of tetranuclear complexes $N_mCu_4X_4$ is complete (in *I*) or partial (in *II*) insertion of O_2 into the Cu_4X_4 molecular core. One way to distinguish between structures *I* and *II* is by their behavior towards CO_2: *I* forms a dicarbonate $N_4Cu_4X_4(CO_3)_2$ while *II* is unreactive (1-3).

Complexes $N_4Cu_4X_4Y_2$ (*I*; Y = O or CO_3) and other tetranuclear copper(II) complexes can be partially or completely transmetalated with M(NS)$_2$ reagents (NS is a mono-anionic S-methyl-hydrazinecarbodithioate Schiff base) in aprotic solvents to give stable, tetranuclear products like [(ENCA)CuNi(H$_2$O)Cl$_2$]$_2$O$_2$ (ENCA = ethylnico-tinate; core structure is *I*, both isomers obtained) and [(DENC)Ni(H$_2$O)Cl]$_4$Cl$_4$ (DENC = N,N-diethylnicotinamide) (5,6). These direct transmetalation reactions are rapid, stepwise, quantitative processes and the products are easily separated by gel permeation chromatography (5,6).

The molecular structure of the neutral, tetranuclear complex L$_4$Cu$_4$, (L = 6-methyl-2-oxopyridinate, *I*), is known (Figure 1) (7). We have investigated the stoichiometry and kinetics of its oxidation by dioxygen to give the tetranuclear complex L$_4$Cu$_4$O$_2$, *2*. The presence of two μ_2-oxo groups in *2* is indicated by its ready reaction with CO$_2$ to give L$_4$Cu$_4$(CO$_3$)$_2$, *3* (1-4). We have studied the direct transmetalations of *1-3* by M(NS)$_2$ reagents (M = Ni, Cu, Zn), which give dinuclear and trinuclear (from *1*) and tetranuclear (from *2* and *3*) products.

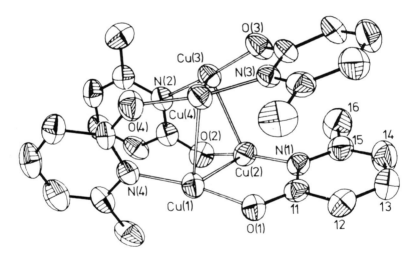

Figure 1. Molecular structure of L$_4$Cu$_4$, *I* (reproduced with permission of the American Chemical Society from ref 7).

Experimental Section

The reactant L$_4$Cu$_4$ was obtained by literature methods (7). All other reagent preparations and experimental procedures have been described previously (1-6).

Results and Discussion

Stoichiometry and Kinetics of Oxidation of 1

Cryoscopic data (Table I) indicate that *I* also is tetranuclear in nitrobenzene.

Manometric dioxygen uptake by solutions of *1* in nitrobenzene follows equation 1 (8) and the same product is obtained in methylene chloride. Low temperature ESR measurements (9) confirm that *2* is the sole product with either *1* or O$_2$ in excess. Although single crystals of *2* have not yet been obtained, its rapid reaction with excess CO$_2$ to give L$_4$Cu$_4$(CO$_3$)$_2$ (*3*, eq 2), indicates that *2* contains two μ_2-oxobridges outside the L$_4$Cu$_4$ core, analogous to structure *I* (1-3). Analytical and other data for *2* and *3* are collected in Table I.

Table I
Analytical and Spectral Data for Reactants and Transmetalation Products

Complex	Analytical Data[a] Found (calcd.)	Mol. Wt.[b] Found (calcd.)	Band Maxima, nm ($\epsilon M^{-1}cm^{-1}$) in CH$_2$Cl$_2$ Soln
L$_4$Cu$_4$O$_2$ (*2*)	Cu 35.27 (35.40)	720 ± 20 (718)	650 (301)
L$_4$Cu$_4$(CO$_3$)$_2$ (*3*)	Cu 31.62 (31.49)	810 ± 20 (807)	650 (274)
L$_3$Cu$_2$Ni(OH)O·4H$_2$O (*4*)	Cu 18.50 (20.66) Ni 10.59 (9.55)	650 ± 20 (615)	700 (110)
L$_3$Cu$_2$Ni(OH)CO$_3$·8H$_2$O (*5*)	Cu 16.7 (17.38) Ni 7.7 (8.03)	695 ± 20 (730)	700 (130)
L$_3$Cu$_3$(OH)CO$_3$ (*5'*)	Cu 33.15 (32.2)	560 ± 20 (590)	600sh (610)
L$_3$Cu$_2$Ni(OH)Br$_2$·3H$_2$O (*6*)	Cu 19.10 (17.15) Ni 6.15 (7.92)	760 ± 20 (740)	610 (300)
L$_2$Ni$_2$(OH)$_2$·6H$_2$O (*7*)	Ni 22.95 (23.23)	520 ± 20 (505)	1125(18), 675(69), 375sh (215)
L$_4$Cu$_2$Ni$_2$O$_2$·4H$_2$O (*8,9*)	Cu 16.96 (16.27) Ni 15.40 (15.04)	720 ± 20 (780)	600 (210)
L$_4$Cu$_3$NiO$_2$·6H$_2$O (*10*)	Cu 25.47 (23.20) Ni 7.51 (7.15)	790 ± 20 (821)	600 (350)
L$_4$CuNi$_3$O$_2$·4H$_2$O (*11*)	Cu 8.13 (8.19) Ni 24.24 (22.70)	760 ± 20 (776)	600 (600)
L$_4$CuNiZnCoO$_2$ (*G*)	Cu 9.47 (8.95) Ni 8.13 (9.27) Zn 9.08 (9.21) Co 7.29 (8.30)	720 ± 20 (710)	550sh (300) 425sh (1600)
L$_4$CuNiZnCo(CO$_3$)$_2$ (*G*)	Cu 8.32 (7.95) Ni 7.21 (7.35) Zn 8.13 (8.18) Co 7.07 (7.38)	750 ± 20 (799)	600sh (370) 425sh (1650)

[a]Complete analytical data will be published elsewhere.
[b]Measured cryoscopically in nitrobenzene.

The kinetics of reaction 1 have been monitored spectrophotometrically at 650nm in nitrobenzene and methylene chloride with freshly prepared L$_4$Cu$_4$ in large excess (10). The rate law is eq 3 and no reaction precursor or intermediates have been

$$L_4Cu_4 + O_2 \Rightarrow L_4Cu_4O_2 \qquad\qquad (1)$$
$$\quad \mathbf{1} \qquad\qquad\qquad \mathbf{2}$$

$$L_4Cu_4O_2 + 2CO_2 \Rightarrow L_4Cu_4(CO_3)_2 \qquad (2)$$
$$\quad \mathbf{2} \qquad\qquad\qquad \mathbf{3}$$

$$d[\mathbf{2}]/dt = k_T[\mathbf{1}][O_2] \qquad\qquad (3)$$

detected. Comparison of the kinetic parameters with those for oxidation of tetranuclear $[N_mCuX]_4$ complexes (m = 1 or 2; X = Cl or Br) (1-3) by dioxygen is made in Table II. Of particular note are similar, large negative entropies of activation, $\Delta S_T^{\ddagger}$, and similar, small ratios of k_T in nitrobenzene and methylene chloride. These parameters are characteristic of (associative) insertion of O_2 into the reactant cores as the rate determining step (1-3). The structure proposed for **2** is consistent with complete insertion before rapid electron transfer (3 electrons minimum) (3) from copper(I) to dioxygen. Insertion in reaction 1 is presumed to occur through a Cu-Cu edge of L_4Cu_4, Figure 1, rather than through one of the roughly orthogonal channels created by the aromatic ligand rings (7) because 1) there are 4 unrestricted edges but only 2 channels offering a narrower solid angle of O_2 approach and an inhibiting π-electron density; and 2) large carbonato bridges created in reaction 2 can much more easily be formed and accommodated outside the L_4Cu_4 core.

Table II
Kinetic Data for Oxidation of $[N_mCuX]_4$ and L_4Cu_4 Complexes by Dioxygen in Nitrobenzene

N	m	$k_T M^{-1}sec^{-1}$	$\Delta H_T^{\ddagger}$, Kcalmol^{-1}	$-\Delta S_T^{\ddagger}$, caldeg^{-1}mol^{-1}
(a) X = Cl				
py	2	770	2.9	36
ENCA	1	28	4.4	35
	2	110	4.3	35
DENC	1	15	3.9	40
		6.9[a]		
		5.4[b]	2.1	48
(b) X = Br				
ENCA	2	1.2	5.7	40
DENC	1	0.58	5.9	40
(c)L_4Cu_4		0.32	6.7	39
		0.12[a]		

[a] Solvent is methylene chloride.
[b] Solvent is benzene.

Our previous work (1-3) indicated no prior O_2 coordination by 4- and 5-coordinate copper(I) centers in the oxidation of $[N_mCuX]_4$ complexes, and we are surprised to find no evidence for precursors with the formal 2-coordinate (7) centers of **1**. The activation enthalpy $\Delta H_{\ddagger}^{\ddagger}$ for reaction 1 is the largest so far observed for aprotic tetranuclear copper(I)-dioxygen reactions (Table II). Since the Cu-Cu distance is 2.6-2.8 Å in all these systems and there are no intervening halogen atoms in *1*, we conclude that there is considerable electron density in the Cu-Cu vector in *1*.

Transmetalation of 1 by M(NS)₂ Reagents

Two distinct stoichiometries, eqs 4 and 5, are observed for direct transmetalation (5,6,11) of *1* in aprotic solvents.

$$L_4Cu_4 + M(NS)_2 \Rightarrow [L_3Cu_2M]L + 2Cu(NS) \tag{4}$$

$$[L_3Cu_2M]L + M(NS)_2 \Rightarrow [L_2M_2]L_2 + 2Cu(NS) \tag{5}$$

Reaction of one mol of *1* with one mol of M(NS)₂ under dinitrogen in methylene chloride gives two mols of white, virtually insoluble Cu(NS), which can be separated (Schlenk) and analyzed gravimetrically, eq 4. Eq 4 proceeds even with M = Cu because Cu(NS)(s) is more thermodynamically stable than soluble Cu(NS)₂. The product in this case is a mixed-valence copper complex. The two remaining copper(I) centers of the trinuclear product in eq 4 are oxidized by excess dioxygen (in the absence or presence of carbon dioxide) or by one mol of bromine. Because traces of dissolved Cu(NS) are also oxidized, it is then necessary to separate the oxidized solution by aprotic gel permeation chromatography (4,5). During this process reaction with water results in the loss of LH and the coordination of OH⁻ and H₂O to give typical isolated products *4-6* in Table I, all of which are trinuclear and contain three bridging ligands L⁻ (12).

Reaction of one mol of *1* with 2 mols of M(NS)₂ under dinitrogen in methylene chloride gives 4 mols of Cu(NS), estimated gravimetrically, eq 5. Treatment of the filtrate with excess dioxygen followed by gel permeation chromatography (to remove traces of oxidized Cu(NS), see above) results in the loss of LH and coordination of OH⁻ and water, leading to the typical product *7* (Table I), which is dinuclear and contains two bridging ligands L⁻.

The simplest explanation for these results is that the replacement of each pair of copper(I) centers in *1* by M from M(NS)₂ also results in the loss of one bridging ligand L⁻ (eq 4 and 5), which is then protonated by water during chromatographic separation.

Transmetalation of L₄Cu₄Y₂ (Y = O or CO₃)

The transmetalation reactions of products 2 and 3 with M(NS)₂ reagents are stepwise, quantitative processes in aprotic solvents, eq 6 (13).

$$L_4Cu_4Y_2 + xM(NS)_2 \Rightarrow L_4Cu_{4-x}M_x + xCu(NS)_2 \tag{6}$$

8-11

Analytical and other data for typical transmetalation products *8-11* (Table I) result from coordination of water during chromatographic separation.

The Y_2 bridges in *2* and *3* give rise to two geometrical isomers *8* and *9* of $L_4Cu_2M_2Y_2$, Figure 2, and six geometrical isomers G_1-G_6 of $L_4CuMM'M''Y_2$, Figure 3. Any permanent distortion of *2, 3* or these isomers from square planar towards tetrahedral makes *2, 3* and each isomer racemic. Spectral evidence (Table I) indicates that the species $L_4Cu_2Ni_2O_2 \cdot 4H_2O$ is isomer *8* (14), which does not spontaneously isomerize (5,6) to isomer *9* in aprotic solvents. This establishes that the kinetic *trans*-directing influence (5,6) across Y bridges decreases Cu > Ni (15).

Preparation of Tetranuclear Complexes Containing Four Different Metals

The complexes $L_4CoNiCuZnY_2$ (Table I) have been obtained by consecutive treatments of $L_4Cu_4Y_2$ with one equivalent each of $M(NS)_2$ in the order M = Zn, Ni, Co. If the kinetic *trans*-effect order is Cu > Zn > Ni > Co then this product is isomer G_2 in Figure 3.

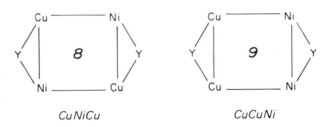

CuNiCu   CuCuNi

Figure 2. Core structures for geometrical isomers *8* and *9* (Y = O or CO_3). Square planar geometry is shown for simplicity and L is omitted. These isomers correspond to tetrahedral isomers *V* and *VI*, respectively, in Scheme I of ref 5. Note that the third isomer, CuNiNi (not shown), does not exist in T_d symmetry.

We are in the process of 1) establishing the *trans*-effect order (previous section) and 2) structurally characterizing these new homo- and hetero-nuclear transmetalation products.

Advantages of Direct Transmetalation

The major obvious advantages of direct aprotic transmetalation are these:

1. Entirely new products, even those which contain aqueous- and acid-sensitive ligands, can be isolated easily. Polynuclear reactants give polynuclear transmetalation products.

2. The reactions are actually *substoichiometric,* which means that they proceed in single steps which can be controlled experimentally. They are thus direct sources of heteropolymetallic complexes.

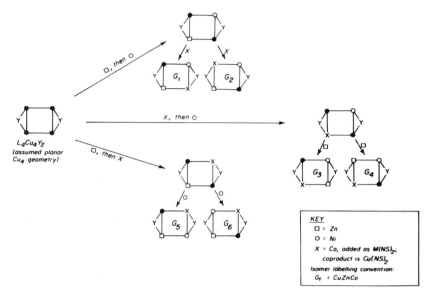

Figure 3. Geometric isomers produced by consecutive, equimolar additions of $M(NS)_2$ reagents to $L_4Cu_4Y_2$, based on the kinetic *trans*-effect order Cu > Zn, Ni, Co. If this is the case, then the product of the first two transmetalations is independent of the order of addition. *Trans*-effect order Ni > Zn gives G_1, Zn > Ni gives G_2, etc. (see text).

3. On the basis of work completed to date we can predict that direct transmetalation will be a source of:

   a. an almost unlimited number of new polynuclear metal complexes; with

   b. retention, reduction and (possibly) expansion of the original number of metal centers present; with

   c. polymetallic complexes containing different oxidation states of elements; with

   d. the likelihood of aprotic reactions of new metal centers with dioxygen to give entirely new oxo metal structures with as yet unknown catalytic properties.

4. There is reason to suppose that the principle of direct transmetalation is widely applicable to the synthesis of new polymetallic structures. All that is needed are soluble reactants, favorable thermodynamics, convenient rates under mild conditions and easy product separation. All these requirements are met by the copper(I)- and copper(II)/$M(NS)_2$ systems that we have investigated and we can be sure that they are met by other systems as well.

Acknowledgements

This work was supported financially by the Department of Health and Human Services (Biomedical Research Support Grant RRO7143), by Northeastern University (Faculty Research Grant 7590) and by the Egyptian Government. We are very grateful for this support.

References and Footnotes

1. M.R. Churchill, G. Davies, M.A. El-Sayed, J.P. Hutchinson and M.W. Rupich, *Inorg. Chem., 21*, 995 (1982).
2. G. Davies and M.A. El-Sayed, *Inorg. Chem., 22*, 1257 (1983).
3. G. Davies and M.A. El-Sayed, in *"Inorganic and Biochemical Perspectives in Copper Coordination Chemistry,"* K.D. Karlin and J.A. Zubieta, Eds., Adenine Press, Guilderland, NY, p. 281 (1983).
4. M.R. Churchill, G. Davies, M.A. El-Sayed, J.A. Fournier, J.P. Hutchinson and J.A. Zubieta, *Inorg. Chem., 23*, 783 (1984).
5. A. El-Toukhy, G.-Z. Cai, G. Davies, T.R. Gilbert, K.D. Onan and M. Veidis, *J. Amer. Chem. Soc., 106*, 4596 (1984), and preceeding Abstract.
6. G.-Z. Cai, G. Davies, A. El-Toukhy, T.R. Gilbert and M. Henary, *Inorg. Chem. 24*, 1701 (1985).
7. M. Berry, W. Clegg, C.D. Garner and I.A. Hillier, *Inorg. Chem., 21*, 1342 (1982).
8. Very slow ligand oxidation, presumably of the 6-methyl group, occurs when $L_4Cu_4O_2$ is stored in aprotic solvents saturated with dioxygen, as observed in other systems (4). This process does not affect the stoichiometry of eq 1 on the time scale of kinetic measurements (4).
9. G.-Z. Cai, G. Davies, M.A. El-Sayed, A. El-Toukhy, T.R. Gilbert, K. Nabih and K.D. Onan, to be published.
10. Good yields of solid L_4Cu_4 are obtained by the literature procedure (7). Two consecutive first-order processes are observed if solid L_4Cu_4 is stored for more than a few days in a desiccator and then reacted in excess with dioxygen in an aprotic solvent. The extent of reaction associated with the first process increases with increasing storage time, and is due to slow air oxidation of solid L_4Cu_4. Only one first-order process is observed if solid L_4Cu_4 is stored under vacuum, the rates corresponding to those for the second process for oxidized solid L_4Cu_4. We therefore recommend storage of L_4Cu_4 under vacuum.
11. G. Davies, A. El-Toukhy, K.D. Onan and M. Veidis, *Inorg. Chim. Acta, 84*, 41 (1984).
12. Overlapping L^- absorption prevents ir distinction of bridging and terminal OH^- in products *4-7*.
13. The presence of bridging Y groups limits transmetalation of $N_mCu_4X_4Y_2$ to $N_mCu_2M_2X_4Y_2$ products even in the presence of a large excess of $M(NS)_2$ (5,6); $L_4Cu_4Y_2$ can be transmetalated beyond the $L_4Cu_2M_2Y_2$ stage (Table I), albeit at lower rates than for the first two steps (9).
14. Isomers *8* and *9* contain Cu-Y-Ni and Ni-Y-Ni units, respectively. Unlike the case for $[N_mCuX]_4O_2$ systems (5,6), the spectrum of the transmetalation product $L_4Cu_2Ni_2(H_2O)_2O_2$ is independent of the $Ni(NS)_2$ reagent and this species does not isomerize (5,6) in aprotic solvents. We suggest that the transmetalation product with both (5,6) $Ni(NS)_2$ reagents is isomer *8* because the drastic spectral difference between $L_4Cu_2Ni_2(H_2O)_2O_2$ and $L_4CuNi_3(H_2O)_3O_2$ (Table I) must be due to the presence of a Ni-0-Ni unit in the latter.
15. The kinetic *trans*-effect presumably only operates across Y bridges. If $L_4Cu_4Y_2$ is treated consecutively with one equivalent each of $Ni(NS)_2$ and $Zn(NS)_2$ (to give isomer *8*) and then $Ni(NS)_2$ and the product contains a Ni-Y-Ni unit (14), then the order is Ni > Zn, etc.

Biological & Inorganic Copper Chemistry,
ISBN 0-940030-11-X, Eds., K. D. Karlin & J. Zubieta, Adenine Press, ©Adenine Press, 1985

Micellar Hemin-Copper(I) Binuclear Ions. Potential Models for Reduced and Mixed-Valent Oxygen Reductase Sites in Cytochrome Oxidase

Scott S. Sibbett and James K. Hurst

Department of Chemical, Biological, & Environmental Sciences
Oregon Graduate Center
Beaverton, Oregon 97006

Abstract

Optical spectroscopic and Raman vibrational evidence is presented indicating that Cu(I) and SDS-solubilized ferriprotoporphyrin IX "self-assemble" in acidic aqueous environments to form porphyrin-bridged binuclear ions. The Cu(I) ligation site is either of the two vinyl substituent groups located at the ring 2- and 4-pyrrole positions. Iron is slowly lost from the heme, indicating some reduction to the ferrous state has occurred. The results are interpreted in terms of the dynamic equilibrium:

$$Fe(III)PPIX\text{-}Cu(I) + Cu(I) \rightleftarrows Fe(II)PPIX\text{-}Cu(I) + Cu(II).$$

From the copper ion dependencies of the demetalation rate constant, the equilibrium constant was determined to be $K = 1.8$ in 0.1 M HTFA; this value compares fairly well with one calculated from spectroelectrochemical titration data taken at pH 3.0.

The rate law for electron transfer from Fe(II)PPIX to Cu(II) was determined by stopped-flow spectrophotometry. Comparison of the rate constant, $k = 2 \times 10^3 \, M^{-1} \, s^{-1}$ at 25 C, pH 3.0, in 1% SDS, with the value for Fe(II)mesohemin IX oxidation under the same conditions, $k = 6 \times 10^3 \, M^{-1} \, s^{-1}$, gave no evidence for preferential electron transfer occurring via a peripheral pathway with the vinyl substituent as lead-in group. The results are discussed in terms of possible similar structural organization of the reduced cytochrome a_3 site in cytochrome c oxidase.

Introduction

Cytochrome c oxidase, the terminal oxidase of the mitochondrial and some microbial respiratory redox chains, is an exceptionally complex biological redox particle (1). The mitochondrial enzyme is comprised of at least seven nonidentical subunits, which are variously encoded in both mitochondrial and nuclear DNA. The oxidase contains two heme and two copper redox sites, and is capable of a functional four-equivalent reduction of dioxygen to water. Several intermediate oxidation states of the particle have been described from low-temperature optical and magnetic studies; these species are presumed to be chemical intermediates of the physiological redox reaction. The heme prosthetic group is unique, possessing an unusual polyisoprenyl substituent attached at the 2-β-pyrrolic position and an 8-formyl substituent (Figure 1c). The heme and copper binding sites are nonequivalent and, to varying extents, interacting. Oxygen reduction in both mitochondria and reconstituted cytochrome oxidase-liposome assemblies occurs with electrogenic proton translocation across the membrane bilayer. Electron transfer is thereby tightly coupled to the transmembrane electrochemical potential of the inner mitochondrial membrane. Given this complexity it is not surprising that, despite intensive research for nearly half a century, the structural organization and dynamic behavior of the oxidase are relatively poorly understood.

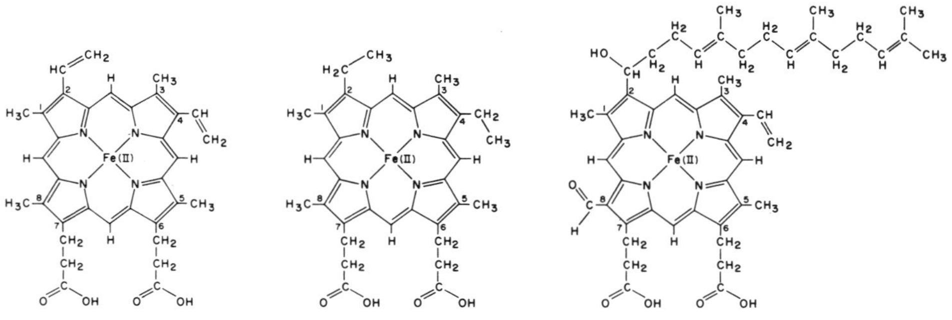

Figure 1. Heme molecular structures. a. ferroprotoporphyrin IX (ferrohemin). b. ferromesoporphyrin IX. c. ferroheme *a*.

Considerable evidence has been advanced indicating that cytochrome a_3, the oxygen reductase site, is a spin-coupled (S=2) diamagnetic ferriheme-Cu(II) binuclear center (1,2). Alternative models that have been proposed feature metal centers that are axially linked by imidazolato (2), oxo (3-5), or mercapto (5) bridges. Since the porphyrin macrocycle possesses few functional groups capable of assisting in Cu(II) coordination, it is evident that the protein matrix of the oxidase must provide at least some of the Cu(II) ligands at the a_3 active site. Attempts at building inorganic models of cytochrome a_3 are challenged by the need to construct a Cu(II) ligand binding environment on the heme that mimics the ill-defined protein sites. Nonetheless, several mixed binuclear systems containing ligand-bridged Fe(III) and Cu(II) ions have been devised (6). The models generally feature cofacially oriented macrocyclic ligands or copper binding harnesses which cap the heme (Figure 2); Fe(III)-Cu(II) ions have also been formed within the framework of macrocyclic binucleating ligands. The primary criterion used to gauge the appropriateness of the various models has been the magnitude of antiferromagnetic coupling between the metal centers. Comparison of spectroscopic properties has generally been less valuable because either the Cu(II) site is quite unlike the protein environment, i.e., is macrocyclic, or considerable structural modification of the iron macrocycle is required to covalently attach the Cu(II) ligating groups.

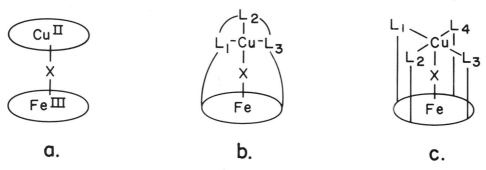

Figure 2. Several classes of axial models for the cytochrome a_3 binuclear site: a. coaxially aligned macrocycles. b. porphyrin-capped chelating ligands. c. picket-fence models.

Our approach to building cytochrome a_3 models has been somewhat different. Rather than constructing ligand environments that constrain the Fe(III) and Cu(II) centers to align axially, we have sought to explore to what extent self-assembly of the biological components might occur in environments that mimic the biological milieu. The notion that the forces of interaction leading to biomolecular organization are inherent in the bonding properties of the component structural units is supported by numerous examples. Among metalloproteins, the relative ease of formation of the unusual iron-sulfur cubane analogs of ferredoxin redox centers (7) and of binuclear iron analogs of hemerythrin (8) can be cited as examples. Previously we observed that addition of cuprous ion to acidic aqueous micellar dispersions of heme a and other hemes possessing olefinic substituents gives rise to small red-shifting of the heme visible and Soret absorption bands, and to the appearance of a new band in the near ultraviolet region (9). Since similar shifts were observed when Cu(I) was added to the corresponding micellar solubilized porphyrin dications, but not with a variety of hemes and porphyrins lacking vinyl groups, we ascribed the effect to π-complexation of the olefin, forming porphyrin-bridged heme-copper(I) binuclear ions. Given this interpretation, the near-ultraviolet band can be assigned to Cu(d)$\Rightarrow$olefin(π^*) charge transfer. For ferriprotoporphyrin IX, analysis of the optical changes by the method of continuous variations indicated predominantly 1:1 binding stoichiometry. Acid dependent demetalation of the heme slowly occurs in the binuclear ions, which we took as evidence for electron transfer from Cu(I) to Fe(III). By appropriate manipulation of reagent concentrations, it appeared possible to prepare both the Fe(II)-Cu(I) and Fe(III)-Cu(I) π-ions, which are putative models for the reduced cytochrome a_3 site and a postulated spin-uncoupled intermediate oxidation state, respectively (1,2).

Several ways in which olefin functional groups on heme a might contribute to Cu(I) binding and/or formation of electron transfer pathways in the oxidase are suggested schematically in Figure 3. Certain structural details are not included in this figure, e.g., proximal heme ligation or out-of-plane character of the high-spin a_3 iron. The notation Cu_B identifies copper ion that is antiferromagnetically coupled to heme a in the oxidized a_3 site; Cu_A indicates the other oxidase copper ion. The double-

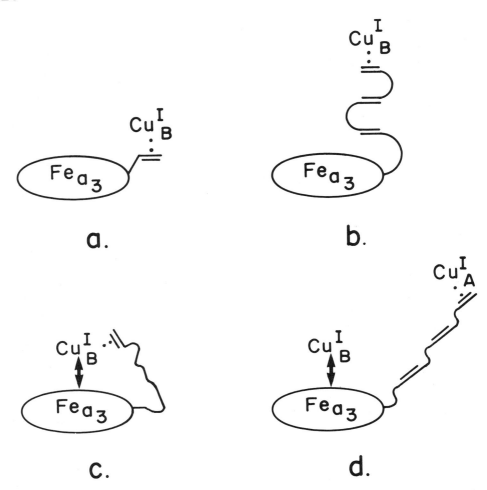

Figure 3. Alternate structural and dynamic roles for olefin bonds in cytochrome oxidase.

headed arrows between Cu and Fe_{a_3} in structures c and d illustrate possible axial electron transfer pathways, and are not intended to address the question of axial bridging ligation between the metal ions. Other specific structures can be envisioned, but those shown constitute examples of the four basic types of olefin contribution that are possible, namely, (a) coordination to the pyrrolic 4-vinyl substituent and electron transfer through a peripheral π-conjugated system, (b) coordination to the 2-hydroxyethylfarnesyl substituent and electron transfer via the heme periphery, (c) coordination to the polyisoprenyl substituent, but electron transfer by an axial pathway, and (d) coordination to the other oxidase copper by an extended conformer of the farnesyl group. In (b), the isoprenyl chain is shown in a folded, π-stacked conformation. Structures of this type have previously been proposed for electron transfer pathways in cytochrome a_3 (10) and photoredox-active binuclear ions (11).

The studies described in this report examining the reactivity of Cu(I) with SDS-solubilized ferriprotoporphyrin IX are directed primarily at evaluating the plausibility of type (a) structures as models for the reduced a_3 active site.

It should be noted that olefin bonds are not good coordination sites for cupric ion; by the same token, the types of bridging ligands that generally give strong antiferromagnetic coupling in Cu(II)-containing binuclear ions (12), i.e., oxo, carboxylato, phenoxo, are not good ligands for copper(I). If Cu(I)-olefin coordination exists in the reduced enzyme, oxidation is likely to be accompanied by a change in coordination environment. Considerable indirect evidence has accumulated indicating that changes in redox states in the oxidase are accompanied by conformational changes in the protein (1,2,13).

Physical Characteristics of SDS Micellar Suspensions Containing Hemin and Cuprous Ion

Electronic Spectra

Hemin dispersed in SDS micelles is monomeric; below about pH 5, it is thought to exist as the six-coordinate diaquo ion (14). EPR analysis of frozen suspension gives a characteristic axial iron signal with $g_{\parallel} = 2.00$ and $g_{\perp} = 5.71$ (Figure 4a) indicating high-spin Fe(III). Spectral changes observed upon Cu(I) addition are illustrated in Figure 5. Except for some slight chromophoric bleaching, oxygenation of the solution causes reversion to the original ferriheme spectrum. As noted previously (9), plots of the absorbancy changes occurring at the Q-band, Soret and near ultraviolet difference maxima all indicate heme-copper association occurs with 1:1 stoichiometry. Assignment of the near ultraviolet band to Cu(I)-olefin ligation follows from the general properties of the π-complexes (15), specifically:

(i) Charge transfer excitation of simple Cu(I)-olefin complexes gives rise to one or more bands in the 270-350 nm region. The wavelength maxima, at least that of the lower energy band, increases progressively with complexation of olefins possessing increasingly electron withdrawing substituents, confirming the $Cu(d) \Rightarrow L(\pi^*)$ character of the transition. These transitions are nearly fully allowed, but because they are extremely broad, molar extinction coefficients for the band maxima are on the order of 10^3 M^{-1} cm^{-1}.

(ii) Cu(I) binds strongly to unsubstituted olefins, with association constants (K_a) in the range of 10^4 M^{-1}. Solutions containing millimolar concentrations of reactants are therefore largely complexed. Binding strengths are sensitive to steric crowding by bulky substituents but are relatively insensitive to electronic and electrostatic effects (16). For this reason, association constants for Cu(I)-olefin complexes are very nearly the same whether the olefin is a pendant ligand of a coordination compound or simply a free ligand. For example, Cu(I) π-ligation to the 4-vinylpyridineH$^+$ ion has an association constant, $K_a = 8.4 \times 10^3$ M^{-1}, while for the (NH$_3$)$_5$Ru-4-vinylpyridine^{3+} and

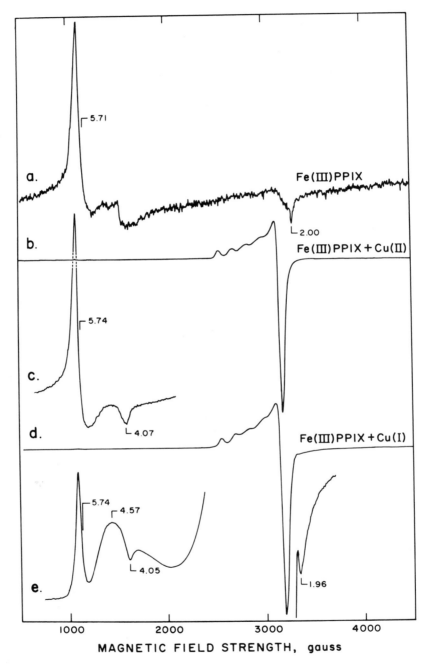

Figure 4. X-band EPR spectra of hemin. Conditions: 2.2% SDS, 0.1 M HTFA. Trace a, 0.12 mM Fe(III)PPIX; trace b, 0.20 mM Fe(III)PPIX, 15 mM Cu(II); trace c, as in b, except 10-fold increased receiver gain; trace d, 0.20 mM Fe(III)PPIX, 13 mM Cu(II), 1.6 mM Cu(I), 1.6 mM Cr(III); trace e, as in d, except 4-fold increased receiver gain. All spectra were recorded with a Varian E-109 spectrometer using a liquid helium cryostat. Magnetic field strengths were determined with an NMR gaussmeter.

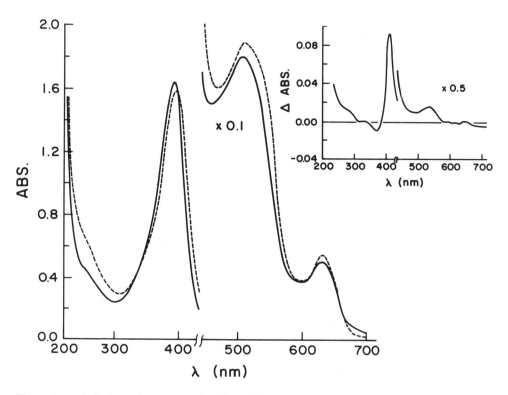

Figure 5. Optical absorption spectra of SDS-solubilized hemin. Solid line: 18 μM Fe(III)PPIX in 2% SDS, 0.1 M NaTFA, pH 4.0, 23 C, 1.0 cm optical pathlength; dashed line: same spectrum after addition of 0.22 mM Cu(I), 0.38 mM Cu(II), 0.22 mM Cr(III). Inset: Fe(III)PPIX + Cu(I) vs. Fe(III)PPIX difference spectrum. Conditions: 0.6 mM Fe(III)PPIX, 1.6 mM Cu(I), 13 mM Cu(II) in 0.1 M HTFA, 0.8% SDS, 23 C, 0.01 cm optical pathlength.

$(NH_3)_5Co$-4-vinylpyridine^{3+} ions the values are $K_a = 8.0 \times 10^3$ M^{-1} and $K_a = 3.4 \times 10^3$ M^{-1}, respectively (17). Hemin-copper(I) solutions at the concentration levels used in our studies would therefore be anticipated to form π-complexes, giving rise to characteristic new spectral bands of about the energy and intensity that we have observed in the optical difference spectra (Figure 5).

Addition of other unreactive metal ions, including Cu(II), has no effect upon the heme optical spectrum, but addition of Eu^{2+} ion (E$^\circ$ = -0.43 V), or excess dithionite ion causes immediate reduction to the ferroheme, which has markedly different spectral properties (Figure 6). Reaction with Eu^{2+} is well behaved, requiring addition of about one equivalent to effect complete reduction of heme. Addition of excess Eu^{2+} causes no immediate further spectral changes. The spectrum obtained is nearly identical to one obtained by pulse radiolytic reduction of hemin-SDS (18). The relative intensities of the Q-band peaks suggest that Fe(II) is low-spin (19) an interpretation supported by the heme resonance Raman spectrum (given below).

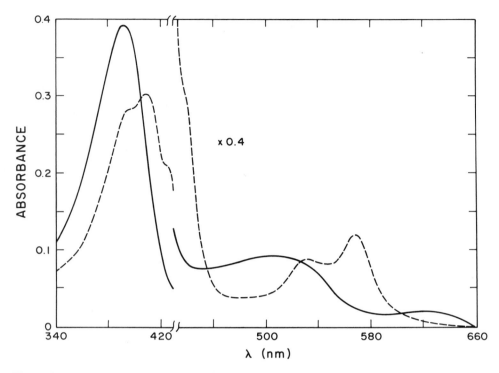

Figure 6. Optical absorption spectra of SDS-solubilized ferri- and ferrohemins. Solid line: 40 μM Fe(III)PPIX in 2% SDS, 0.01 M HTFA, 23 C, 1.0 cm optical pathlength; dashed line, immediately after addition of 40 μM Eu(TFA)$_2$.

Resonance Raman Spectra

Independent evidence of vinyl group complexation in the hemin-copper(I) ions was sought in the vibrational spectra of the ions. Typically, Cu(I)-olefin binding gives rise to a 100-150 cm^{-1} shift in the C=C stretching vibration to lower energies; this effect is illustrated for the (H$_2$O)$_5$Cr(III)-fumarato-Cu(I)$^{3+}$ binuclear ion in Figure 7, where the band at 1660 cm^{-1} shifts to 1526 cm^{-1} upon Cu(I) addition. The (H$_2$O)$_5$Cr(III)-fumarato^{2+} ion was chosen to provide a photoredox-inactive, substitution-inert system.

Resonance Raman spectra of hemin and hemin-Cu(I) ions are given in Figure 8. The band at 1634 cm^{-1} has been assigned to a vinyl stretching mode (20). Its intensity appears to diminish upon Cu(I) addition and a new band appears at 1528 cm^{-1}, in the region expected for the Cu(I)-olefin stretching mode. These results are consistent with binding stoichiometries determined by optical spectroscopy, i.e., hemin contains two vinyl substituents, only one of which appears to coordinate Cu(I).

Additional information on the oxidation and spin states of the heme iron can be obtained from the positions of vibrational bands in the core size (1550-1600 cm^{-1})

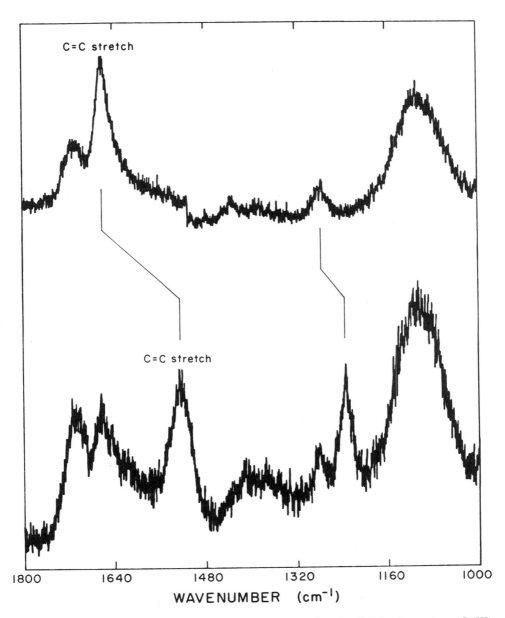

Figure 7. Raman vibrational spectra of the fumaratopentaaquochromium(III) ion. Lower trace: Cr(III)-fumarato-Cu(I) π-ion. The chromium(III) complex was prepared by adding a stoichiometric equivalent of Cr(II) ion to the $(NH_3)_5$Co(III)fumarate ion; the binuclear complex was prepared *in situ* by reducing Cu(II) with Cr(II) in the presence of the Cr(III) complex ion. Conditions: 0.13 M Cr(III)fumarate; 0.10 M Cu(I), 0.05 M Cu(II), in 1.0 M $HClO_4$. The intensity of the Cu(d)$\Rightarrow$L(π^*) optical band indicated that the Cr(III)fumarate ion was about 70% π-complexed under these conditions. Upper trace: same solution after air oxygenation. Laser excitation was at 488.0 nm; samples were irradiated at room temperature. Optical spectra before and after Raman analysis were identical.

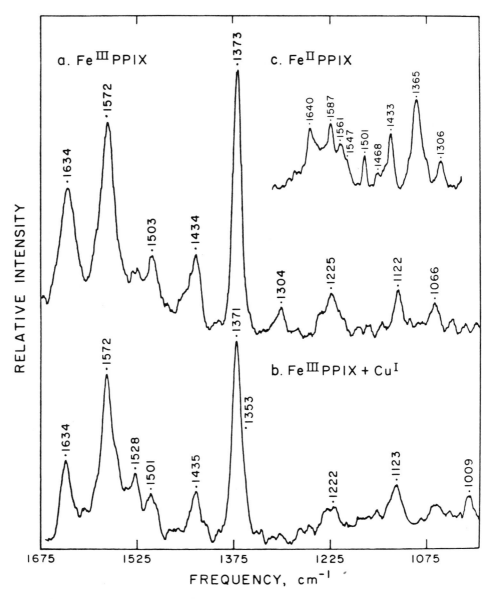

Figure 8. Resonance Raman spectra of SDS-solubilized hemin. Spectrum a: 14 μM Fe(III)PPIX, 0.6 mM Cu(II) in 2.2% SDS, 0.1 HTFA, 23 C, 1 scan, incident laser power 32 mW; spectrum b: 14 μM Fe(III)PPIX, 0.38 mM Cu(II), 0.22 mM Cu(I), 0.22 mM Cr(III) in 2.2% SDS, 0.1 M HTFA, 23 C, 1 scan, incident laser power 32 mW; spectrum c: 24 μM Fe(III)PPIX reduced by addition of slight stoichiometric excess of Eu(II), pH 2.60, 23 C, 4 scans, incident laser power 19 mW. All samples were maintained under rigorously anaerobic conditions. Laser excitation was at 406.7 nm. Spectra were subject to a 25-point smooth.

and oxidation state (1350-1380 cm^{-1}) marker regions (20). Appearance of bands at 1373 and 1572 cm^{-1} are consistent with assignment as a high-spin ferric ion. Upon Cu(I) association, iron remains high-spin ferric except at the highest Cu(I)/Cu(II) ratios used, for which formation of some ferroheme is indicated by the appearance of a low-energy shoulder on the 1371 cm^{-1} band. Europous ion reduction gives rise to a low-spin ferroheme, as indicated by the shift in band maxima to 1365 and 1587 cm^{-1}. No bands appear in the vicinity of 1520 cm^{-1} in the chemically reduced heme.

EPR Spectra

Cupric ion addition to micellar hemin suspensions causes virtually no perturbation of the axial $g_\perp$ band; the $g_\parallel$ band is obscured by the strong axial Cu(II) signal in the $g = 2$ region (Figure 4b). In initial studies, we found that addition of Cu(I) reagent solutions gave rise to a broad new band in the low-field region of the spectrum (Figure 4c). These spectra bear striking similarity to EPR signals generated by partial oxidation of reduced cytochrome oxidase by O_2 (21). In the present instance, however, subsequent experiments established that the broad $g = 4.5$ band was not attributable to Cu(I)-heme ligation, but to hexaaquochromic ion, which was present in solution as a product of the chromous-cupric ion reaction used to generate Cu(I). Interference from $Cr(H_2O)_6^{3+}$ ion was unanticipated, since it is reported to exhibit a single band in the $g = 2$ region (22). Axial perturbations of the magnetic field can cause appearance of low-field bands, e.g., as occurs in trigonally distorted chromic alums (23) or coordination complexes possessing tetragonal ligand environments (24); presumably, the field symmetry about Cr(III) is lowered in this instance upon freezing the micellar suspension.

It is possible to prepare Cu(I) solutions which are devoid of low-field bands by using Eu(II) as chemical reductant. The corresponding Cu(I)-ferriheme π-complexes formed from this reagent solution gave EPR spectra which were indistinguishable from spectra taken in the absence of Cu(I) (Figure 4b). Cu(I) ligation to the porphyrin periphery therefore causes no detectable perturbation of the magnetic field at the central iron.

Dynamics of Hemin-Cu(I) Binuclear Ions

Demetalation

Either reduction by Eu^{2+} or addition of Cu(I) causes slow loss of iron from the heme in these acidic suspensions; because the SDS-solubilized ferriheme is stable in these systems, the metal is clearly being lost as the ferrous ion. Reaction product spectra are identical to the H_4PPIX (25) dication in 0.1 M HTFA when Cu(II) concentration levels are below one millimolar, but Cu(II)PPIX also forms at higher [Cu(II)] values. Demetalation rates are dependent upon the [Cu(I)]/[Cu(II)] ratios, and were found to fit the rate law:

$$dP/dt = a[FePPIX]/(1 + b[Cu(II)]/[Cu(I)]) \qquad (1)$$

When [Cu(I)], [Cu(II)] ≫ [FePPIX], the reaction is pseudo-first-order; under these conditions, plots of the reciprocal of the measured rate constant (k_o) against [Cu(II)]/[Cu(I)] yield straight lines (Figure 9) with the constants a and b defined by the intercept and slope/intercept ratio, respectively, i.e.,

$$1/k_o = 1/a + (b/a)([Cu(II)]/[Cu(I)]) \qquad (2)$$

This unusual rate law can be rationalized by a mechanism in which an equilibrium is rapidly established between the ferri and ferro redox states that is controlled by the Cu(II)/Cu(I) ratio, with demetalation occurring from the ferroheme only, i.e.,

$$Fe(III)PPIX\text{-}Cu(I) + Cu(I) \rightleftarrows Fe(II)PPIX\text{-}Cu(I) + Cu(II) \qquad K_3 \qquad (3)$$

$$Fe(II)PPIX\text{-}Cu(I) + 4H^+ \Rightarrow Fe(II) + H_4PPIX\text{-}Cu(I) \qquad k_4 \qquad (4)$$

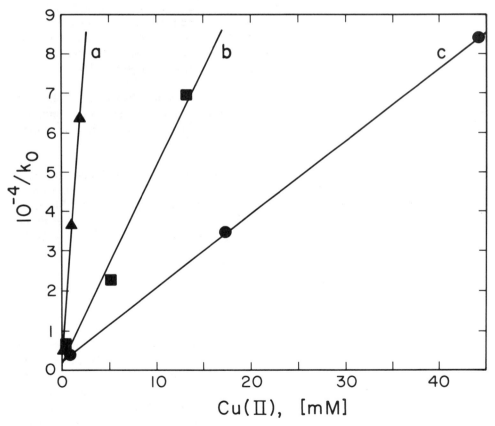

Figure 9. Copper dependence of iron loss from hemin-Cu(I) binuclear ions. Conditions: $12\,\mu M$ Fe(III)PPIX, 2.0-2.2% SDS, 0.1 M HTFA, 23 C. Triangles, 0.073 mM Cu(I); squares, 0.20 mM Cu(I); circles, 0.66 mM Cu(I). Solid lines are least-squares fits to the data. Values for K_3 and k_4 were computed for each line; the means for these values are: $K_3 = 1.7$, $k_4 = 4.2 \times 10^{-4}\,s^{-1}$.

Given this mechanism, the rate law constants are identified as $a = k_4$ and $b = 1/K_3$. From the kinetic data (Figure 9), the redox equilibrium, $K_3 = 1.8$ at 23 C. This value indicates that under most conditions used in this study the equilibrium lies to the left, so that the Fe(III)-Cu(I) binuclear ion predominates in solution. This result is consistent with data from the optical and Raman studies described above. From the magnitude of K_3 and the reduction potential for the $Cu^{2+/+}$ aquo ion, ($E° = 153$ mV) (26), we calculate the potential for the FePPIX-Cu(I)$^{2+/+}$ ion, $E° = 173$ mV at pH 1.0. This number compares fairly well with the value of ~100 mV determined at pH 3.0 from the midpoint potential in a spectroelectrochemical titration (27) using Eu^{2+} as reductant, providing thermodyamic confirmation of the kinetically determined redox equilibrium position.

Electron Transfer Pathways

When redox pairs associate strongly it becomes possible under favorable circumstances to identify by kinetic arguments the pathway for electron transfer. A pertinent example is the one-electron reduction of the $(NH_3)_5$Ru-4-vinylpyridine^{3+} ion by Cu(I). Because strong π-bonding occurs, the binuclear ion accumulates and one observes "saturation" kinetics (17), i.e., conversion from second- to first-order behavior with increasing [Cu(I)]. A general mechanism which accounts for this behavior is given in Figure 10. Here, it is recognized that electron transfer might occur by way of the bridging vinylpyridine ligand (k_a) and by various other pathways (designated collectively by k_b). With [Cu(I)] $\gg$ [Ru(III)], the rate law for this mechanism is:

$$k_5 = (k_a + k_b/K_a)/(1 + 1/K_a[Ru(III)]) \tag{5}$$

From the kinetic analysis, it is possible to determine only the sum $(k_a + k_b/K_a)$. However, by comparing the reactivity of Cu(I) in this system to structurally very similar oxidants lacking the ability to form binuclear π-complexes, it is possible to obtain an independent estimate of k_b. In the present instance, we used the 4-ethylpyridine analog, which proved to be insufficiently reactive with Cu(I) to account for the measured rate of reduction of the $(NH_3)_5$Ru-4-vinylpyridine^{3+} ion (17). This establishes that the predominant pathway for electron transfer in this system is through the bridging ligand.

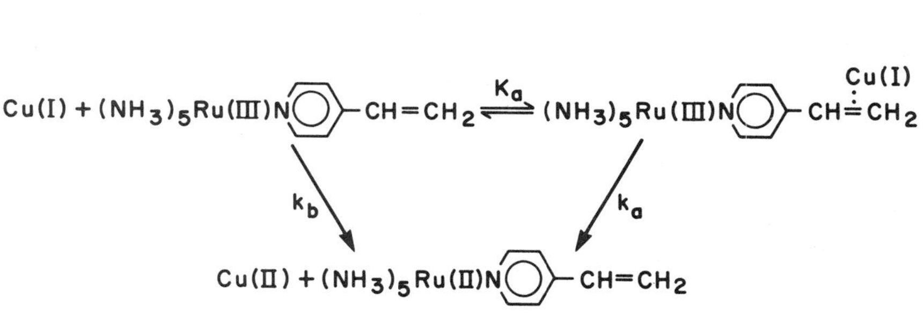

Figure 10. Mechanism for 4-vinylpyridinepentaammineruthenium(III) reduction by Cu(I).

A similar rate comparison was made using the ferrimesoporphyrin IX ion (Figure 1b) as a structural analog of hemin to distinguish between peripheral electron transfer through the bridging porphyrin in the hemin-Cu(I) binuclear ion and electron transfer by other, presumably axial, pathways. The SDS-solubilized ferric mesoIX ion in weakly acidic media displays an optical absorption spectrum nearly identical in shape to the diaquohemin spectrum, although the band maxima are blue-shifted by about 10 nm (λ_{max} = 622, 494, 382 nm); the EPR spectrum shows an axial high-spin ferric signal with $g_{\parallel}$ = 1.99, $g_{\perp}$ = 5.74, essentially identical to hemin, and the resonance Raman spectrum gives bands at 1586 and 1371 cm^{-1}, also indicating the high-spin ferric state. Reduction with Eu^{2+} causes immediate conversion to a spectrum featuring a split Soret (λ_{max} 382, 405 nm), similar to the one observed for ferrohemin (Figure 6), but with visible bands at 560 and 523 nm that differ in shape and relative intensity from ferrohemin. The spectra of the visible bands in both oxidation states appear identical to published spectra of mesohemin in dichloromethane (28). Based upon an analysis of the resonance Raman spectrum, it has been suggested that the ferrous heme exists in an intermediate S=1 electronic ground state (28).

Because the redox equilibria in the heme-copper systems (equation 3) lies to the left, it has not been possible to detect electron transfer from Cu(I) to either of the hemes. However, the back reaction between the ferrohemes and cupric ion is easily measured by stopped-flow spectrophotometry. From the wavelength dependence of the amplitudes of the kinetic traces it was evident that the process being monitored is oxidation of the heme. If reaction between Cu(I) and hemin proceeds preferentially by peripheral attack through the π-complexed intermediate, microscopic reversibility dictates that oxidation of the heme will also occur preferentially by Cu(II)-olefin interaction, even though stable Cu(II)-olefin complexes are not formed. A point of kinetic ambiguity is introduced, however, since binuclear ions do not accumulate. Either the rate-limiting step in the reverse reaction is not electron transfer or the measured rate constant is a composite of the ion-pair formation constant for the precursor complex and the intrinsic electron transfer rate constant.

Ferroheme oxidation was found in both cases to follow a second-order rate law, $-d[Fe(II)heme]/dt = k[Fe(II)heme][Cu(II)]$, with $k = 6.2 (\pm 0.7) \times 10^3$ M^{-1}s^{-1} for ferromesoporphyrin IX and $k = 2.2 (\pm 0.2) \times 10^3$ M^{-1}s^{-1} for ferrohemin at 25 C, pH 3.0 in 1.0% SDS (Figure 11). The magnitudes of the rate constants are too low for the reactions to be limited by diffusion, either in bulk solution or along the micellar surface (29). Since precursor complex stabilities and ferroheme orientations within the micelle should be comparable in the two systems, the rate differences probably reflect intrinsic differences in electron transfer rates. Some differences in reactivity may be expected because the reactant hemes probably are in differing spin states, i.e., for ferrohemin, S=0; for ferromesoIX, S=1, and the reaction driving force is greater for the latter heme. Nonetheless, the absence of any apparent rate enhancing effects accompanying incorporation of vinyl substituents onto the prophyrin ring argues against preferential operation of a peripheral pathway with the olefin as lead-in group in the hemin-copper redox reaction. The question of whether this pathway might operate in cytochrome oxidase remains open, however, since alternate pathways available to the model system involving uncomplexed copper ions will not exist in the biological particle.

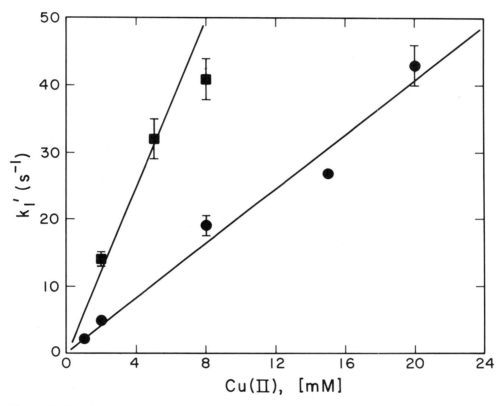

Figure 11. Kinetics of oxidation of ferrohemin and ferromesoporphyrin IX by Cu(II). Conditions: 0.13-0.15 mM Fe(II)mesoIX or 0.06-0.20 mM Fe(II)PPIX in 1% SDS, pH 3.0 at 25 C. k_1' is the first-order rate constant determined by stopped-flow spectrophotometry. Each data point is the mean value of 4-5 individual determinations; error bars give the average deviation from the mean.

Evidence for Cu(I) π-Ligation in Cytochrome Oxidase

Based upon our observations, cuprous ion binding to heme a_3 in the oxidase would be expected to cause only very small changes in the heme visible absorption and EPR spectra, and the ultraviolet charge transfer bands would be obscured by protein absorption bands. In general, then, direct detection of π-complexation by these methods will be difficult.

The vinyl stretching modes of hemes a and a_3 in cytochrome oxidase have been assigned to a band at 1624 cm^{-1} (30). Since other bands overlap in this region, it is

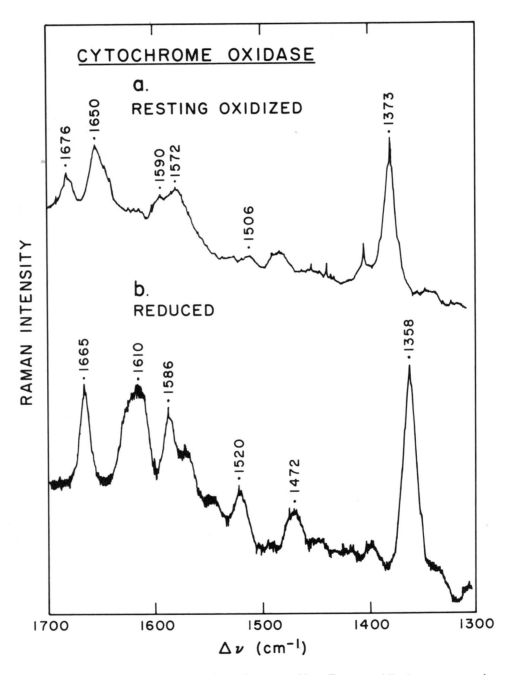

Figure 12. Resonance Raman spectrum of cytochrome *c* oxidase. Trace a: oxidized enzyme; trace b: dithionite reduced enzyme. Spectra are reproduced from reference d listed in Table I, with permission from Gerald Babcock.

difficult to quantify the intensity change of the 1624 cm^{-1} band upon reducing the enzyme. The appearance of a new band at about 1520 cm^{-1} is easily observed, however, in reduced oxidases of both mitochondrial and microbial origin (Figure 12, Table I). This behavior is analogous to that observed in the Raman spectra of Cu(I)-hemin solutions (Figure 8), suggesting that Cu(I)-olefin ligation may occur in the reduced form of the oxidases as well. In examining the vibrational spectra of

Table I

Raman Bands of Cytochrome Oxidase[a], 1500-1540 cm^{-1}

Excitation wavelength, nm	Oxidized enzyme	Reduced enzyme	References
406.7	1506 (vw)	1520 (m)	d
	1506 (vw)	1519 (m)	e
	1506 (vw)	1519 (m)	f
	1509 (vw)	1518 (w)[b]	g
413.1	~1509 (vw)	~1520 (m)	h,i
	~1504 (vw)	~1520 (m)	d
	Bands absent	1525 (m)	g
	1504 (vw), 1520 (vw)	Not reported	l
	~1520 (m)[c]	~1520 (m)	j,k
441.6	Bands absent	1527 (w)	m
	Not reported	~1520 (w)	d
	Not reported	~1520 (w)	n
	Not reported	1519 (w)	o
	Bands absent	1517 (w)[p]	o
	Not reported	1519 (w)[q]	o
	Not reported	1519 (w)[r]	f

[a] Mitochondrial cytochrome oxidase, except where noted.

[b] Partially-reduced form.

[c] Reported spectrum is nearly identical to that of partially-reduced enzyme (ref. *g*), and bears little resemblance to other spectra of oxidized enzyme reported by these workers (ref. *h*).

[d] G.T. Babcock, P.M. Callahan, M.R. Ondrias and I. Salmeen, *Biochemistry 20*, 959 (1981).

[e] M. Callahan and G.T. Babcock, *Biochemistry 22*, 452 (1983).

[f] G.T. Babcock and P.M. Callahan, *Biochemistry 22*, 2314 (1983).

[g] M.R. Ondrias and G.T. Babcock, *Biochem. Biophys. Res. Commun. 93*, 29 (1980).

[h] W.H. Woodruff, R.J. Kessler, N.S. Ferris, R.F. Dallinger, K.R. Carter, T.M. Antalis and G. Palmer, *Adv. Chem. Ser. 201*, 625 (1982).

[i] Reference 27.

[j] W.H. Woodruff, R.F. Dallinger, T.M. Antalis and G. Palmer, *Biochemistry 20*, 1332 (1981).

[k] K.R. Carter, T.M. Antalis, G. Palmer, N.S. Ferris and W.H. Woodruff, *Proc. Natl. Acad. Sci. USA 78*, 1652 (1981).

[l] Reference 26.

[m] G.T. Babcock and I. Salmeen, *Biochemistry 18*, 2493 (1979).

[n] J. Van Steelandt-Frentrup, I. Salmeen and G.T. Babcock, *J. Am. Chem. Soc. 103*, 5981 (1981).

[o] T. Ogura, N. Sone, K. Tagawa and T. Kitagawa, *Biochemistry 23*, 2826 (1984).

[p] For PS3 thermophilic bacterium.

[q] For yeast (*Saccharomyces cerevisiae*).

[r] For *Thermus thermophilus*.

other hemes and heme proteins, we have found no similar changes accompanying change of oxidation state of the central iron; in particular, the 1520 cm^{-1} band is absent from the spectra of several ferroheme *a* complexes. The only data of which we are aware that cast doubt on this assignment are Raman spectra of the copper-depleted derivatives of the mitochondrial enzyme, which are also reported to show the appearance of 1520 cm^{-1} bands upon heme reduction (31).

As previously mentioned, the micellar hemin-copper(I) ions are models for type a π-complexation in cytochrome a_3 (Figure 3). Comparison of physical properties and dynamic behavior with heme *a*-based binuclear ions will provide a basis for evaluating the potential role of the Cu(I) binding polyisoprenyl heme substituent (Figure 1c) in electron transfer. These studies are in progress.

Acknowledgements

JKH expresses his gratitude to former colleagues and associates who have contributed to our understanding of the principles underlying this research, including Paulette A.'G. Carr, Eugene A. Deardorff, James K. Farr, Leslie G. Hulett, Robert H. Lane, Kenneth A. Norton, Jr., and Alan Quenelle. The authors are grateful to Dr. Takeshi Sakurai for assistance in obtaining the EPR spectra, and to Thomas M. Loehr for helpful discussions. Financial support has been provided by the National Institute of Health under grants GM-20943 and GM-31620.

References and Footnotes

1. Recent reviews include: M. Wikström, K. Krab and M. Saraste, "Cytochrome Oxidase—A Synthesis," Academic Press, 1981; D.F. Wilson and M. Erecinska, *Porphyrins 7*, 1 (1980); T.E. King, Y. Orii, B. Chance and K. Okunuki, "Cytochrome Oxidase," Elsevier: Amsterdam, 1979; W.S. Caughey, W.J. Wallace, J.A. Volpe and S. Yoshikawa, *Enzymes 13*, 299 (1976); B. G. Malmstrom, *Q. Rev. Biophys. 6*, 389 (1974); D.C. Wharton, in "Inorganic Biochemistry," Vol. 2, G.I. Eichhorn, ed., Elsevier: Amsterdam, 1973, p. 955.
2. G. Palmer, G.T. Babcock and L.E. Vickery, *Proc. Natl. Acad. Sci. USA 73*, 2206 (1976).
3. C.A. Reed and J.T. Landrum, *FEBS Lett. 106*, 265 (1979).
4. C.H.A. Seiter, in "Frontiers of Biological Energetics," L.P. Dutton, J.S. Leigh and A. Scarpa, eds., Academic Press: New York, 1979, p. 798.
5. L. Powers, B. Chance, Y. Ching and P. Angiolillo, *Biophys. J. 34*, 465 (1981); L. Powers, W.E. Blumberg, B. Chance, C.H. Barlow, J.S. Leigh, J. Smith, T. Yonetani, S. Vik and J. Peisach, *Biochim. Biophys. Acta 546*, 520 (1979).
6. C.K. Shauer, K. Akabori, C.M. Elliott and O.P. Anderson, *J. Am. Chem. Soc. 106*, 1127 (1984); R.J. Saxton, L.W. Olson and L.J. Wilson, *J. Chem. Soc. Chem. Commun.* 984 (1982); S.E. Dessens, C.L. Merrill, R. J. Saxton, R.L. Ilaria, J.W. Lindsey and L.J. Wilson, *J. Am. Chem. Soc. 104*, 4357 (1982); C.K. Chang, M.S. Koo and B.J. Ward, *J. Chem. Soc. Chem. Commun.* 716 (1982); B. Lukas, J.R. Miller, J. Silver, M.T. Wilson and I.E.G. Morrison, *J. Chem. Soc. Dalton* 1035 (1982); M.J. Gunter, L.N. Mander, K.S. Murray and P.E. Clark, *J. Am. Chem. Soc. 103*, 6784 (1981); M.J. Gunter, L.N. Mander, G.M. McLaughlin, K.S. Murray, K.J. Berry, P.E. Clark and D.A. Buckingham, *J. Am. Chem. Soc. 102*, 1470 (1980); R.E. Petty, B.R. Welch, L.J. Wilson, L.A. Bottomly and K.M. Kadish, *J. Am. Chem. Soc. 102*, 611 (1980); J. Jaud, Y. Journaux, J. Galy and O. Kahn, *Nouv. J. Chim. 4*, 629 (1980); H. Okawa, W. Kanda and S. Kida, *Chem. Lett.* 1281 (1980); T. Prosperi and A.A.G. Tomlinson, *J. Chem. Soc. Chem. Commun.* 196 (1979).

7. J.A. Ibers and R.H. Holm, *Science 209,* 223 (1980).
8. W.H. Armstrong, A. Spool, G.C. Papaefthymiou, R.B. Frankel and S.J. Lippard, *J. Am. Chem. Soc. 106,* 3653 (1984).
9. E.A. Deardorff, P.A.G. Carr and J. K. Hurst, *J. Am. Chem. Soc. 103,* 6611 (1981).
10. W.S. Caughey, G.S. Smythe, D.H. O'Keeffe, J.E. Maskasky and M.L. Smith, *J. Biol. Chem. 250,* 7602 (1975).
11. K.A. Norton, Jr. and J.K. Hurst, *J. Am. Chem. Soc. 104,* 5960 (1982).
12. M.S. Haddad, S.R. Wilson, D.J. Hodgson and D.N. Hendrickson, *J. Am. Chem. Soc. 103,* 384 (1981); R.J. Butcher, C.J. O'Connor and E. Sinn, *Inorg. Chem. 18,* 1913 (1979); J.A. Moreland and R.J. Doedens, *Inorg. Chem. 17,* 674 (1978); R.L. Lintvedt, M.D. Glick, B.K. Tomlonovic, D. P. Gavel and J.M. Kusjaz, *Inorg. Chem. 15,* 1633 (1976).
13. G.W. Brudvig, T.H. Stevens, R.H. Morse and S.I. Chan, *Biochemistry 20,* 3912 (1981); G.T. Babcock, L.E. Vickery and G. Palmer, *J. Biol. Chem. 253,* 2400 (1978); D.W. Urry, W.W. Wainio and D. Grebner, *Biochem. Biophys. Res. Commun. 27,* 625 (1967).
14. J. Simplicio and K. Schwenzer, *Biochemistry 12,* 1923 (1973); J. Simplicio, *Biochemistry 11,* 2525 (1972).
15. J.K. Hurst and R.H. Lane, *J. Am. Chem. Soc. 95,* 1703 (1973).
16. F.R. Hartley, *Chem. Rev. 73,* 163 (1973).
17. K.A. Norton, Jr. and J.K. Hurst, *J. Am. Chem. Soc. 100,* 7237 (1978); J.K. Hurst, *J. Am. Chem. Soc. 98,* 4001 (1976).
18. E.L. Evers, G.G. Jayson and A.J. Swallow, *J. Chem. Soc. Faraday 74,* 418 (1977).
19. R.J.P. Williams, in "Haematin Enzymes," J.E. Falk, R. Lemberg and R. K. Morton, eds., Pergamon Press: London, 1961, p. 41.
20. See, e.g., T.G. Spiro, in "Iron Porphyrins," Part 2, A.B.P. Lever and H.B. Gray, eds., Addison-Wesley: Reading, MA, 1983, p. 91.
21. R.W. Shaw, R.E. Hansen and H. Beinert, *J. Biol. Chem. 253,* 6637 (1978).
22. H. Levanon, S. Charbinsky and Z. Luz, *J. Chem. Phys. 53,* 3056 (1970); K.M. Sancier, *J. Phys. Chem. 67,* 1317 (1968).
23. A.G. Danilov and A. Manoogian, *Phys. Rev. B 6,* 4097 (1972); C.F. Davis, Jr. and M.W.P. Strandberg, *Phys. Rev. 105,* 447 (1957).
24. E. Pedersen and H. Toftlund, *Inorg. Chem. 13,* 1603 (1974).
25. Abbreviations used: PPIX, protoporphyrin IX; mesoIX, mesoporphyrin IX; HTFA, trifluoroacetic acid; SDS, sodium dodecyl sulfate.
26. W.M. Latimer, "Oxidation Potentials," 2nd ed., Prentice-Hall: Englewood Cliff, NJ, 1952.
27. P.L. Dutton, *Methods Enzymol. 54,* 411 (1978).
28. T.G. Spiro and J.M. Burke, *J. Am. Chem. Soc. 98,* 5482 (1976).
29. M.D. Hatlee, J.J. Kozak, G. Rothenberger, P.P. Infelta and M. Grätzel, *J. Phys. Chem. 84,* 1508 (1980).
30. S. Choi, J.J. Lee, Y.H. Wei and T.G. Spiro, *J. Am. Chem. Soc. 105,* 3692 (1983).
31. R.J. Kessler, Thesis, University of Texas, Austin, University Microfilms 8217896 (1982).

Biological & Inorganic Copper Chemistry,
ISBN 0-940030-11-X, Eds., K. D. Karlin & J. Zubieta, Adenine Press, ©Adenine Press, 1985

Copper Chelates with Azole-Containing Ligands as Corroborative and Speculative Model Compounds for Copper Proteins

Jan Reedijk, Willem L. Driessen, Jacobus van Rijn
Department of Chemistry
Gorlaeus Laboratories
State University Leiden
P. O. Box 9502, 2300 RA Leiden
The Netherlands

Abstract

This review describes the most recent results of copper coordination compounds with chelating ligands containing at least two azole ligands (i.e. imidazoles, benzimidazoles, pyrazoles). The strategy and design of the ligand systems is briefly described, as well as the synthetic routes. The synthesis and characterisation of the copper(I) and copper(II) compounds with these ligands is presented, together with a variety of X-ray structures. The details of the structures are discussed in relation with the known or proposed geometries of Cu(I) and Cu(II) in copper proteins and enzymes. Finally, some preliminary results of catalysis studies with some dinuclear copper compounds are presented.

Introduction

The bioinorganic chemistry of copper is one of the most rapidly expanding areas of chemistry and enjoys the interest of e.g. biochemists, microbiologists, clinical chemists, spectroscopists, synthetic organic chemists, and coordination chemists. The area has frequently been reviewed (1-5), even in recent years, with the previous book in this series (6) as one of the most complete overviews of the field.

In non-biological systems the coordination chemistry of copper(I) and copper(II) continues to yield surprising structures and coordination geometries. In case of copper(I) coordination numbers of 2 (linear), 3 (T-shape, planar trigonal, trigonal pyramidal), 4 (tetrahedrally based), 5 (tetragonal pyramidal) have been reported (1-6). The d^{10} system of Cu(I) does not seem to have a preference for a certain coordination geometry and therefore the steric and/or electronic properties of the ligand systems are playing an important role in the determination of the structure of Cu(I) compounds. In the case of copper(II) coordination compounds the so-called "plasticity" of the Cu(II) ion is now generally accepted to be responsible for great variation of coordination numbers, sometimes even changing as a function of temperature (3,4,7). Often observed are coordination number 4 (square planar and

143

distorted tetrahedral), 5 (trigonal bipyramidal and square pyramidal), 6 (octahedral and distorted octahedral, such as tetragonally elongated or bicapped square pyramidal), 7 (capped octahedral) and 8 (dodecahedral). The resulting coordination geometry for a Cu(II) coordination compound is therefore mainly determined by either direct steric effects of the ligands, or indirect steric effects of the counter ions and the crystal lattice.

Realising this versatility in the coordination chemistry of both Cu(I) and Cu(II), it is not surprising that copper proteins also exhibit a variety of coordination geometries, some of which are now known in detail through X-ray analysis and advanced spectroscopic studies (6,8-10). From these spectroscopic studies, copper proteins have been divided in three groups, i.e.:

(i) *Type I copper proteins,* also called "blue copper" after the deep blue color in the Cu(II) state. The origin of this intense color (molar extinction above 3000 $1.mol^{-1}.cm^{-1}$ at about 600 nm) seems to be related to the distorted tetrahedral geometry of the CuN_2S_2 chromophore and in particular to the Cu-S(cys) charge-transfer band. The same coordination geometry seems to be present in the colorless Cu(I) form of the protein (proven only for plastocyanin); (11).

(ii) *Type II copper proteins.* These proteins do not have unusual spectral properties in the Cu(II) state. A coordination of Cu(II) by four nitrogen donor ligands is expected to be present in most of these proteins, although this has so far only been proven for bovine superoxide dismutase (12). The coordination in the Cu(I) state is expected to be lower (13).

(iii) *Type III copper proteins.* In these proteins (or parts of them) pairs of Cu(II) are believed to be present, which are strongly antiferromagnetically coupled. Such a coupling requires the Cu(II) ions to be rather close together, or to be connected by a bridging ligand, to understand the diamagnetism. In the Cu(I) state, the copper ions are also close together as deduced from EXAFS and, recently, from X-ray diffraction measurements (14).

It should be noted that many complicated copper-containing proteins, such as laccase, ceruloplasmin and others (6), contain more than one type of copper. It has been proposed by Hill (15), to designate these as type IV proteins. In addition to these classes some copper proteins are known, e.g. metallothionein, that only contain Cu(I) and that—most probably—have a role as a copper transport, storage or detoxification protein (16,17). These proteins and their analogs are not discussed in the present review.

With the exception of the above-mentioned copper(I) metallothionein, all so far reported copper proteins of type I, type II and type III do contain copper ions that are coordinated by at least two imidazole ligands from histidine side chains of the protein. This not only appears to be the case in the copper(II) proteins, but also in the copper(I) state of the proteins (known only in two cases with evidence from single-crystal studies) (11,14).

The study of low-molecular weight compounds as analogs (models) for metalloproteins is usually undertaken with the following aims:

a) To help in discovering the metal chromophore and deducing the structure of the active site, by comparing the spectroscopic properties of the protein with the analog (of known structure). These models have been named *"speculative models"* (18).

b) To contribute to a better understanding of the structure and reactivity of the active sites in metalloproteins. For instance when the X-ray structure of the active site is known in some detail, small variations (both structural and electronic) in the low-molecular weight analogs may yield important information about ligand effects, ligand constraints, hydrophobic interactions, etc. on the catalytic reactions occurring at the active site. These models have been named previously *"corroborative models"* (18).

c) To apply the knowledge of the structure and properties of the active site in metalloproteins. In this respect one could think about metal detoxification (such as the albumin models in the treatment of Wilson's disease (19)) and specific catalytic reactions (such as oxidative coupling reactions (20)). Such models can be named *"applicative models"*.

The present review deals with chelating ligands containing at least two azole rings (heterocyclic five-membered rings). The study is limited to this type of chelates, realising that the copper proteins known so far (vide supra) do contain at least two coordinating imidazoles. For reasons of comparison, not only imidazoles have been studied but also pyrazoles (easy synthesis and simple variations in steric strain) and benzimidazoles (easy synthesis) were investigated. Compounds already covered in our previous review (21) will only briefly be dealt with. The main part of the paper will therefore consider results obtained since June 1982.

After a brief section about ligand design and synthesis, first the Cu(I) compounds will be treated, followed by the Cu(II) compounds. Finally, some recent results on the use of our compounds in oxidation catalysis will be mentioned.

Ligand design and synthesis

For the synthesis of chelating ligands that have at least two azole ligands that cannot be oriented independently—our basic requirement—several strategies are possible.

Starting from simple imidazoles usually elaborate procedures are required to obtain chelating ligands. In some cases, however, ligands have been obtained by proce-

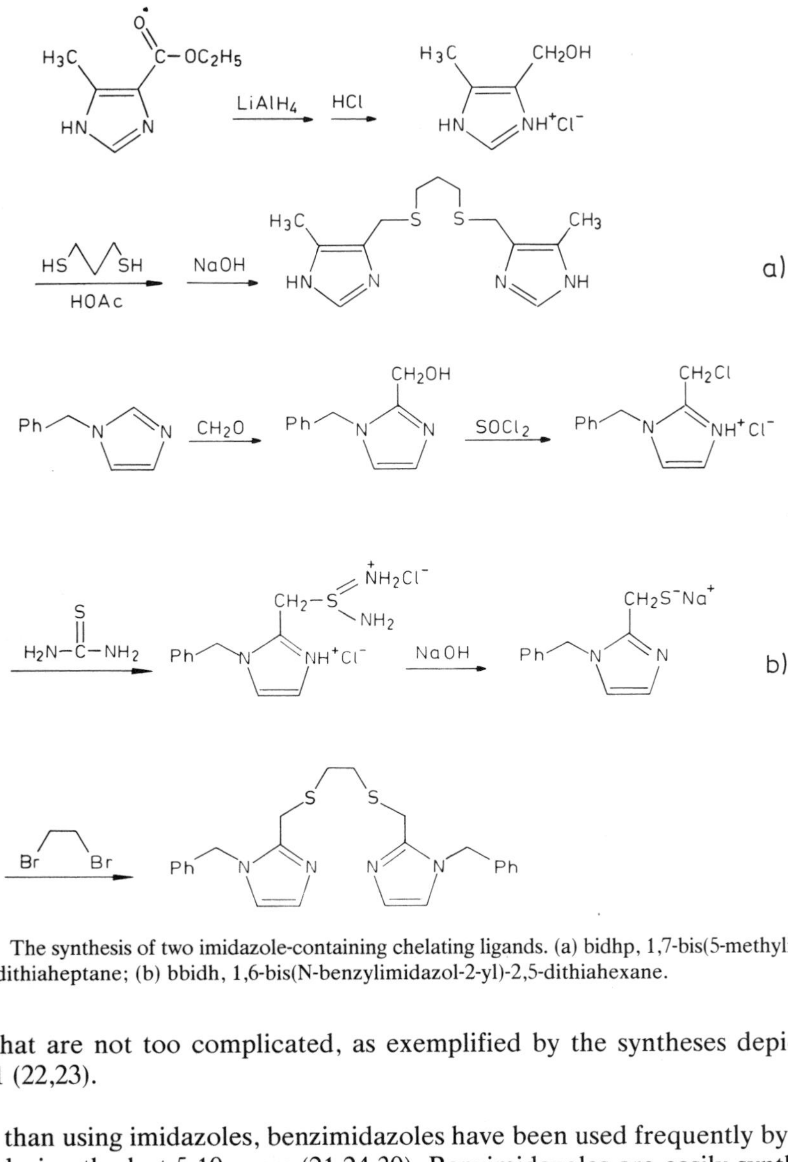

Figure 1. The synthesis of two imidazole-containing chelating ligands. (a) bidhp, 1,7-bis(5-methylimidazol-4-yl)-2,6-dithiaheptane; (b) bbidh, 1,6-bis(N-benzylimidazol-2-yl)-2,5-dithiahexane.

dures that are not too complicated, as exemplified by the syntheses depicted in figure 1 (22,23).

Rather than using imidazoles, benzimidazoles have been used frequently by us and others during the last 5-10 years (21,24-30). Benzimidazoles are easily synthesized via a condensation reaction of 1,2-diaminobenzenes and substituted carboxylic acids. Some examples taken from our work are schematically presented in figure 2 (31,32). In a further step these benzimidazole-type chelating ligands can be modified, such as N-alkylation (31,33).

More recently, rather than using (benz)imidazoles, pyrazole-type chelating ligands have been used. These ligands are easily synthesized and have the advantage that quite cheap starting materials can be used, and that a wide variation of steric

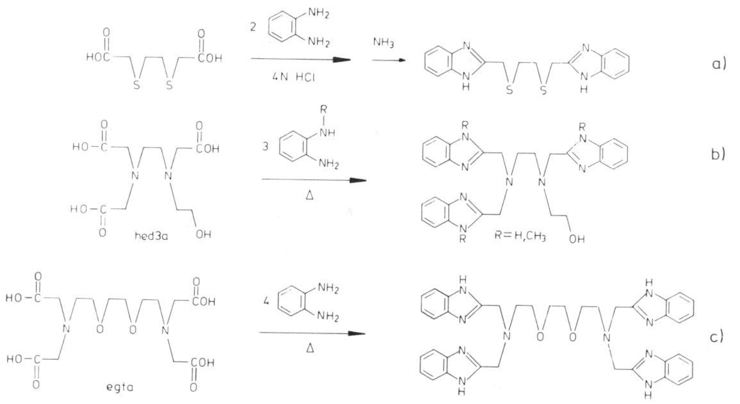

Figure 2. The synthesis of benzimidazole-containing chelating ligands. (a) bbdh, 1,6-bis(benzimidazol-2-yl)-2,5-dithiahexane; (b) hed3b, N,N,N′-tris(benzimidazol-2-ylmethyl)-N′-(2-hydroxyethyl)-1,2-ethane-diamine; (c) egtb, 1,1,10,10-tetrakis(benzimidazol-2-ylmethyl)-1,10-diaza-4,7-dioxadecane.

arrangements can be performed. A few synthetic routes are schematically depicted in figure 3 (34-36).

The variation of the examples shown in figures 1-3 will make clear that synthetic possibilities are almost unlimited and allow the study of the consequences of subtle variations in steric effects and electronic influences of the ligands (37,38). Chelating ligands of these classes should be able to structurally mimick type I copper (two azole and two S-donor ligands), type II copper (four azoles) including superoxide dismutase (6 azoles including a bridging one) and type III (6 azoles and some other ligands).

In the next section the Cu(I) and Cu(II) compounds of these and other ligands will be described, with special emphasis on the compounds prepared in our laboratory.

Copper(I) azole chelates

The number of copper(I) compounds with coordinated azoles is growing rapidly. Linearly coordinated Cu(I) has been proposed or proven for the simple non-chelating pyrazoles and imidazoles (39-41). Recently, also tetrahedral Cu(I) has been reported for the compound Cu(N-Meim)$_4$ClO$_4$ (N-Meim = N-methylimidazole) as proven by X-ray diffraction (42).

In the case of chelating imidazole ligands, initially only linear Cu(I) was observed, i.e. in Cu$_2$(edtb)(ClO$_4$)$_2$ and in Cu(bbdhp)(PF$_6$) (43,44), although in the latter compound Cu...S contacts of 2.9 A occur. However, T-shape coordination with two short colinear Cu−N bonds and somewhat longer Cu−X contacts have been found for both imidazoles (45) and pyrazoles (35). Some schematic ligand structures are redrawn in figure 4.

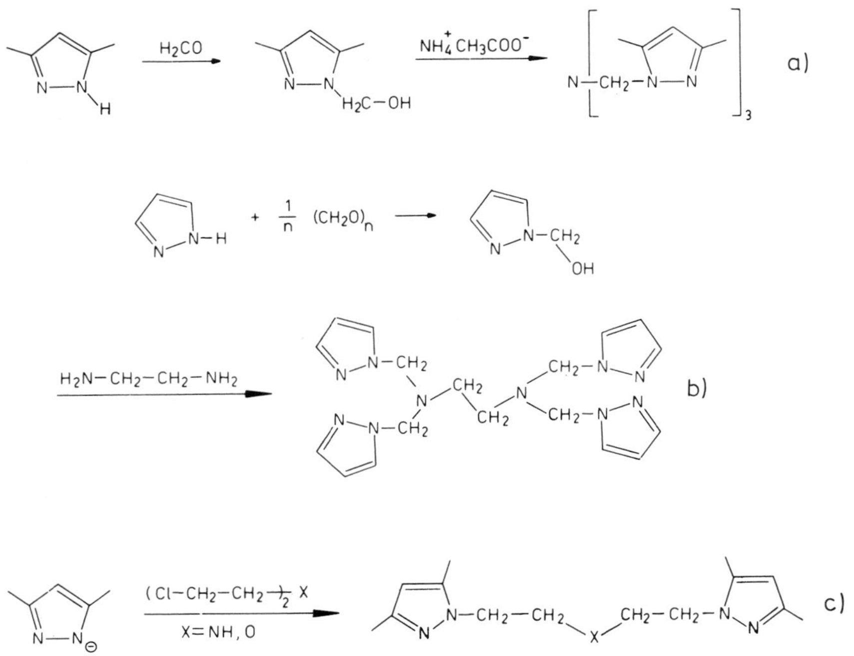

Figure 3. The synthesis of pyrazole-containing chelating ligands. (a) amtd, tris(3,5-dimethyl-1-pyrazolyl-methyl)amine; (b) edtp, N,N,N',N'-tetrakis(1-pyrazolylmethyl)-1,2-ethanediamine; (c) pzo, bis(2-(3,5-dimethyl-1-pyrazolyl)ethyl)oxyde (X = O).

When, in addition to azoles, alkenes are present as ligands, such as in the hydrotris(pyrazolyl)borates of Cu(I) (46), other trigonal coordination geometries with non-colinear Cu—N bonds do occur. Very recently, we have found that tetrahedral Cu(I) brought about by sterically hindered pyrazoles, can also occur. Figure 5 describes the cationic species Cu(edtp)$^+$ as it has been found in the compound Cu(edtp)(BF$_4$)(CH$_3$CN) (47).

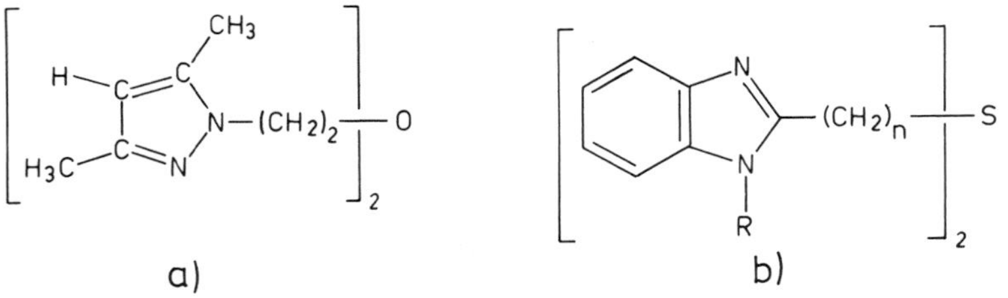

Figure 4. Some schematic structures of tridentate azole chelating ligands,resulting in T-shape co-ordination. (a) the pzo ligand (35); (b) the benzimidazole thioether ligands; when R = propyl and n = 2 the X-ray structure of the Cu(I) compound is known (45).

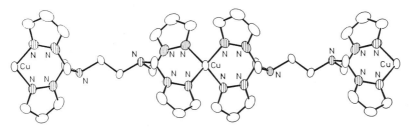

Figure 5. Part of the polymeric chain structure of the cation Cu(edtp)$^+$. Cu$-$N distances are 2.03 Å (47).

Realizing that with other ligands for Cu(I) a variety of coordination geometries has been observed, it is to be expected that future work in this area will reveal more about the structural variations that can occur in the case of the azole ligands coordinated to copper(I). In this respect it is tempting to speculate whether or not all the three histidine imidazoles in deoxyhemocyanin (14) are coordinated to each Cu(I). The possible presence of one protonated histidine, as observed in Cu(I)-plastocyanin (11), might well result in linear coordination for Cu(I).

Copper(II) azole chelates

The number of Cu(II) compounds with non-chelating azole ligands is extremely large, and coordination number 4 (square planar or distorted tetrahedral), 5 (square pyramidal and trigonal bipyramidal) and 6 (distorted octahedral) have frequently been found. Only in a few cases all ligands for Cu(II) were found to be azoles, such as in Cu(imH)$_6$(NO$_3$)$_2$ (48). Usually, however, also other ligands are coordinated to Cu(II) (49).

With chelating azole ligands, containing at least two azoles, the number of crystallographically characterized Cu(II) compounds is quite large and has significantly increased since the previous overview (6,21). The more recent results will be discussed according to the classification of the copper proteins.

Models for type I copper proteins. Tridentate chelating ligands with the donor set N$_2$S have been studied for benzimidazoles (39,45) in combination with copper(II). In these cases the Cu(II) adopts a five-coordinated geometry with two additional ligands, such as H$_2$O, ClO$_4^-$ or MeOH (30,45).

Tetradentate ligands with the donor set N$_2$S$_2$ have been studied both for imidazoles and benzimidazoles in combination with Cu(II) (21,22,28,29,49). Five-coordinate Cu(II) compounds with one additional ligand (Cl,Br,H$_2$O) and a trigonal bipyramidal geometry were already briefly mentioned in the previous review (21). More recently we have found a Cu(II) species with intermediate geometry, having water as the fifth ligand, but with the benzimidazoles not colinear (50). The structure of the cationic species is redrawn in figure 6.

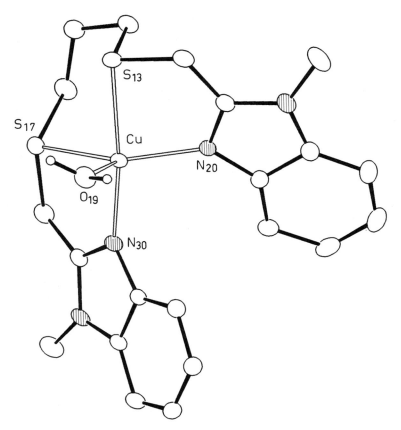

Figure 6. Structure of the Cu(II) cation [Cu(dmbbdhp)(H$_2$O)]$^{2+}$. Distances are: Cu−S = 2.33-2.34 Å, Cu−O = 2.23 Å and Cu−N = 1.95-2.00 Å (50).

As we have shown earlier, enlargement of the number of CH$_2$ groups between the 2 thioether sulfur atoms may also result in changed redox properties: Copper(I) compounds are easily formed in many cases (44), and the reduction can be even enhanced by irradiation with visible or UV light (51). Taking imidazoles, rather than benzimidazoles, it appears that the copper(II) state is quite stable, and a very interesting structure has been found for the compound Cu(bidhp)Cl$_2$ (ligand structure in figure 1). The X-ray structure (redrawn in figure 7) has indicated that in the six-coordinate Cu(II) ion, the Cu...S distances are 2.89-2.97 Å, which is unprecedented for a cis-octahedral geometry. As a result of these long bands, the Cu(II)−N bonds of 1.95 Å are rather short (23). Further enlargement of the number of CH$_2$ groups or other atoms between the two thioether atoms, has not yet resulted in crystal structures. The number of potential ligands, however, is significant (37,52,53). A challenge for the coming years will be the inclusion of a thiol ligand in the chelating N$_2$S$_2$ groups. Up to now, this has not yet been reported.

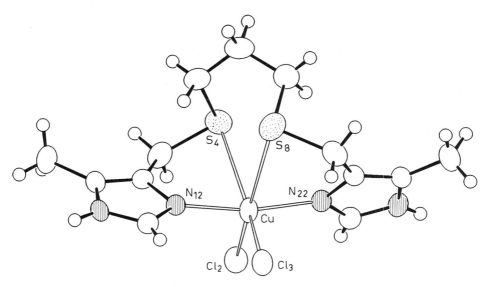

Figure 7. Structure of the distorted octahedral species Cu(bidhp)Cl$_2$. Distances are: Cu—Cl = 2.395 and 2.457 Å; Cu—S = 2.886 and 2.970 Å; Cu—N = 1.949 and 1.955 Å; (23).

Models for type II Cu(II) proteins. In this section we will deal with chelating ligands that result in mononuclear Cu(II) compounds, not having a sulfur atom in the ligand. With benzimidazole groups we and others (54-56) have previously described Cu(II) compounds formed from ntb, mntb and edtb. Related ligands containing also an oxygen-donor atom have been reported by Kida (56) and also (31) by us (see figure 2c and figure 8). Several crystal structures are now available for Cu(II) compounds with these ligands. Other ligands of this type have been developed by other workers, although the Cu(II) compounds have not yet or hardly been reported (57-59). See figure 9 for some ligands.

With pyrazoles also several ligands are available now and the copper compounds have been prepared and analysed for several (60-65) of them (see figure 10). The crystal structures are available (63,64) for Cu(amtd)(NO$_3$)$_2$ in which amtd (see figure 3a) coordinates tripodal tetradentate (see figure 11) and also for Cu(bidhp)Cl$_2$ which contains five-coordinate copper (see figure 12). Mononuclear copper(II) compounds with the pyrazole ligands described by Sorrell (35) have not yet been reported.

The close resemblance of the spectral behaviour of Cu(edtb)(ClO$_4$)$_2$ and bovine superoxide dismutase has been mentioned before (21). Some related benzimidazole type ligands have been described meanwhile (66,67).

Models for type III Cu-proteins. In this section chelating azole ligands will be dealt with that are capable of binding two copper ions. Our previous review (21) has already dealt with the benzimidazole-type ligands edtb (25,68), dtpb (69) and ehpdtb

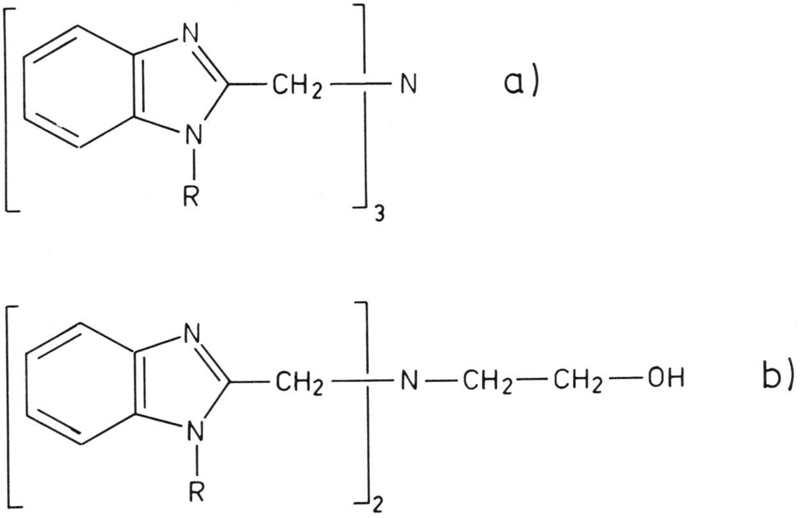

Figure 8. Some potential tetradentate benzimidazole ligands. (a) ntb with R = H (54) and mntb with R = CH$_3$ (33); (b) ligand structure in which one benzimidazole group has been replaced by $-$C$_2$H$_4$OH (56).

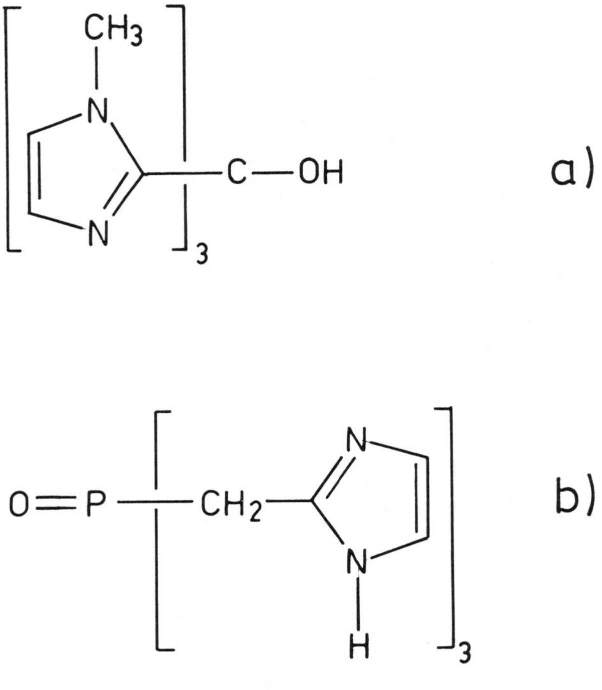

Figure 9. Some tripodal imidazole-type ligands (57,58) for which Cu-compounds have hardly been studied as yet.

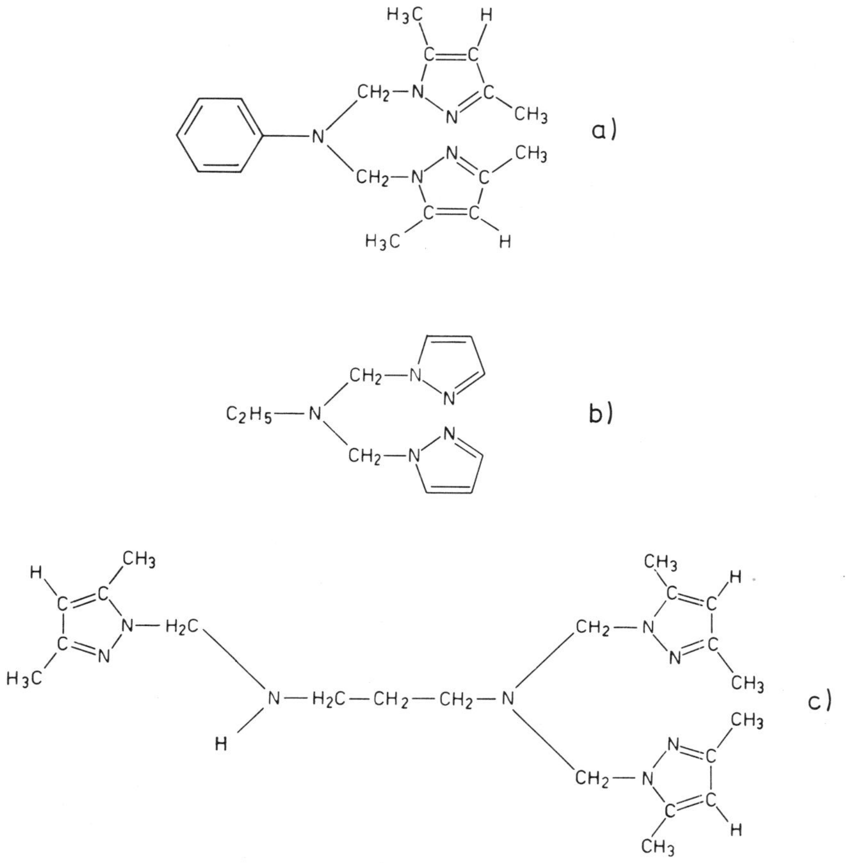

Figure 10. Some new pyrazole-type ligands for which copper compounds have already been studied. (a) pabd, bis(3,5-dimethylpyrazol-1-ylmethyl)phenylamine (64); (b) eabp, bis(pyrazolyl-1-ylmethyl)ethylamine; (c) aptd, N,N,N'tris(3,5-dimethylpyrazol-1-ylmethyl)-propane-1,3-diamine (65).

(70) and their Cu(I) and Cu(II) compounds. In $Cu_2(edtb)^{2+}$ the Cu-ions are separated by 3.04 Å, whereas in $Cu_2(ehpdtb)(N_3)^{2+}$ (with azide as the exogeneous bridging ligand) a Cu−Cu distance of 3.61 Å has been observed (68,70). This latter distance is quite close to that observed recently for crystalline deoxyhemocyanin (14).

Karlin and others (71-73) have developed related systems with pyridine groups, instead of azoles. These compounds show also very interesting properties in oxidation reactions (see elsewhere in this book).

With azole ligands Sorrell and co-workers have developed the interesting dinucleating system based on 2,6-diformylphenol (74). A schematic drawing of the crystal structure of the dinuclear Cu(II) compound with an exogeneous OH ligand is depicted in figure 13. The magnetic exchange coupling between the copper ions is quite strong

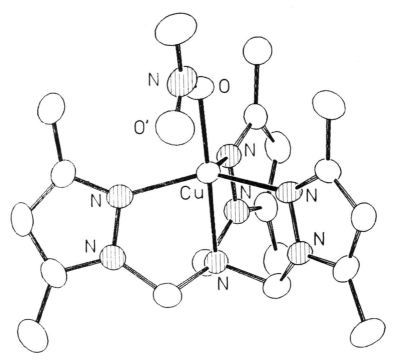

Figure 11. Schematic structure of the cationic species $[Cu(amtd)(NO_3)]^+$ (amtd = tris(3,5-dimethylpyrazol-1-ylmethyl)amine). Distances are: Cu−N(pyrazole): 2.02-2.19 Å; Cu−N(amine) = 2.09 Å; Cu−O = 1.94 Å; Cu−O' = 2.75 Å (63).

(just as found by Reed (70) for the benzimidazole azide compound). Completely reversible dioxygen binding has not yet been found for these and related compounds in the Cu(I) state.

Since the X-ray structure of deoxyhemocyanin (14) suggests that no bridging ligand group is present, azole-containing chelating ligands of the type shown in figure 2c remain of great interest. Without exogeneous ligands, megtb (the tetra-N-methylated derivative of egtb, figure 2c), however, has so far only resulted in bis-Cu(II) complexes of the open form (31,38). A structure of the cationic species of the $CuCl_2$ adduct with formula $Cu_2(megtb)Cl_2^{2+}$ is depicted in figure 14.

However, when ligands are added to solutions of these and other compounds, dinuclear species are formed, probably of the structure depicted in figure 15, with a bridging exogeneous ligand. The strongest evidence for these dinuclear species comes from the EPR spectra, that clearly show the signals expected for S = 1 systems, characteristic for Cu(II) dimers. Also in the solid state such EPR signals have been observed, although definite proof has to await crystal structure determinations.

Finally, it should be mentioned that some, apparently mononuclear Cu(I) compounds with ligands of the type given in figure 16, exhibit some reversible oxygen-binding

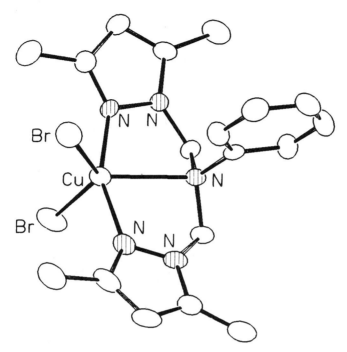

Figure 12. Schematic structure of Cu(pabd)Br$_2$ (ligand see figure 10a). Distances are: Cu−N(pyrazole) = 1.98 Å; Cu−N(amine) = 2.42 Å; Cu−Br = 2.43 Å (64).

behaviour (75,76). As a ligand type, they more resemble the ligands treated above as models for type II copper.

Reactivity

Redox potentials. One of the characteristic properties of the blue copper proteins (type I) is the high redox potential compared with ordinary Cu(II) compounds. Recently, it has become clear that Cu(II) compounds with a N$_2$S$_2$ chromophore very often may have redox potentials close to those of the blue copper proteins. However, the intense blue colour has not yet been reproduced for such simple compounds. The redox potential of Cu(bbdh)Cl$_2$ has been studied in detail in CH$_3$CN (77) and the value of 0.62 V (against normal hydrogen electrode) is quite close to those found for the blue copper proteins (5,6).

A related compound, containing imidazole groups instead of benzimidazoles, i.e. Cu(bidh)(ClO$_4$)$_2$ was found by Tanaka et al. (52) to have a slightly lower redox potential (0.51 V against normal hydrogen electrode). It appears (78) that small changes in the ligand coordination behaviour, resulting in slightly different geometries, may have variations of about ±0.5 V. A variation of this amount is also known for the several blue Cu proteins (5).

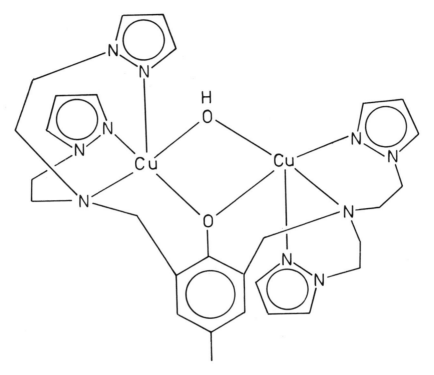

Figure 13. Schematic representation of the structure of the dinuclear cationic species $[Cu_2L(OH)]^{2+}$ as described by Sorrell (74).

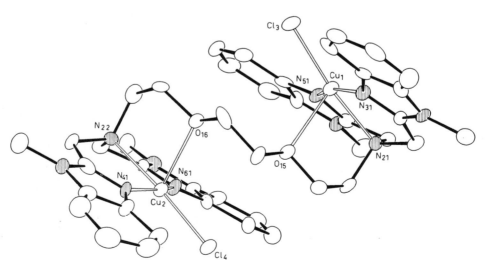

Figure 14. Structure of the compound Cu_2Cl_4(megtb). Some relevant distances are: Cu−N(azole) = 1.92-1.95 Å; Cu−N(amine) = 2.09-2.14 Å; Cu−O = 2.41-2.46 Å; Cu−Cl....... = 2.22-2.23 Å.

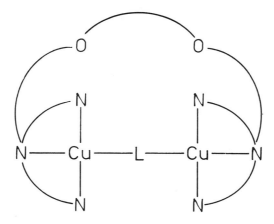

Figure 15. Schematic structure of a dinuclear unit with a bridging exogeneous ligand (L) between two copper ions.

Oxidation reactions. The most interesting reactions of copper proteins undoubtedly are the reactions with dioxygen and derivatives (O_2 and H_2O_2). Mimicking these reactions with copper coordination compounds has been the aim of many chemists. In fact many Cu(I) and Cu(II) coordination compounds do catalyse the oxidation of a variety of organic compounds (6), although very often the organic ligands are also (slowly) oxidised or degraded during the course of the reactions.

The most fascinating aspect of these reactions is the reversible dioxygen binding, analogous to hemocyanin (14). Although several reports are available describing such reactions, it seems that up to the present, none of the systems shows reversible behaviour for more than 90%. A very recent observation by Karlin et al. (79) has led to the conclusion that the bound oxygen is present as a peroxo ligand bridging between two copper ions. In case of imidazole-containing chelates, Wilson (76) and Casella (75) have reported interesting results for—apparently—mononuclear Cu(I) compounds (dimerisation may of course occur in solution), whereas Hendriks (43,68) observed such reactions in a dinuclear Cu(I) compound. Oxidation of substrate organic molecules, such as phenoles, with the aid of copper azole-chelating ligands has—contrary to pyridine or amine compounds (6,80-82)—hardly been studied so far. In fact only with imidazole-substituted polystyrene and polyvinylimidazole copper compounds, oxidation of 2,6-dimethylphenol has been studied (83). Recently, we have started using copper benzimidazole-type chelates for the oxidation of 2,6-dimethylphenol and 2,6-di-t-butylphenol into the quinones and the commercially interesting polyphenoles (84). The first results are encouraging, although the catalytic effects are still somewhat smaller than those for the substituted pyridine copper compounds.

Concluding remarks

The present overview on copper-azole compounds with imidazoles, benzimidazoles

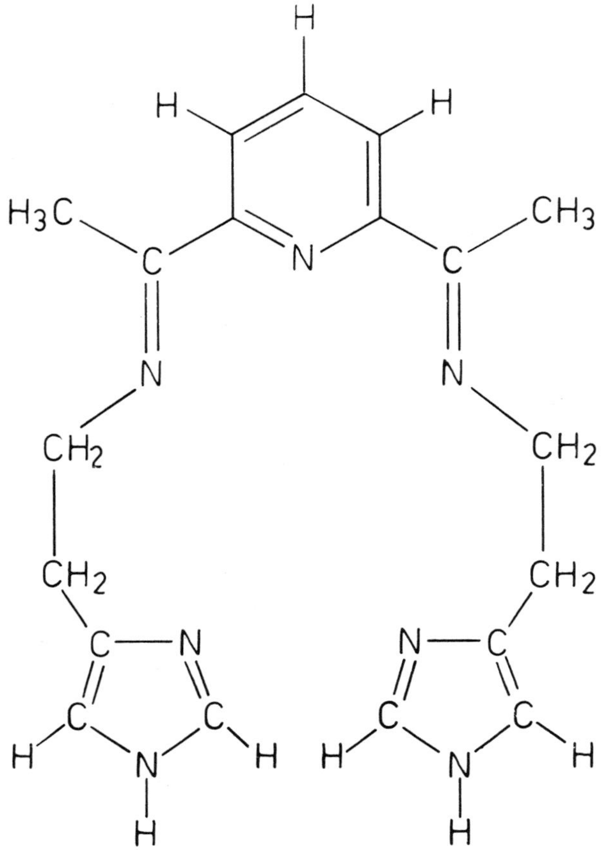

Figure 16. The structure of the pentadentate imidazole ligand developed by Wilson (76).

or pyrazoles as coordinating groups in the chelating ligands, has necessarily been focussed on results obtained from our laboratory. However, related work of other workers has been included as completely as possible. For details, the reader is referred to the respective papers of these authors, many of which have contributed to the present book.

We have shown that the chelating ligands containing two or more azole groups in a—more or less—constrained geometry, may yield very interesting copper coordination compounds. Several compounds have unusual structures and spectroscopic properties and may mimick properties of copper proteins to significant detail. Further work in this area is expected to deal with:

a) fine-tuning of the molecular shape of the structure of the ligand and the resulting copper compounds;

b) application of the copper compounds in reactivity studies, such as catalytic oxidation of organic subtrates.

Acknowledgements

The authors are indebted to all collaborators and colleagues from our laboratory and elsewhere, whose names appear as co-authors of publications in the list of references.

References and Footnotes

1. R. Osterberg, *Coord. Chem. Rev. 12,* 309 (1974).
2. J. A. Fee, *Struct. Bonding 23,* 1 (1975).
3. J. Gazo, I. B. Bersuker, L. Garaj, M. Kabesova, J. Kohout, H. Langfelderova, M. Melnik, M. Serator and F. Valach, *Coord. Chem. Rev. 21,* 253 (1976).
4. H. Beinert, *Coord. Chem. Rev. 23,* 119 (1977).
5. H. Beinert, *Coord. Chem. Rev. 33,* 55 (1980).
6. K. D. Karlin and J. Zubieta (eds), *Copper Coordination Chemistry: Biochemical and Inorganic Perspectives,* Adenine Press, New York, (1983).
7. B. J. Hathaway, *Struct. Bonding 57,* in press (1984).
8. J. M. Guss and H. C. Freeman, *J. Mol. Biol. 169,* 521 (1983).
9. E. T. Adman and L. H. Jensen, *Isr. J. Chem. 21,* 8 (1981).
10. T. G. Spiro (Ed.), *Copper Proteins,* Wiley, New York, (1981).
11. H. C. Freeman, personal communication.
12. J. A. Tainer, E. D. Getzoff, J. S. Richardson and D. C. Richardson, *Nature 306,* 284 (1983).
13. K. G. Strothkamp and S. J. Lippard, *Acc. Chem. Res. 10,* 318 (1982).
14. W. P. J. Gaykema, W. G. J. Hol, J. M. Vereijken, N. M. Soeter, H. J. Bak and J. J. Beintema, *Nature 309,* 23 (1984).
15. A. E. G. Cass and H. A. O. Hill, Exerpta Medica 1980, *Biological Roles of Copper (Ciba Foundation Symposium 79),* 71 (1980).
16. K. Lerch and M. Beltramini, *Chemica Scripta 21,* 109 (1983).
17. M. Vasak, *J. Mol. Catal. 23,* 293 (1984).
18. H. A. O. Hill, *Chem. Brit. 12,* 119 (1976).
19. T. P. A. Kruck and B. Sarkar, *Inorg. Chem. 14,* 2383 (1976).
20. M. M. Rogic, M. D. Swerdloff and T. R. Demmin, ref. 6, p. 259.
21. P. J. M. W. L. Birker and J. Reedijk, ref. 6, p. 409.
22. P. J. M. W. L. Birker, E. F. Godefroi, J. Helder and J. Reedijk, *J. Am. Chem. Soc. 104,* 7556 (1982).
23. J. van Rijn, W. L. Driessen, J. Reedijk and J. M. Lehn, *Inorg. Chem. 23,* 3584 (1983).
24. L. K. Thompson, B. S. Ramaswany and E. A. Seymour, *Can. J. Chem. 55,* 878 (1977).
25. H. M. J. Hendriks, W. O. ten Bokkel Huinink and J. Reedijk, *Recl. Trav. Chim. Pays-Bas 98,* 499 (1979).
26. J. V. Dagdigian and C. A. Reed, *Inorg. Chem. 18,* 2623 (1979).
27. Y. Nishida, N. Oishi and S. Kida, *Inorg. Chim. Acta 44,* L257 (1980).
28. A. W. Addison and P. J. Burke, *J. Heterocyclic Chem. 18,* 803 (1981).
29. F. J. Rietmeijer, P. J. M. W. L. Birker, S. Gorter and J. Reedijk, *J. Chem. Soc. Dalton Trans.,* 1191 (1982).
30. A. W. Addison, P. J. Burke, K. Henrick, T. N. Rao and E. Sinn, *Inorg. Chem. 22,* 3645 (1983).
31. J. van Rijn and J. Reedijk, *Recl. Trav. Chim. Pays-Bas 103,* 78 (1984).
32. P. J. M. W. L. Birker, J. Helder, G. Henkel, B. Krebs and J. Reedijk, *Inorg. Chem. 21,* 357 (1982).
33. H. M. J. Hendriks, P. J. M. W. L. Birker, G. C. Verschoor and J. Reedijk, *J. Chem. Soc. Dalton Trans.,* 623 (1982).
34. W. L. Driessen, *Recl. Trav. Chim. Pays-Bas 101,* 441 (1982).
35. T. N. Sorrell adn M. R. Malachowski, *Inorg. Chem. 22,* 1883 (1983).
36. F. B. Hulsbergen, W. L. Driessen, J. Reedijk and G. C. Verschoor, *Inorg. Chem. 23,* 3588 (1984).
37. A. W. Addison, T. N. Rao and C. G. Wahlgren, *J. Heterocyclic Chem. 20,* 1481 (1983).

38. J. Reedijk, P. J. M. W. L. Birker and J. van Rijn, *J. Mol. Catal. 23,* 369 (1984).
39. H. Okkersen, W. L. Groeneveld and J. Reedijk, *Recl. Trav. Chim. Pays-Bas 92,* 945 (1973).
40. H. M. J. Hendriks and J. Reedijk, *Recl. Trav. Chim. Pays-Bas 98,* 95 (1979).
41. T. N. Sorrell and D. L. Jameson, *J. Am. Chem. Soc. 105,* 6013 (1983).
42. W. Clegg, S. R. Acott and C. D. Garner, *Acta Cryst. C40,* 768 (1984).
43. H. M. J. Hendriks, P. J. M. W. L. Birker, J. van Rijn, G. C. Verschoor and J. Reedijk, *J. Am. Chem. Soc. 104,* 3607 (1982).
44. M. J. Schilstra, P. J. M. W. L. Birker, G. C. Verschoor and J. Reedijk, *Inorg. Chem. 21,* 2637 (1982).
45. J. V. Dagdigian, V. McKee and C. A. Reed, *Inorg. Chem. 21,* 1332 (1982).
46. J. S. Thompson and J. F. Whitney, *Acta Cryst. C40,* 756 (1984).
47. W. L. Driessen, F. B. Hulsbergen, J. Reedijk and G. C. Verschoor, in preparation.
48. D. L. McFaddeb, A. T. McPhail, C. D. Garner and F. Mabbs, *J. Chem. Soc. Dalton Trans,* 263 (1975).
49. N. Aoi, G. Matsubayashi and T. Tanaka, *J. Chem. Soc. Dalton Trans.,* 1059 (1983).
50. A. W. Addison, T. N. Rao, J. Reedijk, J. van Rijn and G. C. Verschoor, *J. Chem. Soc. Dalton Trans.,* in press (1984).
51. P. L. Verheydt, J. G. Haasnoot and J. Reedijk, *Inorg. Chim. Acta 76,* L43 (1983).
52. N. Aoi, G. Matsubayashi and T. Tanaka, *Inorg. Chim. Acta 85,* 123 (1984).
53. O. Yamauchi, H. Seki and T. Shoda, *Bull. Chem. Soc. Jap. 56,* 3258 (1983).
54. A. W. Addison, H. M. J. Hendriks, J. Reedijk and L. K. Thompson, *Inorg. Chem. 20,* 103 (1981).
55. T. Sakurai, H. Oi and A. Nakahara, *Inorg. Chim. Acta 92,* 131 (1984).
56. K. Takahashi, Y. Nishida and S. Kida, *Polyhedron 3,* 113 (1984).
57. A. J. Canty, J. M. Patrick and A. H. White, *J. Chem. Soc. Dalton Trans.,* 1873 (1983).
58. K. D. Gallicano, N. L. Paddock, S. J. Rettig and J. Trotter, *Inorg. Nucl. Chem. Letters 15,* 417 (1979).
59. A. J. Canty, N. J. Minchin, J. M. Patrick and A. H. White, *J. Chem. Soc. Dalton Trans.,* 1253 (1983).
60. J. S. Thompson, R. L. Harlow and J. F. Whitney, *J. Am. Chem. Soc. 105,* 3522 (1983).
61. M. A. Mesubi, *Trans. Met. Chem. 9,* 181 (1984).
62. C. Benelli, I. Bertini, M. Di Vaira and F. Mani, *Inorg. Chem. 23,* 1422 (1984).
63. G. J. Kleywegt, G. J. van Driel, W. G. R. Wiesmeijer, W. L. Driessen and J. Reedijk, *J. Chem. Soc. Dalton,* in press.
64. H. L. Blonk, W. L. Driessen and J. Reedijk, *J. Chem. Soc. Dalton,* 1699 (1985).
65. E. Bouwman, W. L. Driessen and J. Reedijk, in preparation.
66. Y. Nishida, K. Takahashi, H. Kuramoto and S. Kida, *Inorg. Chim. Acta 54,* L103 (1981).
67. T. Sakurai, H. Kaji and A. Nakahara, *Inorg. Chim. Acta 67,* 1 (1982).
68. P. J. M. W. L. Birker, H. M. J. Hendriks and J. Reedijk, *Inorg. Chim. Acta 55,* L17 (1984).
69. P. J. M. W. L. Birker, A. J. Schierbeek, G. C. Verschoor and J. Reedijk, *J. Chem. Soc. Chem. Commun.,* 1124 (1981).
70. V. McKee, J. V. Dagdigian, R. Bau and C. A. Reed, *J. Am. Chem. Soc. 103,* 7000 (1981).
71. K. D. Karlin, P. L. Dahlstrom, S. N. Cozzette, P. M. Scensny and J. Zubieta, *J. Chem. Soc. Chem. Commun.,* 881 (1981).
72. K. D. Karlin, J. Shi, J. C. Hayes, J. W. McKown, J. P. Hutchinson and J. Zubieta, *Inorg. Chim. Acta 91,* L3 (1984).
73. K. D. Karlin, J. C. Hayes, Y. Gultneh, R. W. Cruse, J. W. McKown, J. P. Hutchinson and J. Zubieta, *J. Am. Chem. Soc. 106,* 2121 (1984).
74. T. N. Sorrell, D. L. Jameson and C. J. O'Connor, *Inorg. Chem. 23,* 190 (1984).
75. L. Casella, M. E. Silver and J. A. Ibers, *Inorg. Chem. 23,* 1409 (1984).
76. M. G. Simmons, C. L. Merrill, L. J. Wilson, L. A. Bottomley and K. M. Kadish, *J. Chem. Soc. Dalton Trans.,* 1827 (1980).
77. M. F. Cabral, J. de O'Cabral, J. van Rijn and J. Reedijk, *Inorg. Chim. Acta 87,* 87 (1984).
78. A. W. Addison, J. van Rijn and J. Reedijk, to be published.
79. K. D. Karlin, Y. Gultneh, R. W. Cruse, J. C. Hayes and J. Zubieta, *J. Am. Chem. Soc. 106,* 3372 (1984).
80. M. R. Churchill, G. Davies, M. A. El-Sayed, J. A. Fournier, J. P. Hutchinson and J. Zubieta, *Inorg. Chem. 23,* 783 (1984).
81. H. C. Meinders, F. van Bolhuis and G. Challa, *J. Mol. Catal. 5,* 225 (1979).
82. A. J. Schouten, G. Challa and J. Reedijk, *J. Mol. Catal. 9,* 41 (1980).
83. J. P. J. Verlaan, C. E. Koning and G. Challa, *J. Mol. Catal. 20,* 203 (1983).
84. A. G. T. M. Bastein, J. van Rijn and J. Reedijk, in preparation.

Biological & Inorganic Copper Chemistry,
ISBN 0-940030-11-X, Eds., K. D. Karlin & J. Zubieta, Adenine Press, ©Adenine Press, 1985

Binuclear Copper Complexes Containing Hydroxo, Phenoxo, Alkoxo or Thiolato Bridging Groups in Models for a Copper Binding Polymer (Sirorez Cu) and Related Systems

Keith S. Murray

Department of Chemistry
Monash University
Clayton, Victoria
Australia 3168

Abstract

In Part A the synthesis, solution chemistry, structure and magnetism of some copper(II) complexes coordinated to 2,6−piperazylmethyl-substituted phenol ligands are described. These compounds are low molecular weight models of a selective copper-binding polymer, Sirorez-Cu. 1:1 and 2:1 copper:ligand species were obtained, the former involving tridentate coordination of the ligand, the latter involving pentadentate coordination within a binuclear structure. A crystal structure determination and magnetic studies on a 2:1 complex show some interesting and unusual features, especially with respect to the influence which the bridging phenoxo-oxygen geometry has on the exchange-coupling. This feature is further elaborated in Part B where magentostructural correlations are described for a range of dibridged copper(II) complexes containing phenoxo or alkoxo bridging groups within binucleating ligands. A comparison of a ferromagnetic and antiferromagnetic isomer of the same molecule is emphasised. Finally a short appraisal of sulfur-bridging ligands and their copper(II) complexes is given.

Introduction

This article combines material relevant to both the lecture and the poster given in the Conference. In Part A a study of copper coordination to low molecular weight analogs of a new copper-binding polymer is described. This is followed in Part B by a discussion of some of our current work on the magnetochemical and bioinorganic aspects of binuclear copper systems containing a variety of bridging groups. Emphasis will be placed on magnetostructural correlations and it will be seen that a new and important relationship between the geometry of the bridging phenoxo (phenolate) or alkoxo oxygen atom in pentadentate binucleating ligands and the exchange constant, J, has been found. This relationship was also observed in a doubly-bridged binuclear compound described in Part A. A progress report on S-bridging in copper(II) complexes is included, and comparisons with O-bridged analogs are given where appropriate.

161

Part A. A Study of Copper(II) Coordination to Piperazine-Phenol Ligands,
Models for the Copper Binding Polymer Sirorez Cu

(G. D. Fallon, J. H. Hodgkin‡, B. J. Kennedy, B. C. Loft‡, K. S. Murray, B. Spethmann,
J. K. Yandell.
‡CSIRO Division of Applied Organic Chemistry, Melbourne)

The recently synthesized condensation polymer, Sirorez-Cu, (Figure 1) has been shown to have a high capacity and selectivity for Cu(II) ions with which it forms a dark green complex. Details of the polymer synthesis, properties and copper-binding studies have been described elsewhere (1-4). Sirorez-Cu is a different type of material to the common chelating resins which are generally produced by the addition of known chelating groups onto the side group of a preformed polymer such as polystyrene or a condensation reaction with a known chelating monomer (5,6). In the present case the main polymer chain is the chelating structure and it possesses potential copper binding sites at the phenolic oxygen and piperazine nitrogen atoms. Because of their relative ease of synthesis and ability to selectively remove copper from aqueous solutions (and iron under different pH conditions) these resins clearly have good potential for commercial and industrial applications.

In order to try to understand the way that copper binds to a resin of the Sirorez type and to deduce reasons for the high selectivity it was decided to investigate complex formation (or lack of it) with a range of 'monomeric' model ligands, L^nH, shown in Figure 1. A combination of solution studies, synthesis, spectral, magnetic and X-ray crystallographic measurements were employed to obtain a detailed picture of the coordination environment. The results are described herein.

Materials and Methods

The ligands, L^nH, were synthesized by the Mannich reaction of the appropriate phenol, formaldehyde and secondary amine (N—methylpiperazine or piperidine) in refluxing aqueous ethanol. Details of reaction conditions and purification procedures are given elsewhere (7). A wide range of reaction conditions were employed in order to prepare crystalline derivatives of the copper(II) complexes, the chief aim being to obtain crystals suitable for X-ray crystallographic measurements. Complexes of 1:1 and 2:1 Cu:ligand stoichiometry were obtained (8). The 1:1 species were obtained as dark bottle-green colored solids on extraction of toluene solutions of the ligand into an aqueous solution of copper(II) sulphate in which the pH was adjusted to 6-8. In some cases a blue basic sulphate, $CuSO_4 3Cu(OH)_2$, was deposited and filtered off. The 1:1 compounds were very soluble and could only be isolated on evaporation to dryness. C, H, N, S and Cu analytical data were in agreement with the formula $Cu(L^nH)SO_4(H_2O)_y$. Spectroscopic properties are given in Table I. A 1:1 complex, $CuL^6(ClO_4)$, could also be isolated using the 'one-armed' ligand L^6H.

A 2:1 compound of formula $[Cu_2(L^1)(OH)](ClO_4)_2 \cdot 3H_2O$ was obtained in the form of blue/green needle shaped crystals by reaction of copper(II) perchlorate hexahydrate

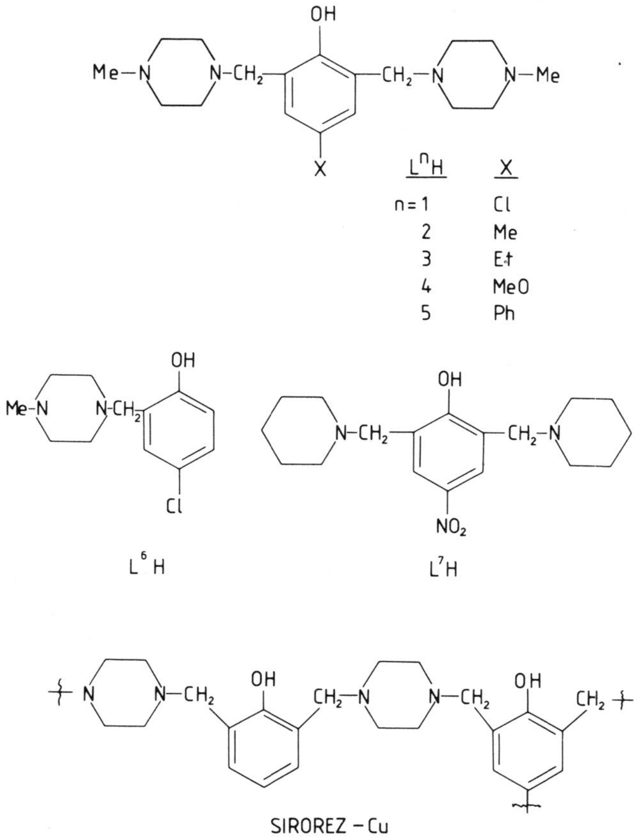

Figure 1. Structure of the ligands and of the polymer, Sirorez-Cu.

Table I
1:1 Cu:ligand Complexes, $Cu(L^nH)SO_4(H_2O)_y$

n	y	μ_{Cu} (295K, μ_B)	$\lambda_{max[\epsilon]}$ (nm)	$g_\parallel$	$A_\parallel$ (10^4 cm^{-1})	$g_\perp$
1	4	1.71	636 [189] 419 [608]	2.26	169	2.03
2	2	(a)	631 [137] 420 [419]	2.25	163	2.03
3	2	1.67	628 [186] 418 [539]	2.26	177	2.04
4	2	1.58	622 [208] 434 [541]	2.26	168	2.04
5	5	1.80	630 [229] 440 [595]	2.26	169	2.03

(a) Sample hygroscopic. Visible spectra are of aqueous solutions. ESR spectra are of frozen dmf/H$_2$O solutions.

with the p-chlorophenol derived ligand, L^1H, either in ethanol or aqueous ethanolic solutions. In the latter solution sodium hydroxide was added to the ligand to produce the sodium salt in-situ. Crystals suitable for X-ray determination were recrystallized from aqueous ethanol. Spectroscopic properties of this compound are given in Table II.

Table II
Properties of the Binuclear Complex *4*; $[Cu_2L^1(OH)(H_2O)_2](ClO_4)_2 \cdot H_2O$

λ_{max} in $H_2O[\epsilon]$ (nm)	μ_{Cu} (μ_B at 295K)	$g_{\parallel}$	$A_{\parallel}$ (10^4 cm^{-1})	$g_{\perp}$
614[170] d−d	1.94	2.25	146	2.06
388[364] Cu−OPh, C.T.				

e.s.r. spectrum measured using a d.m.f. glass.

The methods and instruments used for uv-visible, e.s.r. and magnetic susceptibility measurements have been described previously (9). Potentiometric titrations were carried out using a computer controlled automatic burette and a pH electrode calibrated with pH = 4 potassium hydrogen phthalate buffer. Solutions containing 10^{-3} M ligand (in dilute HNO_3), 0.1 M KNO_3 and the required concentration of Cu(II) in water were titrated against 1 M sodium hydroxide. Samples were periodically removed to record the visible spectrum and then returned to the vessel.

Results and Discussion

Complex formation in Solution

Potentiometric titrations were performed in order to determine the stoichiometry and pH range of Cu complex formation. The solution properties of a range of substituted ligands have been studied but details only of the ligand L^1H and the 'one-armed' analog L^6H will be given here. Potentiometric titration of the ligands in the presence and absence of copper(II) along with uv-visible spectra as a function of pH has enabled a fairly clear understanding of the coordination behaviour of the ligands. Ligand L^6H was found to have three accessible pK_a's 9.8, 7.8, 3.7 corresponding to the three basic groups. Since in isolation all three groups will have similar pK_a's the assignment of the pK_a's to individual groups is pointless though the lowest pK_a is probably associated with the piperazine. In ligand L^1H four of the five basic groups had accessible pK_a's with the remaining pK_a too low to measure by our methods. The pK_a's were determined to be 10.4, 8.2, 7.0, 3.6, <2. Again assignment of these pK_a's to individual groups is not possible or fruitful.

Copper complexes form in 1:1 mixtures of copper(II) and the ligand above pH 5 with both ligands. With the potentially tridentate ligand L^6H the potentiometric data are consistent with the formation of the 1:1 complex with fully deprotonated ligand $[CuL^6]^+$ and a stability constant of 8.1 (i.e. $\log_{10} K_1$). Any complex formation with protonated forms of the ligand is slight as judged by both the potentiometric and visible spectral data ($\log_{10} K_1 [Cu(L^6H)]^{2+} < 4$). The visible spectrum of $[CuL^6]^+$ shows a band at 412 nm which is associated with phenolate coordination and the stability constant is too high for piperazine coordination alone or for phenol and piperazine. It seems clear therefore that the ligand is acting primarily as a tridentate ligand coordinating to copper(II) through the phenolate oxygen and both piperazine nitrogen atoms.

For the ligand L^1H copper coordination is more complicated. The visible spectra and the potentiometric data are consistent with the following observations. At low copper concentration and low pH the main species formed has the stoichiometry $Cu(L^1H)^{2+}$ and the similarity of the visible spectra to those of the $[CuL^6]^+$ suggest coordination of a phenolate oxygen and two piperazine nitrogens. At higher copper concentration ($Cu:L^1H = 2:1$) and higher pH the visible spectra change and this is probably associated with the formation of the binuclear species $[Cu_2L^1(OH)]^{2+}$, the same species which has been isolated as a crystalline perchlorate salt (Figure 3).

It is noteworthy that the piperidine ligand L^7H, and a 'one-armed' analog, does not form copper complexes under the same conditions further suggesting that both nitrogens of piperazine contribute to copper coordination.

Synthesis and Visible Spectra of 1:1 and 2:1 Copper:Ligand Complexes

After exploring a range of different reaction conditions it was possible to obtain analytically pure samples of formulae $Cu(L^nH)SO_4(H_2O)_y$, $CuL^6(ClO_4)$ and $[Cu_2L^1(OH)(H_2O)_2](ClO_4)_2 \cdot H_2O$. Details are given in the Experimental section and in Tables I and II. Aqueous solutions of the bottle-green 1:1 species show a d−d band at 624 nm and $Cu \Leftarrow OPh$ charge-transfer band at 412 nm while the blue/green 2:1 species exhibit a d−d band in similar position (618 nm) but with a shift of the C.T. band to 389 nm. These bands are in the ranges generally observed for Cu(II)phenolate complexes (10). Infra-red frequencies of the sulphate and perchlorate vibrations suggest that the SO_4 group is probably bonded in a unidentate fashion to Cu in the solid state while the ClO_4 group is ionic and not coordinated. Attempts to prepare crystals of the 1:1 complexes suitable for X-ray study have so far been unsuccessful, however it was possible to obtain appropriate crystals of the 2:1 species, prepared as the perchlorate salt.

Structures

At the outset molecular models had shown that in order for all four piperazine N atoms in ligands of type L^nH (n = 1-5) and the phenolic oxygen to coordinate to Cu then only a limited number of conformations were possible and considerable steric strain seemed likely. Little is known in general about the donor properties and stereochemical preferences of piperazines towards Cu (11), although phenolate to copper coordination is better understood (10). Solution and preparative studies of the 1:1 complexes show the presence of protonated ligand in a ratio $1Cu:1L^nH:1SO_4$. Even though the Cu—phenolate C.T. band is shifted from its position in the structurally characterized 2:1 (deprotonated) species its presence would still suggest that the proton resides on one of the N atoms rather than on the phenol oxygen. In the light of the e.s.r. parameters, which suggest tetragonally {N,O} coordinated Cu(II) (12,13), the potentiometric and other spectroscopic data, a plausible structure for the 1:1 species in the solid state is that shown in Figure 2. However the susceptibility studies, described below, clearly show that association of these monomeric units occurs, possibly via the phenoxide oxygen which is a well known bridging group. Similar tridentate coordination seems likely in the 1:1 complex $CuL^6(ClO_4)$, as discussed in the solution chemistry section.

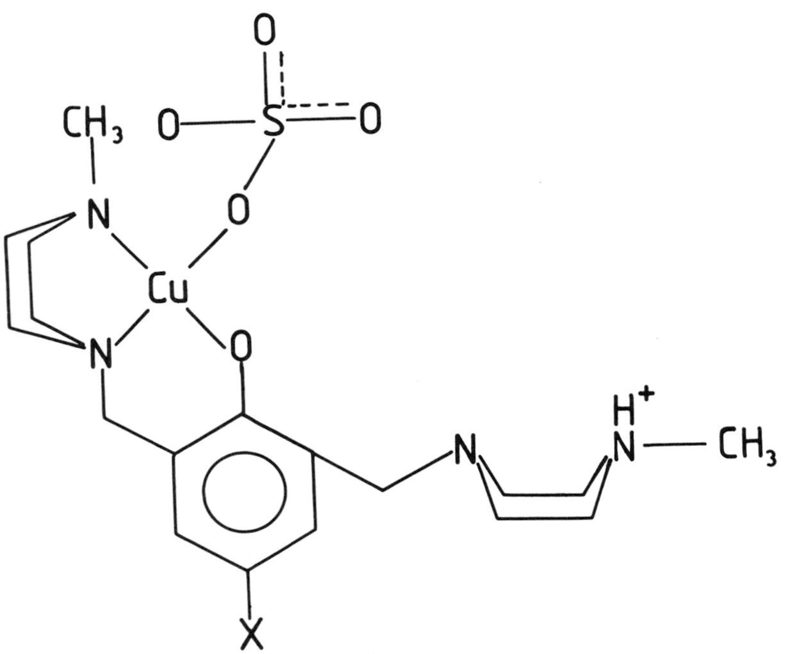

Figure 2. Possible coordination geometry for 1:1 $Cu(L^nH)(SO_4)$ complexes.

A crystal structure determination of the 2:1 complex $[Cu_2(L^1)OH(H_2O)_2](ClO_4)_2 \cdot H_2O$ shows that the 2,6—di(N—methylpiperazylmethyl)p—chlorophenol ligand is acting as a binucleating ligand, coordinated to two Cu atoms via phenoxide and hydroxide bridging oxygens. There are two crystallographically distinct half molecules in the asymmetric unit such that each molecule has the same gross stereochemistry with only minor differences in detail (14). The structure is shown in Figure 3 and geometrical details are given in Table III. (Bond lengths and angles for only one molecule will be discussed in the text). In general the molecules exhibit a binuclear structure similar to those of other recently reported m-xylyl phenol ligands (15) but

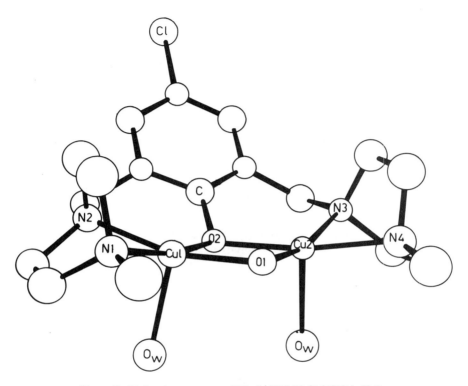

Figure 3. Molecular structure of $[Cu_2L^1(OH)(H_2O)_2](ClO_4)_2 \cdot H_2O$.

there are some significant and important differences which, as shown below, affect the magnetic properties of the compound. Each Cu is coordinated in an essentially square pyramidal arrangement to the piperazine nitrogens, hydroxo oxygen, phenoxo oxygen and a water molecule. The axial water molecules on each Cu are cis to each other. A Cu—Cu distance of 2.871(3) Å is the shortest yet observed in these kinds of binuclear structures, although similar distances are known in roof-shaped dihydroxo-bridged dimers (16). The small bridging angles, Cu(OH)Cu 96.5(4)°, Cu(OPh)Cu 91.7(4)°, yield a flat almost square Cu_2O_2 cycle. One of the most pertinent and unusual features of the structure, which in part arises from the short Cu—Cu distance and concomitant bonding to the piperazine N atoms, is the non-trigonal (planar) nature of the bridging phenoxo O atom. In contrast to other examples of this general type (15a,17,18), the angles around the phenoxo O are closer to tetrahedral than to trigonal values indicating an sp^3 (pyramidal) arrangement of orbitals rather than sp^2. There are no nearby intermolecular contacts in the vicinity of the non-bonded pair of electrons on the phenoxo O. A "dihedral" angle of 48.4° between the C—O bond and the Cu_2O_2 plane results from this bonding arrangement. Presumably the H—O bond of the bridging hydroxo group is disposed at a similar (non-coplanar) angle.

Magnetic Properties

Room temperature moments of the "monomeric" $Cu(L^nH)SO_4(H_2O)_y$ complexes are generally reduced a little from the spin-only value and are lower, surprisingly, than that of the doubly-bridged binuclear complex $[Cu_2L^1(OH)(H_2O)_2](ClO_4)_2 \cdot H_2O$. These initially rather puzzling results can be interpreted as follows. The 1:1 molecules associate in the solid state into dimeric (or higher oligomeric) species. This is evidenced by the χ_{Cu}/T data which, as shown in Figure 4 for the n = 3 derivative, shows a temperature dependence typical of an antiferromagnetically coupled Cu(II) dimer. The susceptibility maximum occurs at 105 K which corresponds to a best-fit J value of -64 cm^{-1} and $\bar{g}$ value of 2.08. The steep increase in χ_{Cu} at very low temperatures is due to the presence of ca. 10% monomeric impurity. Similarly, for the complex with n = 4; J = -80 cm^{-1}, g = 2.0 and for n = 5; J = -58 cm^{-1}, g = 2.25. We unfortunately do not have crystal structures on any of these $Cu(L^nH)SO_4$ derivatives which would help to identify the bridging group and geometrical features responsible for the observed magnetism. E.s.r. spectra of frozen dmf/water glasses of these materials all show two g values with $g_\parallel//A_\parallel$ ratios of ca. 133 cm compatible with tetragonal symmetry and {O,N} coordination around Cu (12,13).

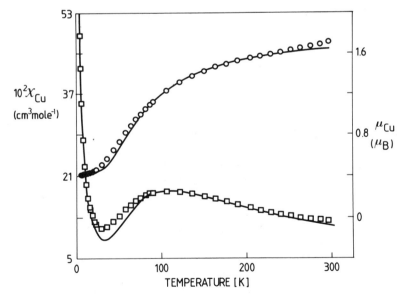

Figure 4. Temperature dependence of χ_{Cu} and μ_{Cu} for $Cu(L^3H)(SO_4) \cdot 2H_2O$. Solid lines are those calculated using the g and J values given in the text.

The temperature dependence of χ_{Cu}^{-1} and μ_{Cu} vs. T for the binuclear complex $[Cu_2L^1(OH)(H_2O)_2](ClO_4)_2 \cdot H_2O$ is shown in Figure 5. The data presumably represent a weighted average of the behaviour of the two similar, but not identical, molecules on the unit cell. The results are symptomatic of essentially uncoupled

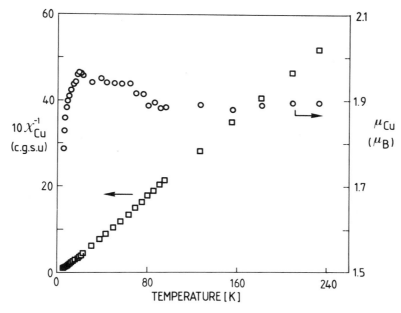

Figure 5. Temperature dependence of χ_{Cu}^{-1} and μ_{Cu} for $[Cu_2L^1(OH)(H_2O)_2](ClO_4)_2 \cdot H_2O$.

Cu(II) pairs, with a weak intramolecular ferromagnetic contribution probably responsible for the small increase in μ_{Cu} occurring as the temperature decreases. The rapid decrease at low temperatures is a feature which has been observed previously in related systems (19,20) and is due to either inter-molecular antiferromagnetic coupling or zero-field splitting of a ground triplet state.

In view of the medium to strong antiferromagnetic coupling observed in other structurally characterized μ−phenoxo−μ−hydroxo binuclear species of the present general type, it is important to be able to explain the zero to weak ferromagnetic coupling displayed here. We (19), and others (17,21,22,23), have considered the superexchange pathways in asymmetric binucleated species and have attempted to correlate the overall exchange coupling (i.e. ferromagnetic plus antiferromagnetic contributions) with chemical and structural features. Despite a lack of extensive crystallographic data within closely related systems, it appears that the changes in J for phenoxo/hydroxo or alkoxo/hydroxo pathways generally follow the dependence on Cu−Cu distance and Cu−OR−Cu angle (R = H) found in the symmetrical dihydroxo-bridged dimers (24,25). Thus, in the present molecule, the Cu−Cu distance of 2.87 Å and Cu−OR−Cu angles of 91.7° and 96.5° should lead to J being close to zero or positive overall. While these structural features will probably dominate the nature of the overlap of the magnetic orbitals on the Cu atoms with the bridging oxygen orbitals, we feel that the non-planarity of the latter orbitals (brought about through the non−coplanar phenoxo C-O vector) plays a significant role. The question as to the interdependence between a structural distortion of this type, possibly brought about by a sterically demanding ligand, and the concomitant electronic structure is somewhat of the chicken and egg variety! Nevertheless, comparison with related antiferromagnetically coupled 'coplanar' {Cu(OR)(OH)Cu} complexes support this proposed dependence on the nature of the bridging oxygen orbitals. The feature is elaborated in more detail in Part B and Table III.

Relations to Sirorez-Cu resin

While further work is required on the polymeric resin and on soluble linear forms of the polymer, the following points can be made based on the model studies described here.

(i) The selectivity of the resin for copper appears at this stage to be primarily a consequence of the preference of copper for phenolate oxygen and ammine nitrogen donor systems as reflected in published stability constants. A combination of low-ligand-field strength and favorable stability constant makes the phenolate group ideally suited to selectively bind Cu.

(ii) Cu(II) binds to the resin and to soluble linear forms of the polymer at a lower pH than it does with the model ligands (4). This may arise through a combination of (a) mutual interactions between groups in the polymer which may change the pK_a's and affect the relative binding of Cu(II) and H^+ and (b) a lowering of the dielectric constant of the coordination environment. Model studies using less polar solvents than water could perhaps show some trends supporting postulate (b).

(iii) The similarity of the colour and e.s.r. spectra of resins loaded with copper to those of the 1:1 model complexes suggests tridentate coordination of a phenolate oxygen and two piperazine nitrogens (Figure 2) by the resin at low copper loading. Binuclear species of the type shown in Figure 3 may also occur at higher copper loading.

Part B. *Electronic and Structural Features of Binuclear O– and S– bridged Copper(II) Complexes*

Magnetostructural Correlations in di-bridged Complexes Containing Alkoxo- or Phenoxo Bridging Moieties. The Importance of the Bridging-Oxygen Geometry

(G. D. Fallon, B. J. Kennedy, W. Mazurek[‡], K. S. Murray, M. J. O'Connor[‡], P. Zwack. [‡]La Trobe University, Melbourne)

Our studies (19,22,26) on di-bridged copper(II) complexes of pentadentate binucleating ligands based on 1,5–diaminopentan–3–ol or 1,3–diaminopropan–2–ol, shown in Figure 6, nos. *1-3,* have shown that small changes to the ligand backbone, or to the exogenous bridging group, can have quite dramatic effects on the sign and size of the exchange constant J. Similar observations have been made

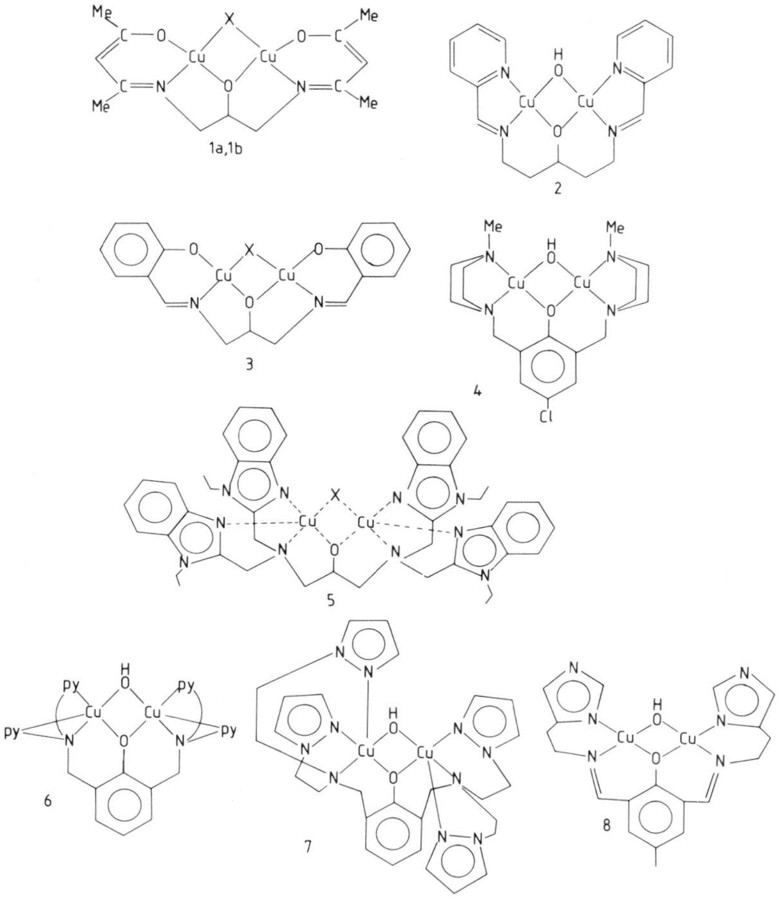

Figure 6. Structures of representative di-bridged copper(II) complexes containing alkoxo- or phenoxo-bridging groups. Charges are not shown.

in binuclear species based on the Robson-type 2,6−diformylphenol derived ligands, *8* (17,27). Arguments were put forward to try and correlate variations in J with systematic changes to the molecule but a lack of crystal structure data on key compounds has hampered us in obtaining good correlations (19). Features such as Cu−Cu distance, Cu−OR−Cu angle and Cu ground state orbital symmetry, found to be important in the more symmetrical dihydroxo-bridged dimers (24,25), were clearly playing important roles in the present systems. However, the two different 'exogenous' and 'endogenous' superexchange pathways complicate an understanding of the antiferromagnetic and ferromagnetic contribution to the observed J value. Some important structures have recently become available which are helping to clarify the situation. For instance Reed and coworkers (21,28) have found that the structures of acetate-bridged (J = +12 cm^{-1}) and 1,3−azido-bridged (J = > −500 cm^{-1}) complexes of their alkoxo-bridging benzimidazole ligand *5* appears to be compatible with a change in symmetry around the Cu atoms i.e. square pyramidal in the azide leading to $Cu(d_{x^2-y^2})$ overlap with alkoxo O and azido N orbitals, and trigonal bipyramidal in the acetate leading to $Cu(d_{z^2})$ overlap chiefly with acetate O orbitals

Recently Nishida and coworkers have published the structure of complex *1b*, an acetate bridged derivative displaying antiferromagnetic exchange with J = −82.5 cm^{-1} (29). This molecule, and related multiatomic exogenous bridged derivatives, had been investigated concurrently by Bertrand et al. (30) and ourselves (26) some five or six years ago. Since our "isomer", *1a*, displayed ferromagnetic coupling and a J of +19 cm^{-1}, the rare opportunity was created of being able to make magnetostructural correlations on two structural forms of the same molecule (N.B. Complex *1b* contains a molecule of water which could be bonded to one of the Cu atoms but the authors do not indicate this (29); complex *1a* is not hydrated). The structure of *1a* is shown in Figure 7 and geometrical comparisons with *1b* are shown in Table III. The most notable features of *1a* are

(i) the non-coplanarity of the two {CuO$_3$N} coordination planes; this is evidenced by a dihedral angle of 119.2° between the best planes Cu(1),N(2), O(3),C(9),C(10) and Cu(2),N(1),O(3),C(9),C(8). The corresponding planes in *1b* are much more coplanar.

(ii) the non-trigonal planar coordination of the bridging alkoxo oxygen, O(3), which adopts a distorted pyramidal geometry.

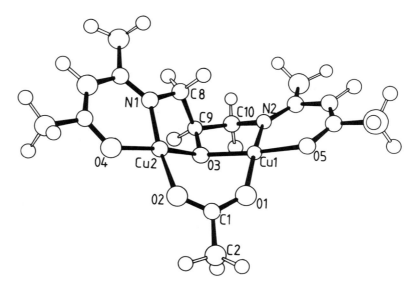

Figure 7. Molecular structure of Complex 1a. The numbering of the atoms is the same as that used for 1b in ref. 29.

(iii) the shorter Cu—Cu distance and smaller Cu—O—Cu angle, γ, in *1a* compared to *1b*.

The pyramidal nature of the alkoxo oxygen in *1a* is of a related kind to that described in Part A for complex *4*. Perusal of Table III and Fig. 8 shows that the summation $(\alpha + \beta + \gamma)$ is 335.5° in *1a* and 329.5° in *4* compared to ca. 360° in seven other trigonal-planar O-bridged compounds listed. The angles for *1b* are not at hand but the solid angle would presumably be close to 360°.

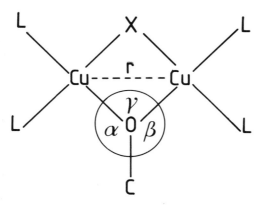

Figure 8. Core geometry showing Cu—Cu distance, r, and angles around bridging oxygen of alkoxide or phenoxide group.

Table III
Geometry around bridging alkoxo— or phenoxo—oxygen atom
(see Figures 6 and 8)

Complex X		α(deg.)	β(deg.)	γ(deg.)	r(Å)	J(cm^{-1})	Ref.
alkoxo bridge							
1a	OAc	111.4	109.8	114.3	3.24	+19	this work (a)
1b	OAc	NG	NG	133.3	3.50	−82	29
2	OH	127.4	129.3	100.4	2.93	−142	19
3	C$_3$H$_3$N$_2$	117.1	117.1	125.1	3.35	−120	22
5	1,3−N$_3$	NG	NG	136.9	3.61	>−550	21
phenoxo bridge							
4	OH	118.9	118.9	91.7	2.87	~+4	this work
6	OH	129.6	127.1	102.5	3.08	NG	15a
7	OH	130.4	127.4	101.9	3.05	−210	17
8	OH	129.7	128.5	101.4	3.05	~−187	18

(a) α = Cu2—O3—C9, β = Cu1—O3—C9, γ = Cu1—O3—Cu2
NG = not given.

In attempting to assess the reasons for a more positive J value in complexes such as *1a* and *4* compared to the others listed in Table III it would appear, as discussed in Part A, that the geometry around the bridging alkoxo or phenoxo oxygen atoms (and presumably about the OH oxygen in *4*) is playing a significant role. Those compounds with pyramidal O display a more positive J value than those with a pseudotrigonal O. At a qualitative level one might say that a pyramidal disposition of orbitals is the norm and that the more common trigonal disposition, with its consequent coplanarity of Cu and O orbitals is unusual and stabilized by π-overlap of $Cu(d_{x^2-y^2})$ and $O(p_z)$ orbitals, the latter leading to enhanced antiferromagnetism. Bertrand argued this possibility some years ago (31). At a more quantitative level the relative contributions of r(Cu—Cu), Cu—OR—Cu angles and bridging O angles to the antiferromagnetic and ferromagnetic exchange integrals within the endogenous pathway would need to be computed. Kahn (16,20,25) has advanced the earlier model of Hatfield and Hodgson (24) to include a dihedral angle between Cu-ligand planes in 'roof—shaped' μ-dihydroxo dimers. In many ways this is a similar but not identical situation to that described for *1a* and *4,* although the Cu—O—H angles are not normally measurable. Each case nevertheless leads to shorter Cu—Cu distance, smaller Cu—OR—Cu angle and less negative J. Kahn's calculations relate these changes to the relative energies of the symmetric and antisymmetric M.O.'s (based on the Cu magnetic orbitals) which ultimately lead to an accidental orthogonality between these magnetic orbitals and a resulting positive J (25). Glerup and coworkers, in their "GHP" model, have also recently detected a dependence on the angle between OR vector and bridging plane in a range of symmetrical di—μ—alkoxo and di—μ—hydroxo Cr(III) dimers (32). In Cr(III) the magnetic orbitals $d_{(xz,yz)}$ will more obviously interact by π-overlap with bridging-oxygen p_z orbitals, and hence be sensitive to the angle of the OR vector, than is the case for Cu(III) which has a $d_{x^2-y^2}$ magnetic orbital. We note also that Hoffman (33) and Gatteschi (34), using M.O. and A.O.M. models which include π-bonding contributions to Cu-ligand overlap, have considered some of the aspects described here but applied to symmetrically bridged systems.

A full quantitative understanding of magnetism and J values in dibridged systems containing two different superexchange pathways still needs to be achieved, although the present results advance our understanding of some of the finer geometrical details within the "endogenous" pathway. It is possible to fine-tune our structural postulates for type 3 Cu geometries from the present 'model' results. The EXAFS and EPR data of Solomon, Powers, Spiro and coworkers (10,35,36) on met-hemocyanin and related derivatives are defining the donor atom and bridging atom geometries with considerable accuracy. The endogenous bridging group, probably a tyrosine phenoxo, provides the dominant pathway for superexchange. A Cu—Cu distance of ca. 3.4 Å and bridging angle of ca. 130° appear to be a minimal structural requirement in the strongly coupled metaquo or metfluoro derivatives. The present work adds the prerequisite that (i) the coordination within the binuclear site be planar overall; (ii) that the phenoxo oxygen atom be trigonally coordinated and coplanar with the Cu—Cu moiety; and (iii) the tyrosine aromatic ring be coplanar with the binuclear moiety.

S-bridging in Binculear Copper(II) Complexes. A brief appraisal.

(P. Iliopoulos and K. S. Murray)

Bridging of Cu—Cu and Cu—Fe pairs in Type 3 copper sites and in cytochrome oxidase heme a_3 sites by sulfur containing residues has been proposed (37) although EXAFS studies on hemocyanins would appear to eliminate the former possibility (36). The synthesis of stable sulfur-bridged binuclear copper(II) complexes nevertheless remains a challenging chemical problem. In the present context sulfur-bridging implies such groups as thiolate RS⁻ (R = alkyl or aryl), thione C=S or thioether C—S—C, and emphasis will be given to these groups forming part of a chelating ligand. The stereochemical, magnetic and redox properties of copper(II) complexes of these ligands are particularly interesting and comparison with oxygen-bridged analogs are desirable. However there are some formidable and well known problems which include (i) redox reaction forming Cu(I) (perhaps bonded to the S-chelate) and a disulfide; (ii) a tendency for the S-chelate to condense and cyclise during synthesis forming stable heterocyclic species which do not bind to Cu (38,39).

These problems can sometimes be alleviated by attaching protective groups to RS⁻ groups prior to coordination to Cu(II) (40), by modifying the redox properties through chemical or stereochemical variations on the ligand and by working under anaerobic conditions.

In Figure 9 a variety of known and unknown (but possible) S-bridged examples are given (41). The associated-dimers *9* have been structurally characterized and show weak ferromagnetic or antiferromagnetic coupling in the case of R = Et and Bu (42-44). Adducts of Cu(salen) of type *10* should form as they do in the Cu(salen) systems (45,46) although the disposition of the non-bonded S orbitals may affect the reaction. Susceptibility studies on both the thiophenolate-bridged binuclear complex *11a* (X = pyrazolate) and its phenolate analog *11b* show much stronger antiferro-magnetic coupling in the phenolate case, i.e. J for *11b* is −207 cm⁻¹ and −2.6 cm⁻¹ for *11a*. We are currently collaborating with R. Robson and G. Williams on crystallographic correlations within this matched pair (47) and are also working on systems *10, 14* and *15*. In the latter case we have obtained the β-keto substituted thioamide ligands after much effort. Reactions with Cu(II) salts yield products which are currently being characterized and comparisons with previously synthesized O-bridged analogs (38) are now possible. Condensation of the terminal keto groups in *15* with diamines gives scope for production of compartmental ligands and subsequent formation of homo- and heterobinuclear metal complexes (39a). Recent studies on reactions of thioamides such as PhCS·NH·py with Cu(II) salts led to some interesting tetrahedral Cu(I) monomeric and dimeric {S,N} bonded chelates (48). The stability of the functionalysed thioamides in *15* towards redox reactions is therefore of interest.

Structural and magnetic studies on complexes of the types shown in Figure 9 should allow an understanding of the factors which influence exchange coupling in S-bridging

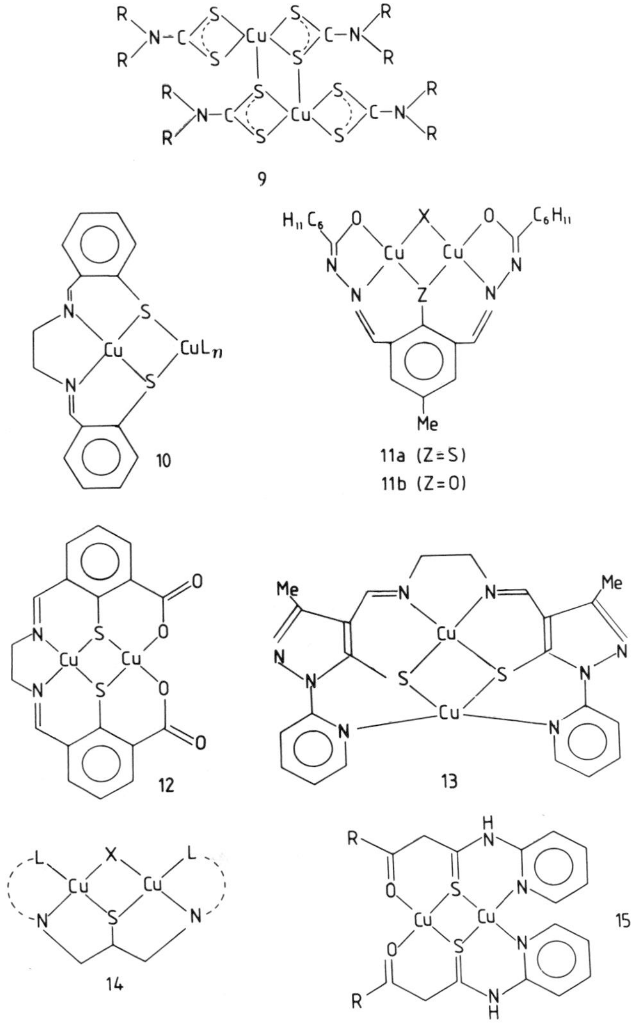

Figure 9. Examples of known and possible S-bridged binuclear copper(II) complexes. Charges are not shown.

pathways. Compared to O-bridging one would expect differences because of size, electronegativity and disposition of bonding and non-bonding orbitals on sulfur (47). Details relevant to these points are also beginning to emerge from synthetic and electronic studies on related complexes of V (49,50), Mn (51,52) and Fe (53) containing monodentate and chelating RS^- groups.

Acknowledgements

KSM wishes to acknowledge the help of colleagues and collaborators whose work is referred to herein, some of which is unpublished. Support from the joint CSIRO/Monash University grants, the Monash University Special Research fund and the Australian Research Grants Scheme is gratefully acknowledged.

References and Footnotes

1. J.H. Hodgkin, *Chem. and Ind. (London)* 153 (1979).
2. J.H. Hodgkin, *Australian Patent* 518,733; *U.S.* 4,190,709.
3. R.W. Murtagh, P.M. Sharples and J.H. Hodgkin, *Australian Water and Wastewater Association, Ninth Federal Convention, Technical Reports,* 8-19 (1981).
4. J.H. Hodgkin and R. Eibl, *Reactive Polymers, 3,* 83 (1985).
5. E. Tsuchida and H. Nishida, *Adv. Polym. Science 24,* 2 (1977).
6. H.C. Yeh, B.E. Eichinger and N.H. Anbdersen, *J. Polym. Science 20,* 2575 (1982).
7. J.H. Hodgkin, *Austral. J. Chem., 37,* 2371 (1984).
8. J.H. Hodgkin, B.C. Loft, K.S. Murray, B. Spethmann and J.K. Yandell, unpublished work.
9. B.J. Kennedy, G.D. Fallon, B.M.K.C. Gatehouse and K.S. Murray, *Inorg. Chem. 23,* 580 (1984).
10. E.I. Solomon, K.W. Penfield and D.E. Wilcox, *Struc. Bonding (Berlin) 53,* 2 (1983).
11. J.G. Gibson and E.D. McKenzie, *J. Chem. Soc.* (A) 1029 (1971).
12. A.W. Addison and U. Sakaguchi, *J. Chem. Soc. Dalton,* 600 (1979).
13. S. E. Blumberg and J. Peisach, *Arch. Biochem. and Biophys., 165,* 691 (1974).
14. G.D. Fallon, K.S. Murray, B. Spethmann, J.K. Yandell, J.H. Hodgkin and B.C. Loft, *J. Chem. Soc. Chem. Commun.,* 1561 (1984).
15. (a) K. D. Karlin, J.C. Hayes, Y. Gultneh, R. W. Cruse, J.W. McKown, J.P. Hutchinson and J. Zubieta, *J. Am. Chem. Soc., 106,* 2121 (1984) and references therein. (b) K. D. Karlin, J.C. Hayes and J. Zubieta, in *Copper Coordination Chemistry: Biochemical and Inorganic Perspectives,* Ed. K.D. Karlin and J. Zubieta, Adenine Press, New York, p. 457 (1983).
16. M.F. Charlot, O. Kahn, S. Jeannin and Y. Jeannin, *Inorg. Chem. 19,* 1410 (1980).
17. T.N. Sorrell, D.L. Jameson and C.J. O'Connor, *Inorg. Chem. 23,* 190 (1984).
18. R.R. Gagne, M.W. McCool and R.E. Marsh, *Acta Cryst. Sect. B, B36,* 2420 (1980).
19. W. Mazurek, K.J. Berry, K.S. Murray, M.J. O'Connor, M.R. Snow and A.G. Wedd, *Inorg. Chem., 21,* 3071 (1982).
20. M.F. Charlot, S. Jeannin, Y. Jeannin, O. Kahn, J. Lucrece-Abaul, J. Martin-Frere, *Inorg. Chem. 18,* 1675 (1979).
21. V. McKee, J.V. Dagdigian, R. Bau and C.A. Reed, *J. Am. Chem. Soc., 103,* 7000 (1981).
22. W. Mazurek, B.J. Kennedy, K.S. Murray, M.J. O'Connor, M.R. Snow, J.R. Rodgers, A.G. Wedd, and P. Zwack, *Inorg. Chem., 24,* 3258 (1985).
23. (a) Y.L. Agnus in *Cooper Cordination Chemistry: Biochemical and Inorganic Perspectives.* Ed. K. Karlin and J. Zubieta, Adenine Press, New York, p. 371 (1983). (b) Y. Agnus, R. Louis, J.P. Gisselbrecht and R. Weiss, *J. Am. Chem. Soc. 106,* 93 (1984).
24. V.H. Crawford, H.W. Richardson, J.R. Wasson, D.J. Hodgson and W.E. Hatfield, *Inorg. Chem. 15,* 2107 (1976).
25. O. Kahn, *Inorg. Chim. Acta 62,* 3 (1982).
26. K. J. Berry, K.S. Murray, W. Mazurek, M.J. O'Connor, A.G. Wedd and M.R. Snow, *Proc. Int. Conf. Coord. Chem. 21st,* 7 (1980).
27. I.E. Dickson and R. Robson, *Inorg. Chem. 13,* 1301 (1974).
28. C.A. Reed, paper read at COMO 12 Conference, University of Tasmania, 1984 (Abstract SL-4).
29. Y. Nishida, M. Takeuchi, R. Takahashi and S. Kida, *Chem. Letter (Japan)* 1815 (1983).
30. C.P. Marabeela, D.G. VanDerveer and J.A. Bertrand, *Proc. 176th ACS Meeting,* INOR 72 (1978).
31. J.A. Bertrand and C.E. Kirkwood, *Inorg. Chim. Acta, 6,* 248 (1972).
32. J. Glerup, D.J. Hodgson and E. Pedersen, *Acta Chem. Scand., A37,* 161 (1983).
33. P.J. Hay, J.C. Thibeault and R. Hoffmann, *J. Am. Chem. Soc. 97,* 4884 (1975).
34. A. Bencini and D. Gatteschi, *Inorg. Chim. Acta 31,* 11 (1978).
35. D.E. Wilcox, J.R. Long and E.I. Solomon, *J. Am. Chem. Soc. 106,* 2186 (1984).

36. G.L. Woolery, L. Powers, M. Winkler, E.I. Solomon and T.G. Spiro, *J. Am. Chem. Soc. 106,* 86 (1984).

37. L. Powers, B. Chance, Y. Ching, and P. Angiolilli, *Biophys. J. 34,* 465 (1981).

38. P. Iliopoulos and K.S. Murray, unpublished work.

39. (a) D.E. Fenton, U. Casellato, R.A. Vigato and M. Vidali, *Inorg. Chim. Acta 62,* 57 (1982). (b) R.C. Coombes and D.E. Fenton, *Phosphorus and Sulfur, 14,* 139 (1983).

40. J. Becher, H. Toftlund and P.H. Olesen, *Chem. Soc. Chem. Commun.* 740 (1983) and references therein.

41. Compound numbers and references:— *9* (ref. 42-44), *10* (ref. 45), *11* (ref. 47), *12* (not known), *13* (ref. 40; this compound may have a trinuclear structure without S-bridging, private communication, J. Becher and H. Toftlund, 1984), *14* (see e.g. I. Murase, S. Ueno and S. Kida, *Bull. Chem. Soc. Japan 56,* 2748 (1983), *15* (ref. 38).

42. W.E. Hatfield, *Inorg. Chem. 22,* 833 (1983).

43. J.A. van Santen, A.J van Duyneveldt and R.L. Carlin, *Inorg. Chem. 19,* 2152 (1980).

44. P.D.W. Boyd, S. Mitra, C.L. Raston, G.L. Rowbottom and A.H. White, *J. Chem. Soc. Dalton Trans.* 13 (1981).

45. M.F. Corrigan, K.S. Murray, B.O. West and J.R. Pilbrow, *Austral. J. Chem. 30,* 2455 (1977).

46. R.B. Coles, C.M. Harris and E. Sinn, *Austral. J. Chem. 23,* 243 (1970).

47. J.G. Hughes and R. Robson, *Inorg. Chim. Acta 35,* 87 (1979).

48. M.W. Fuller, V. Costanzo, K.S. Murray, D. St. C. Black, T.W. Hambley and M.R. Snow, *Austral. J. Chem.,* in press (1985).

49. R.W. Wiggins, J.C. Huffman and G. Christou, *J. Chem. Soc. Chem. Commun.* 1313 (1983).

50. J.R. Dorfman and R.H. Holm, *Inorg. Chem. 22,* 3179 (1983).

51. G. Christou and J.C. Huffman, *J. Chem. Soc. Chem. Commun.* 558 (1983).

52. T. Costa, J.R. Dorfman, K.S. Hagen and R.H. Holm, *Inorg. Chem. 22,* 4091 (1983).

53. K.S. Hagen and R.H. Holm, *J. Am. Chem. Soc. 104,* 5496 (1982).

Biological & Inorganic Copper Chemistry,
ISBN 0-940030-11-X, Eds., K. D. Karlin & J. Zubieta, Adenine Press, ©Adenine Press, 1985

Copper(II) Complexes of Schiff Base Ligands Derived from Pyrrole-2,5-dicarboxaldehyde and from 2-acetoacetylpyrrole

David E. Fenton
Department of Chemistry, The University,
Sheffield S3 7HF, U.K.

Abstract

Copper(II) complexes of acyclic, compartmental Schiff base ligands derived from 2-aceto-acetylpyrrole and of tetraimine, Schiff base macrocycles derived from pyrrole-2,5-dicar-boxaldehyde are described. Relevant crystal structures are presented and trends in structural type are discussed.

Introduction

Compartmental ligands have been defined as compounds which provide adjacent, dissimilar donor sets for complexation (1,2). Such ligands are therefore capable of selectively incorporating one metal ion to provide a mononuclear positional isomer which may then act as a precursor for the formation of homobi- or heterobinuclear complexes (Scheme 1). For example the reaction of o-acetoacetylphenol with α,ω-diamines yields Schiff bases (I) which provide $-N_2O_2$ and $-O_2O_2$ donor sets and so form a range of mono- and binuclear complexes (3).

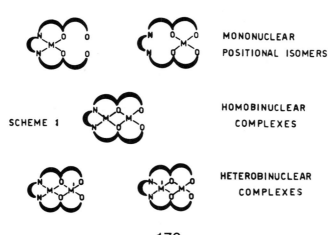

179

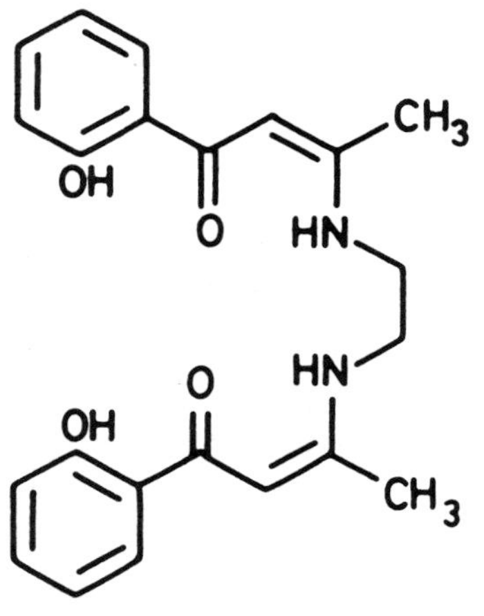

(1)

We have sought to modify the functionality of such systems by preparing Schiff bases derived from the reaction of α,ω-diamines and 2-acetoacetylpyrrole(II). The introduction of pyrrole into the ligand leads to framework modification through

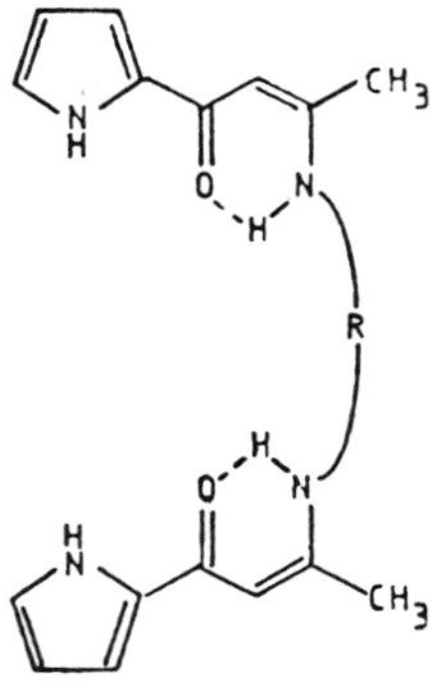

(II)

R	Abbreviation
$-(CH_2)_2-$	H_4paen
$-(CH_2)_3-$	H_4papd
$\overset{CH_3}{-CH-CH_2-}$	H_4papn
$-(CH_2)_4-$	H_4patmd
$-(CH_2)_5-$	H_4papmd
$-(CH_2)_6-$	H_4pahmd
$-(CH_2)_2-O-(CH_2)_2-$	H_4paoden
$-(CH_2)_2-\overset{H}{N}-(CH_2)_2-$	H_4padien
$-(CH_2)_2-S-(CH_2)_2-$	H_4pasden
$-(CH_2)_2-O-(CH_2)_2-O-(CH_2)_2-$	H_4pa(2O)den
$-(CH_2)_2-\overset{H}{N}-(CH_2)_2-\overset{H}{N}-(CH_2)_2-$	H_4pa(2N)den
$-(CH_2)_2-O-(CH_2)_2-O-(CH_2)_2-O-(CH_2)_2-$	H_4pa(3O)den
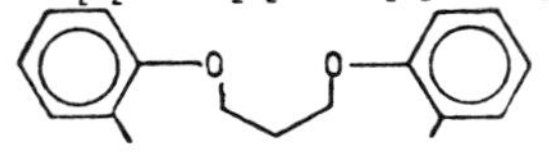	H_4pa(2O)pdphen

change of both the donor environment and the spatiality of the outer compartment. Further modification can then be made by incorporating bridges of varying length, and, in certain instances, having additional potential donor atoms present.

'2 + 2' Tetraimine Schiff base macrocycles have generally been synthesised by template procedures involving alkaline earth or main group metals (4). The resulting complexes have then been applied in transmetallation reactions from which, in the case of copper(II) homobinuclear complexes have been recovered (5). A diverse range of ligands is potentially available through sequential modification of the head and lateral units (Figure 1). The reaction of pyrrole-2,5-dialdehyde with α,ω-diamines generates a series of macrocycles in which there are two ionisable protons present.

This paper reports the application of both types of ligand to copper(II) complexation and presents structural information on several of the products.

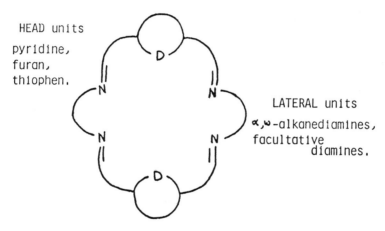

HEAD units

pyridine,
furan,
thiophen.

LATERAL units

α,ω-alkanediamines,
facultative
diamines.

Figure 1. Schematic representation of '2 + 2' tetraimine Schiff base macrocycles.

Complexes of Compartmental Ligands

2-Acetoacetylpyrrole was synthesised from diketene and pyrrole by the method of Treibs and Michl (6). The free compartmental ligands were prepared by reaction of the diketone, dissolved in hot ethanol, with the requisite α,ω-diamine, dissolved in hot chloroform (7) (Figure 2). The bases were characterised by microanalysis, ^{1}H n.m.r., i.r., and m.s.

Mononuclear copper(II) complexes were prepared by reaction of the ligands with copper(II) ethanoate in alcoholic solution. Previous work (3) had shown that with compartmental ligands there is a site preference for complexation, dependent upon the metal used. The pyrrolic ligands present two dissimilar $-N_2O_2$ donor sets for interaction and so the possibility of mononuclear positional isomers arises. A range

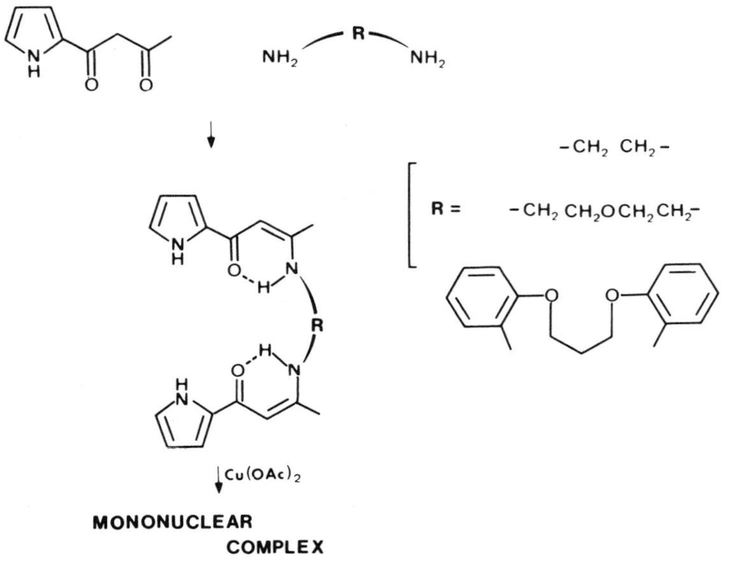

Figure 2. Pyrrole-derived compartmental ligands.

of mononuclear copper(II) complexes was prepared to determine the site preference and to see if bridge extension influenced the choice of occupancy.

The site occupancy was monitored via i.r. spectroscopy; this indicated the presence, or absence, of pyrrolic −NH stretches. The spectra of complexes derived from ligands containing short bridges (2 and 3 carbon atom chains) gave a band *ca.* 3350 cm^{-1} corresponding to the −NH stretch and implying an inner occupancy. As the bridge length was increased from 4 to 6 atoms the −NH stretch was lost and so an outer occupancy was indicated (Figure 3). The d.r.s. spectra of both sets of complexes suggested that the metal was present in an essentially square-planar geometry (bands *ca.* 510, 370, 320 nm).

The X-ray structures of Cu(H$_2$paen) and Cu(H$_2$paoden) confirmed the predicted site occupancies. The structure of Cu(H$_2$paen) consists of two independent, but similar, molecules together with a chloroform molecule of solvation. This latter property appears to be quite a common occurrence with complexes of this general type.

The copper(II) is coordinated in a square planar environment − there is a small tetrahedral distortion of *ca.* 5° − provided by the inner donor set (Figure 4). The bond lengths are normal (Cu−N, 1.93 Å and Cu−O, 1.90 Å) and the two pyrroles are clearly not involved in bonding and are non-ionised (8). The two independent molecules are disposed such that the outer compartments face each other with an angle between the coordination planes of 93.3°. This dimeric appearance leads to the presentation of a cavity having a mean diameter of 4.4 Å; it is conceivable that appropriate cations could be co-crystallised therein.

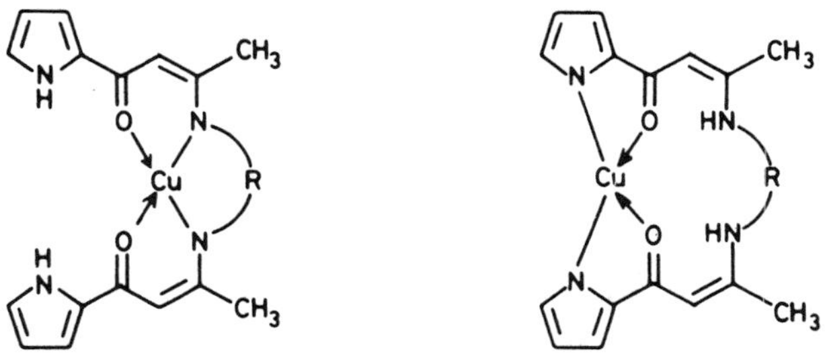

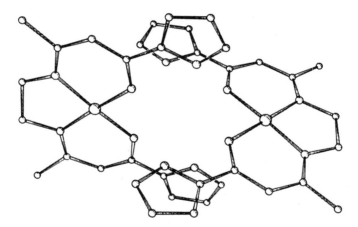

a; R = [CH₂]₂
b; R = [CH₂]₃

a; R = [CH₂]₄
b; R = [CH₂]₅
c; R = [CH₂]₂O[CH₂]₂
d; R = [CH₂]₂S[CH₂]₂

Figure 3. Site occupancy in the mononuclear compartmental complexes.

Figure 4. The molecular geometry of Cu(H₂paen).

The asymmetric unit in the structure of Cu(H₂paoden) comprises one molecule each of two crystallographically independent but chemically similar copper complexes, and one chloroform molecule of solvation (7). The two complexes differ slightly in conformational details and in each molecule the copper(II) is bonded, in an approximately square planar environment in the outer compartment of the ligand (Figure 5). The bond lengths are Cu−N, 1.93 and 1.95 Å; Cu−O, 1.95 and 1.97 Å. The unoccupied inner compartment has a pentagonal shape of mean edge length 2.75 ± 0.15 Å; the slightly different conformational arrangements of the bridge, the oxygen atom of which is non-bonding, lead to differing degrees of planarity for the pentagon. The approximate mean radius of this potential donor set is 2.34 Å and although this would suggest cation accommodation for a large cation such as Pb(II); this has not yet been achieved.

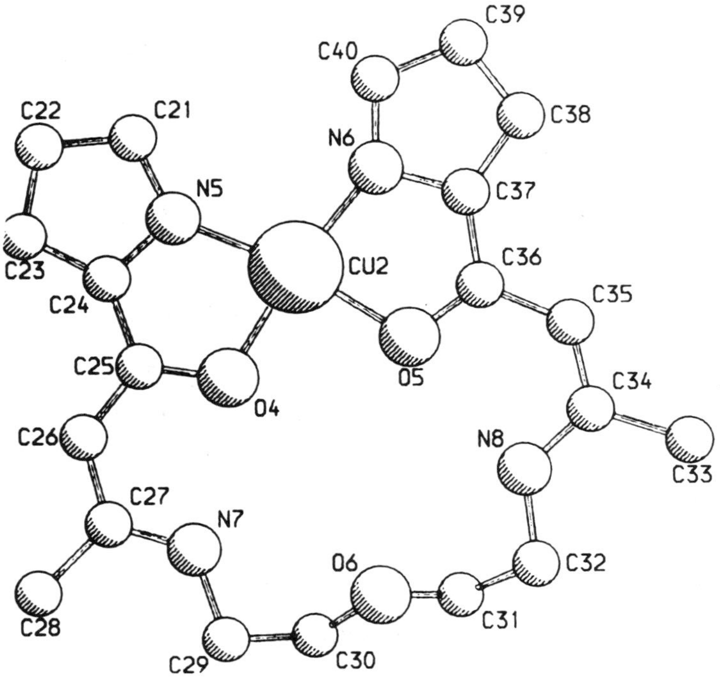

Figure 5. The molecular geometry of Cu(H$_2$paoden).

Interestingly further bridge extension led to a recovery of the $-$NH stretching frequency, and for Cu(H$_2$pa(20)pdphen) two bands were detected at 3405 and 3380 cm^{-1}. The presence of these bands was indicative of an inner compartmental occupancy and this was confirmed by the X-ray structure (8) (Figure 6). The molecule contains a copper atom which is in a tetrahedrally distorted (28.2°) square-planar environment. The donor atoms from the inner compartment are disposed such that the imino nitrogen atoms occupy *trans*-coordination sites at the metal, in contrast to the *cis*- sites in Cu(H$_2$paen). The ether oxygen atoms from the extended bridge and the pyrrolic nitrogen atoms are non-bonded. The bond distances are Cu$-$N, 1.91 Å and Cu$-$O, 2.01 Å. The extended bridge provides a 'cap' for the donor site.

Such 'capped' environments have been reported for a series of complexes of Schiff bases derived from salicylaldehyde or pyrrole-2-carboxaldehyde, and the more rigid and sterically constrained bis(2-aminonaphthyl)-n-alkyl diethers (9,10) (Figure 7a). A further example is found in the heterobimetallic complex illustrated in Figure 7b in which the second metal atom is incorporated in the extended bridge (11). Sterically hindered sites such as these can be viewed as extending the versatility of simple Schiff base ligands by incorporating the protective features introduced into synthetic models for biological molecules. 'Capped' and 'strapped' porphyrins (12) and lacunar iron(II) complexes in which there are persistent voids (13) have been devised as models for haemoglobin and cytochrome P$_{450}$.

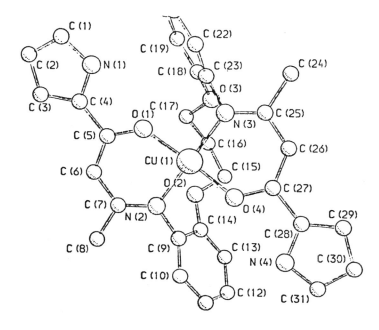

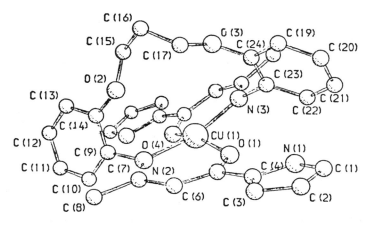

Figure 6. The molecular geometry of Cu(H$_2$pa(20)pdphen).

Simply Square Planar

In studies on related tetradentate Schiff base molecules changing the length of the bridging moiety has led either to geometrical change, or to the generation of homobinuclear complexes. Several groups of workers (14,15,16) showed that with ligands derived from salicylaldehyde and alkane-α,ω-diamines (NH$_2$(CH$_2$)$_n$NH$_2$) nickel(II) complexes remained square planar up to n = 7, and with pyrrole-2-carbaldehyde and the same diamines square planarity was retained up to n = 5.

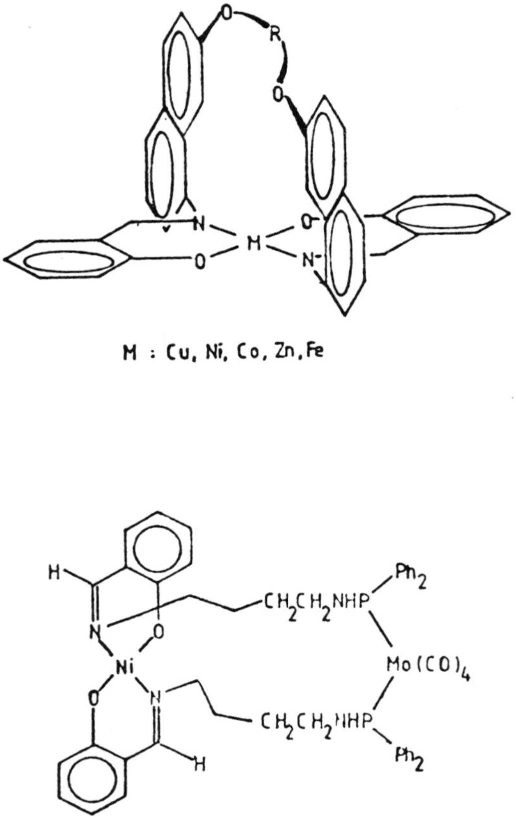

M : Cu, Ni, Co, Zn, Fe

Figure 7. a) Schematic representation of the structure of the 2,2'-tetramethylenedioxydi(8-N-salicyli-deneiminonaphthalene)nickel(II) complex. b) The nickel-molybdenum 'fly-over' system.

In contrast copper(II) (17), manganese(II) (18), and cobalt(III) (19) complexes derived from the salicylaldehyde Schiff bases were found to have an increased tetrahedral distortion as the bridging chain length increased. An alternative proposal (20) was presented for the manganese(II) complexes in which it was suggested that by increasing the length of the polymethylene chain it would be possible to generate homobinuclear complexes of the types depicted in Figure 8.

Recently the X-ray structure of the copper(II) complex of the Schiff base derived from pyrrole-2-carbaldehyde and 1,2-diaminoethane has been solved (Figure 9) and shows a homobinuclear structure of the type I in Figure 8 (21). In contrast the structure of the copper(II) complex of the non-symmetrical Schiff base derived from pyrrole-2-carboxaldehyde, acetylacetone and 1,2-diaminoethane shows the more usual mononuclear square-planar environment (22) (Figure 10). The bond lengths are normal (Cu−N, 1.93 Å and Ni−N, 1.90 Å) and there are long

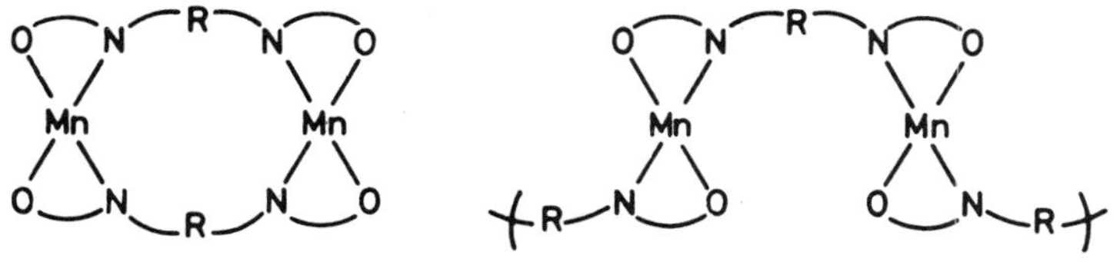

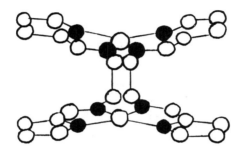

Figure 8. Homobinuclear manganese(II) complexes.

Figure 9. The molecular geometry of bis-μ-N,N'-ethylenebis(pyrrol-2-yl-methyleneaminato)-dicopper(II).

intermolecular contacts to centrosymmetrically related molecular tending towards a weak dimerisation through copper(II) to imine nitrogen interactions.

The difference in structure between these two molecules presumably arises from subtle changes in spatiality at the site caused by replacement of a phenolic moiety by a pyrrolic unit and the accompanying changes in bite sizes, and in chelate ring formation at the metal; 6,5,6 in salen and acen derivatives; 6,5,5 in the nonsymmetrical complex; and 5,5,5 in the symmetrical pyrrole derivative.

In our compounds a monomeric square planar form is maintained throughout. However the metal can move from an increasingly strained inner site into the

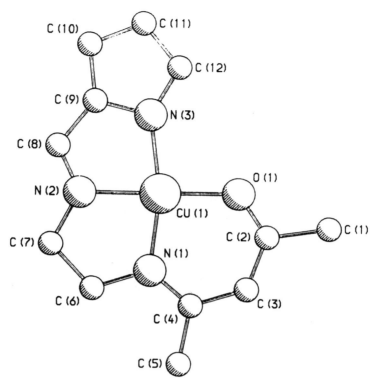

Figure 10. The molecular geometry of the copper(II) complex of the non-symmetric Schiff base derived from pyrrole-2-carboxaldehyde, acetylacetone and 1,2-diaminoethane.

adjacent outer site with the flexible bridge helping to maintain the square planar envi-ronment. Such an environment would be favoured on crystal field stabilisation terms.

Macrocyclic Complexes

The generation of '2 + 2' tetraimine Schiff base macrocycles derived from hetero-cyclic dialdehydes such as pyridine-2,6-; furan-2,5-; and thiophen-2,5-dicarboxalde-hyde has claimed much recent attention (4,5,23). The introduction of pyrrole as a head-unit has now been achieved and mono- and homobi-nuclear copper(II) complexes synthesised.

The addition of copper(II)ethanoate and KOH to a methanolic solution of pyrrole-2,5-dicarboxaldehyde gave a precipitate which was isolated and found to be a dialkoxy-bridged binuclear copper(II) complex containing two dialdehyde anions (Figure 11). Reaction of an excess of α,ω-diamine with this dark green complex in boiling alcohol gave either of two different product types depending on the diamine bridge length. With 2 and 3 carbon bridges mononuclear copper(II) complexes of

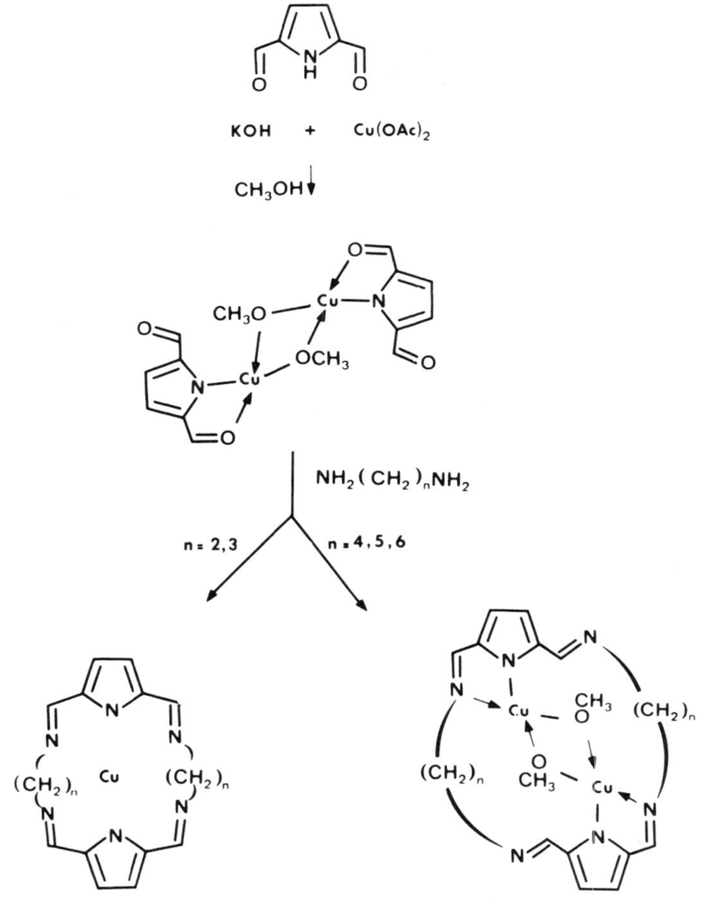

Figure 11. The preparation of '2 + 2' pyrrole-containing macrocycles.

the required macrocycle were obtained, whereas with longer chains a bis-μ-alkoxy-dicopper(II) complex of the required macrocycle were recovered (24).

The i.r. spectra of the complexes exhibit one, or more, absorptions in the region 1600-1630 cm^{-1} due to the imine $\nu_{C=N}$ but show no bands attributable to free carbonyl or amine groups. When available m.s. have given peaks corresponding to the free macrocycle as the principle peak in the spectrum. The macrocyclic nature of the mononuclear complexes is verified by the crystal structure of the compound derived from 1,3-diaminopropane (Figure 12). The copper atom is bound to the two pyrrolic nitrogen atoms and more strongly to the two imine nitrogens from one diamine derived lateral unit (Cu$-$N$_{pyr}$, 2.08 Å and Cu$-$N$_{im}$, 1.83). The metal is in a distorted tetrahedral environment. The near planar pyrrole rings are coplanar with the coordinated imine unit giving planar five-membered chelate rings. The angle between the two symmetry related rings is 38.5°. The uncoordinated imine nitrogen

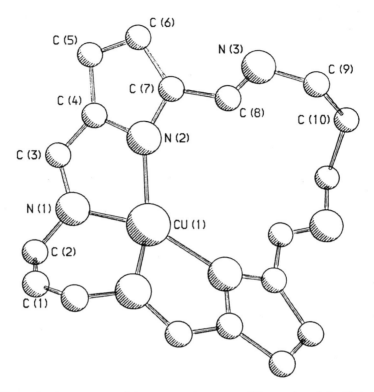

Figure 12. The molecular structure of the mononuclear copper(II) complex of the '2 + 2' pyrrole-containing macrocycle.

atoms are directed away from the cavity and so the head units are in *cis,trans* configurations in contrast to the *cis,cis* arrangements found for pyridinyl, furanyl and thiophenyl head units. It is probable that considerable rearrangement of the ligand would be required to accommodate two metals within the framework. There is some disorder in the 'free' side chain which is still being resolved.

The infrared spectra of the complexes $Cu_2L(OCH_3)_2$ show, in addition to the imine bands, further bands ca. 2800 cm^{-1} which can be assigned to the alkoxide ν_{CH} (25). The d.r.s. exhibit bands indicative of square planar (or slightly distorted planar) copper(II). The structure given in Figure 11 is assigned to these complexes and the use of molecular models indicates that it is sterically favourable to include the $-Cu(OCH_3)_2Cu-$ moiety within macrocycles where n ≥ 4 (n = number of briding methylene units) provided that the uncoordinated imine N atom is directed away from the cavity of the macrocycle. The presence of two distinct imine bands in the i.r. reflects the requirement. Where n < 4 the lateral unit is of insufficient length to provide a cavity of diameter sufficient to enclose the binuclear unit.

For the pyrrole-containing macrocycles the only available structure is of a mononuclear complex. The metal is partly coordinated by the head unit but lies in a lateral compartment; the head unit is in a cis,trans conformation. The proposed structures of the dinuclear alkoxy-bridged copper(II) complexes have the binuclear fragment bonded to the head units but to diagonally opposed pairs of donors (Figure 11). This skewed arrangement is in contrast with the more direct arrangement found in the pyridine-based systems where all of the terminal donors are bound (25), and with the lateral coordination by pairs of imine nitrogens found in the dinuclear copper(II) complex, $Cu_2(m/c)(OEt)_2(NCS)_2$ derived from furan-2,5-dicarboxaldehyde and 1,3-diaminopropane (Figure 13). In this latter complex the furan oxygen atom does not act as a donor.

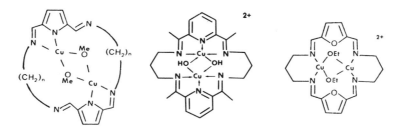

Figure 13. Formula representations of '2 + 2' macrocyclic dinuclear copper(II) complexes with pyridine, furan and pyrrole head units.

It is notable that the pyrrole-containing complexes are synthesised via a copper(II) alkoxy bridged intermediate and not by transmetallation using a preformed macrocycle produced using an alkaline earth or main group metal as a templating agent. This latter technique is generally applicable when the head unit is pyridine, furan or thiophen. In the latter case it has also been possible to prepare free tetraimine macrocyles directly from the organic precursors alone. There is an interesting coincidence concerning conformer distribution and the need for a metal template which, Curtin-Hammett principle notwithstanding (26), may play a contributory role in the reaction mechanism.

The dicarbonyl precursors can exist in different conformations (Figure 14). N.m.r. studies in nematic phases have shown that whereas for pyridine-2,6-dicarboxaldehyde the only important conformer is *trans,trans* (27) and for furan-2,5-dicarboxaldehyde there is a 2:1:1 distribution of *cis,trans:trans,trans:cis,cis* conformers (28), the distribution for thiophen-2,5-dicarboxaldehyde is 80% *cis,cis*:20% *cis,trans* (29). If it is the *cis,cis* conformer which leads most readily to macrocyclisation—and the structures of '2 + 2' macrocycles bearing these head units have *cis,cis* arrangements (see, for example, references 4,5,23)—then it is noted that the conformer distributions correspond with macrocycle formation. Thus for pyridine-2,6- and furan-2,5-dicarboxdehyde the metal ion can be viewed as redirecting conformer distribution to predominately *cis,cis* through complexation prior to macrocyclisation. With thiophen-2,5-dicarboxaldehyde the *cis,cis* conformer is already present in excess and so no metal template is required. Unfortunately there is scant solution phase information available concerning the conformer distributions although dipole moments

c,c   c,t   t,t

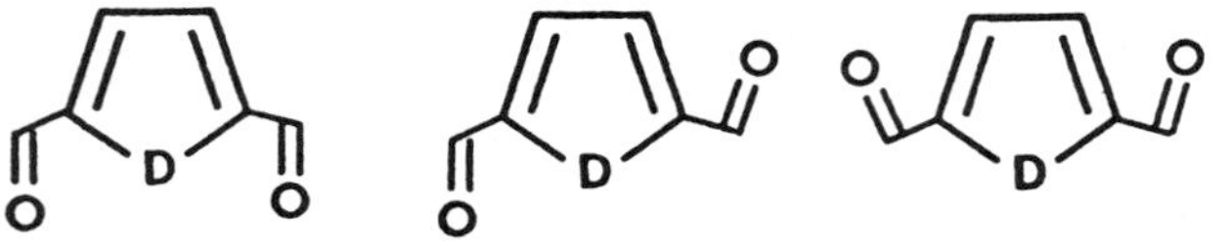

Figure 14. Dialdehyde conformers.

of pyridine-2,6-dicarboxaldehyde and 2,6-diacetylpyridine measured in benzene have been interpreted as being derived from a high *trans,trans* conformer content with ca. 5% *cis,trans* and neglible *cis,cis* presence (30).

N.m.r. studies on pyrrole-2,5-dicarboxaldehyde have indicated an 80% *cis,cis*:20% *cis,trans* conformer ratio (31). This would suggest that metal-free macrocycles could be made directly from the dicarboxaldehyde and α,ω-diamines. Preliminary results have confirmed this hypothesis—albeit in low yield syntheses (32). Similarly the availability of a 25% *cis,cis* conformer presence with furan-2,5-dicarboxaldehyde suggests that metal-free macrocycles should be preparable and this has been achieved in the reaction of the dialdehyde with sterically constrained diamines (33).

As no solid state information was available for the dialdehydes, the structure of pyrrole-2,5-dicarboxaldehyde was undertaken in order to see if there was a strong presence of *cis,trans* conformer in the free dialdehyde. The structure showed a 1:1 presence of *cis,cis:cis,trans* conformers (34) (Figure 15).

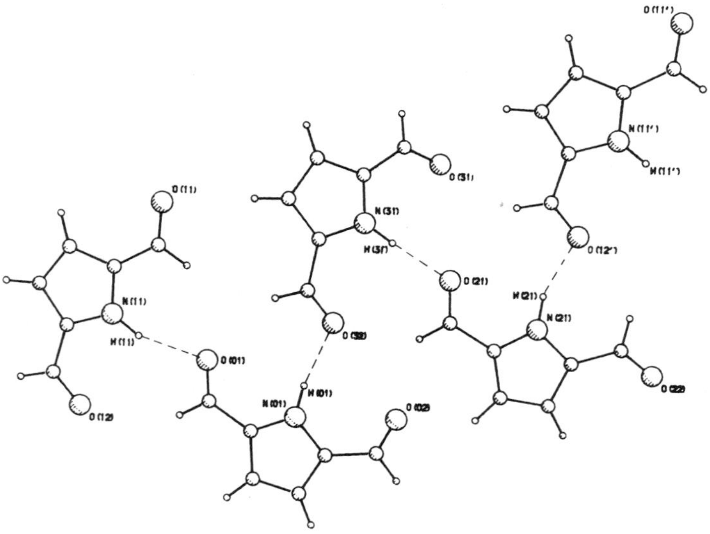

Figure 15. The molecular structure of pyrrole-2,5-dialdehyde.

The Japanese poet Hashin wrote, *'No earth, no sky can be discerned at all; only these ceaseless snowflakes still they fall'.* This is appropriate here as there are obviously many factors which influence the pathway(s) taken when forming tetraimine Schiff base macrocycles in the presence, and absence, of metal ions. The above observations are presented as a provocation to stimulate discussion on this problem.

I would like to acknowledge the contributions made to this work by Martha Leal Gonzalez and Stephen Moss. It is also a great pleasure to draw attention to my collaboration with Neil Bailey and his co-workers without whose crystallographic expertise many forward steps would not be possible. The work prepared here was supported by the S.E.R.C., Conacyt (Mexico) and I.C.I. Ltd. (Pharmaceuticals Division).

References and Footnotes

1. U. Casellato, P.A. Vigato, D.E. Fenton and M. Vidali, *Chem. Soc. Revs. 8,* 199 (1979).
2. D.E. Fenton, U. Casellato, P.A. Vigato and M. Vidali, *Inorg. Chim. Acta 62,* 57 (1982).
3. D.E. Fenton, S.E. Gayda, U. Casellato, P.A. Vigato and M. Vidali, *Inorg. Chim. Acta 27,* 9 (1978).
4. S.M. Nelson, *Pure and Appl. Chem. 52,* 2461 (1980).
5. S.M. Nelson, F.S. Esho, A. Lavery and M.G.B. Drew, *J. Amer. Chem. Soc. 105,* 569 (1983).
6. A. Treibs and K. H. Michl, *Liebigs Annalen. 577,* 129 (1952).
7. H. Adams, N.A. Bailey, D.E. Fenton and M.S. Leal Gonzalez, *J. Chem. Soc., Dalton Trans.,* 1345 (1983).
8. N.A. Bailey, D.E. Fenton, M.S. Leal Gonzalez and C.O. Rodriguez de Barbarin, *unpublished results.*
9. A.R. Hendrickson, J.M. Hope and R.L. Martin, *J. Chem. Soc., Dalton Trans.,* 1479 (1979).
10. A.T. Baker, R.L. Martin and D. Taylor, *J. Chem. Soc., Dalton Trans.,* 1503 (1979).
11. C.S. Kraihanzel, E. Sinn and G.W. Gray, *J. Amer. Chem. Soc. 103,* 960 (1981).
12. J.E. Baldwin and P. Perlmutter, *Topics in Current Chemistry 121,* 181 (1984).
13. N. Herron, J.H. Cameron, G.L. Neer and D.H. Busch, *J. Amer. Chem. Soc. 105,* 298 (1983).
14. R.H. Holm, *J. Amer. Chem. Soc. 82,* 5632 (1960).
15. W.C. Hoyt and G.W. Everett, jun., *Inorg. Chem. 8,* 2013 (1969).
16. J.H. Weber, *Inorg. Chem. 6,* 258 (1967).
17. S.J. Gruber, C.M. Harris and E. Sinn, *J. Inorg. Nucl. Chem. 30,* 1805 (1966).
18. S.J. Ebbs and L.T. Taylor, *Inorg. Nucl. Chem. Lett. 10,* 1137 (1974).
19. M. Nariharan and F.L. Urbach, *Inorg. Chem. 8,* 556 (1969).
20. S.J.E. Titus, W.M. Barr and L.T. Taylor, *Inorg. Chim. Acta 32,* 103 (1979).
21. T. Kikuchi, C. Kabuto, H. Yokoi, M. Iwaizumi and W. Mori, *J. Chem. Soc., Chem. Commun.,* 1306 (1983).
22. H. Adams, N.A. Bailey, J-P. Costes and D.E. Fenton, *unpublished results.*
23. N.A. Bailey, M.M. Eddy, D.E. Fenton, G. Jones, S. Moss and A. Mukhopadhyay, *J. Chem. Soc., Chem. Commun.,* 628 (1981).
24. H. Adams, N.A. Bailey, D.E. Fenton and S. Moss, *Inorg. Chim. Acta 83,* L79 (1984).
25. M.G.B. Drew, J. Nelson, F. Esho, V. McKee and S.M. Nelson, *J. Chem. Soc., Dalton Trans.,* 1837 (1982).
26. J.I. Seeman, *Chem. Revs. 83,* 83 (1983).
27. P.L. Barili, M. Longeri and C.A. Veracini, *Mol. Phys. 28,* 1101 (1974).
28. P. Bucci, C.A. Veracini and M. Longeri, *Chem. Phys. Letters 15,* 396 (1972).
29. L. Lunazzi, G.F. Pedulli, M. Tiecco and C.A. Veracini, *J. Chem. Soc., Perkin II,* 755 (1972).
30. H. Lumbroso, D.M. Bertin and G.C. Pappalardo, *J. Mol. Struct. 37,* 127 (1977).
31. M. Farnier and T. Drakenberg, *J. Chem. Soc., Perkin II,* 337 (1975).
32. D.E. Fenton and R. Moody, unpublished results.
33. D.H. Cook, *Ph.D. Thesis (University of Sheffield)* (1977).
34. N.A. Bailey, D.E. Fenton, S. Moss and C.O. Rodriguez de Barbarin, *unpublished results.*

Biological & Inorganic Copper Chemistry,
ISBN 0-940030-11-X, Eds., K. D. Karlin & J. Zubieta, Adenine Press, ©Adenine Press, 1985

Structures And Properties Of Homo- and Hetero-Binuclear and Polynuclear Complexes Containing Copper

Ekkehard Sinn
Department of Chemistry
University of Virginia
Charlottesville, VA 22901, USA

Magnetic interactions between bridged metal atoms are affected by the metal environment and the nature and geometry of the bridging group.

A general method of forming imidazolate (Im) bridges between similar and dissimilar metal uses unsymmetrical tetradentate ligands containing an Im fragment. It allows magnetic exchange interactions and is of interest in modelling biomolecules which are known or proposed to contain Im bridges. The system can bridge via O and Im.

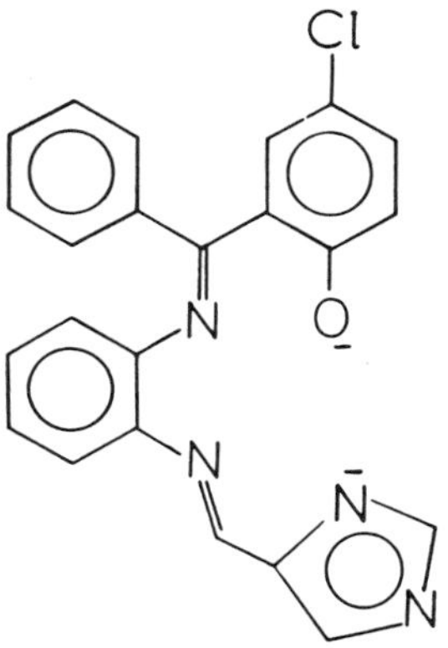

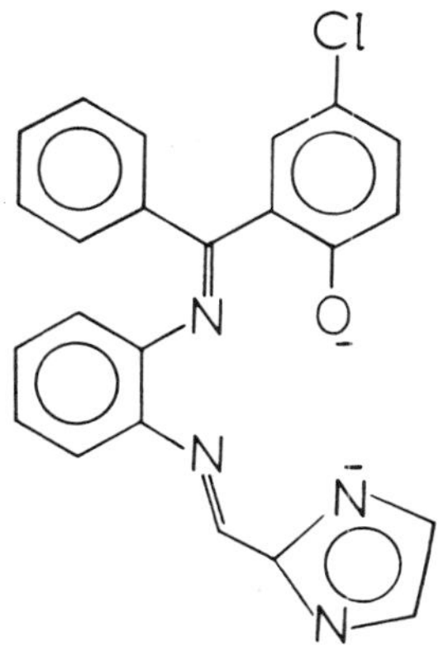

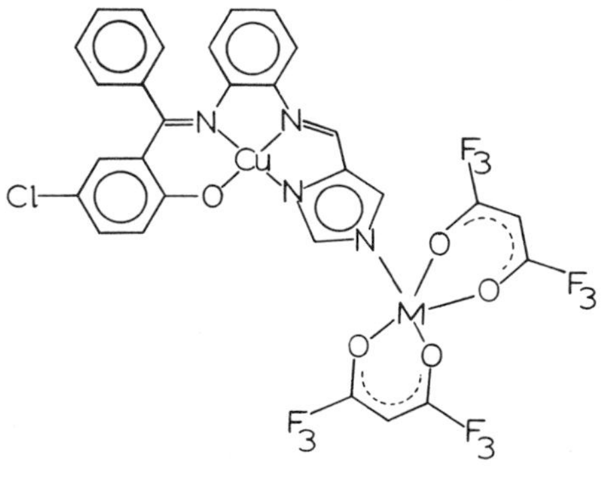

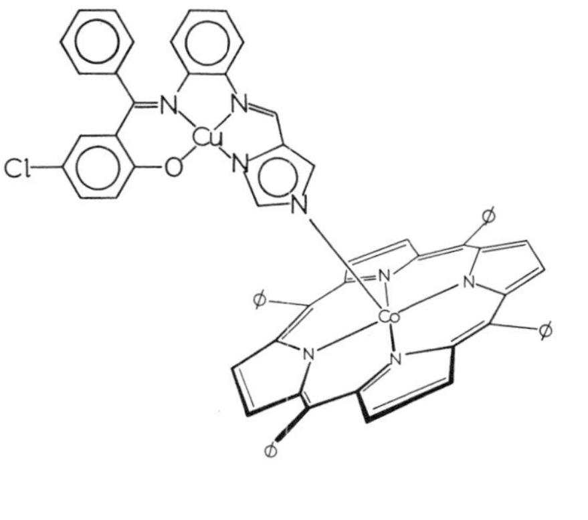

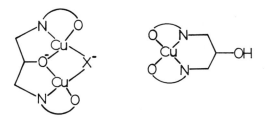

Heavy substitution on unsymmetrical Schiff base ligands tends to produce very different and generally more complex polynuclear compounds than the less substituted ligands and a wide variety of metal geometries and bridging modes is displayed.

Schiff base ligands with alkyl OH centers produce geometry-dependent magnetic interaction strengths: The alkyl chain lengths independently control the metal environment, while bulkiness of the X groups affects the angle between the two principal Cu(II) planes. The possibility of comparison with S-bonded homologs is a further interest in the data.

Introduction: Magnetic Equations

Among binuclear paramagnetic metal complexes, homobinuclears are the easiest to make and have been the most extensively studied (1-4). When two paramagnetic

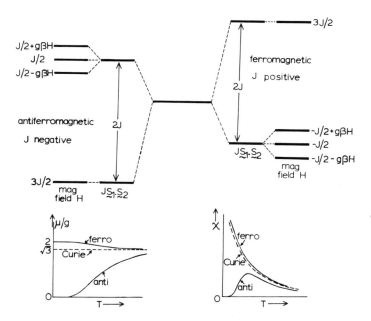

Figure 1. Energy levels, magnetic susceptibility, χ (Eq. 1, based on the Hamiltonian $H = -2JS_1 \cdot S_2$) and "effective magnetic moments", $\mu = \sqrt{7.997\chi T}$ for ferromagnetic and antiferromagnetic coupling in a homobinuclear complex. For this illustration, the simplest case, $S_1 = S_2 = \frac{1}{2}$ is used.

metal atoms are held close enough by the ligands to interact magnetically, their spins will be coupled parallel (ferromagnetic) or anti-parallel (antiferromagnetic), shown schematically in Figure 1. If the metal atom ground state is approximately spherically symmetric, we can use the spin-only Heisenberg Hamiltonian $H = -2J S_1 \cdot S_2$, where $S_1 = S_2 = S =$ spin quantum number of the paramagnetic ion. This enables us to obtain a general equation, Eq. 1, for magnetic susceptibility per gram-atom of metal in homobinuclear complexes:

$$\chi = \frac{Ng^2\beta^2}{6kT} \cdot \frac{\displaystyle\sum_{i=0}^{2S-1}(2S-i)(2S-i+1)(4S-2i+1)y_i}{\displaystyle\sum_{i=0}^{2S}(4S+1-2i)y_i} \quad \text{where } y = e^{i(i-4S-1)J/kT} \tag{1}$$

With copper, this reduces to the Bleaney-Bowers (5) equation, $\mu = g\{1 + \tfrac{1}{3}e^{-2J/kT}\}^{-\frac{1}{2}}$ for the "effective magnetic moment", μ, given by $\chi = \frac{N\beta^2}{3kT}\mu^2$ or $\mu = \sqrt{8.00\chi T}$.

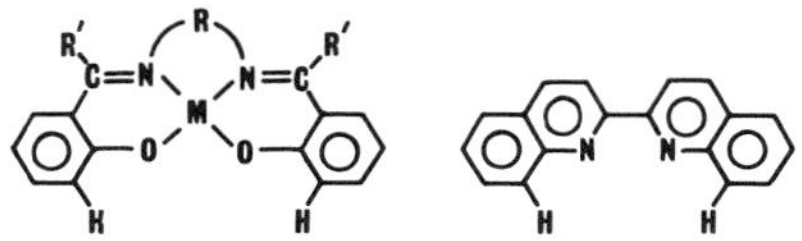

Figure 2. M(TSB) and 2,2′-Biquinolyl which can act similarly as ligands via cis oxygen or as nitrogen donors. The biquinolyl also models the steric constraints imposed by adjacent hydrogen atoms when M(TSB) acts as a ligand.

Tetradentate Schiff base complexes, M(TSB), can act as ligands to other metal atoms, much like 2,2′-biquinolyl, which they somewhat resemble sterically (6) (Figure 2). The second metal atom M′ in the binuclear $M(TSB)M'X_n$ complex may be distorted tetrahedral, five-coordinated or octahedral, but steric crowding prevents it from being planar. When both metals are copper, the complexes are homobinuclear with inequivalent metal sites, and they exhibit moderate to strong antiferromagnetic coupling, depending on the metal and geometry (Figure 3).

In heterobinuclear complexes containing copper, for example $Cu(TSB)MX_n$, spin-only coupling is described by Eq. 2:

$$\chi = \frac{Ng^2\beta^2(2S+1)}{6kT} \cdot \frac{S(S-\frac{1}{2})x+(S+1)(S+\frac{3}{2})}{Sx+S+1} \quad \text{where } x = e^{-J(2S+1)/kT} \tag{2}$$

S is the spin of metal M

This assumes equal g values for the two metals, which is frequently a good representation of reality (2,7,8). Using g_1 and g_2 for the metals Cu and M, we obtain the general equation, Eq. 3, for the cases where the g-values cannot be taken as equal in heterobinuclears:

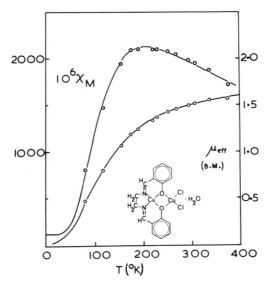

Figure 3. Magnetic properties of the CuCu' binuclear complex shown.

$$\chi = N\beta^2 \cdot [\{(S+1)(2S+3)(2Sg_1+g_2)^2 + \frac{8}{x}S(S+1)(g_1-g_2)^2\}e^x + S(2S-1)\{2(S+1)g_1-g_2\}^2$$
$$(3)$$
$$- \frac{8}{x}S(S+1)(g_1-g_2)^2] / [12(2S+1)kT\{(S+1)e^x + S\}]$$

where $x = (2S+1)J/kT$

Thus, for example, the spin-only equation for a heterobinuclear complex containing interacting d^9 and high spin d^5 species (e.g. Fe^{III}-Cu^{II}) is obtained by substituting S = $\frac{5}{2}$:

$$\chi = \frac{N\beta^2}{18kT} \cdot \frac{\{14(5g_1+g_2)^2 + \frac{35}{x}(g_1-g_2)^2\}e^x + 5(7g_1-g_2)^2 - \frac{35}{x}(g_1-g_2)^2}{7e^x + 5}$$

$$x = \frac{6J}{kT}$$

For (S = $\frac{3}{2}$)-Cu^{II} heterobinuclears (e.g. Co^{II}-Cu^{II}), Eq. 3 becomes:

$$\chi = \frac{N\beta^2}{8kT} \cdot \frac{\{5(3g_1+g_2)^2 + \frac{10}{x}(g_1-g_2)^2\}e^x + (5g_1-g_2)^2 - \frac{10}{x}(g_1-g_2)^2}{5e^x + 3}$$

$$x = \frac{4J}{kT}$$

For binuclear copper(II) complexes with markedly different metal sites, the Bleaney-Bowers equation (5) is replaced by the form of Eq. 3 for the S = $\frac{1}{2}$ case:

$$\chi = \frac{N\beta^2}{2kT} \cdot \frac{\{(g_1+g_2)^2 + \frac{1}{x}(g_1-g_2)^2\}e^x - \frac{1}{x}(g_1-g_2)^2}{3e^x + 1}$$

$$x = \frac{2J}{kT}$$

Such complexes are of interest because of the presumed Fe-Cu couple in cytochrome oxidase and the synthetic Fe-Cu derivative of purple acid phosphatases, vide infra. Such magnetic couplings are also relevant to the imidazolate-bridged heterobinuclear couple in bovine erythrocyte superoxide dismutase in which the zinc atoms of the Zn^{II}-Cu^{II} units (9) can be replaced by other metals such as Cu^{II} (10) and Co^{II} (11).

Trinuclear Complexes

Heterotrinuclear complexes containing copper, such as $(CuTSB)_2M(ClO_4)_n$, which contain two chemically equivalent copper sites, have magnetic properties given in the spin-only case by Eq. (4):

$$\chi = \frac{N\beta^2}{3kT} \cdot \frac{\sum\limits_{i=1}^{3} a_i y_i + a_2 z}{\sum\limits_{i=1}^{3} b_i y_i + b_2 z} \tag{4}$$

where $y_i = e^{-E_i/kT}$; $z = e^{-2J'/kT}$; $a_i = (S+i-1)(S+i-2)b_i g^2$; $b_i = (2S+2i-3)g^2$; $E_i = J(4S-2iS+3i-i^2)$

J and J′ represent the couplings for Cu-M and Cu-Cu respectively. When the g values g_1, g_2 for Cu, M are significantly different, the terms in Eq. (4) are modified

$$y_1' = \frac{y_1}{g^2}\{g_2 - \frac{g_1-g_2}{S}\}^2 \qquad y_2' = \frac{y_2}{g^2}\{g_2 + \frac{g_1-g_2}{S(S+1)}\}^2 \qquad y_3' = \frac{y_3}{g^2}\{g_2 + \frac{g_1-g_2}{S+1}\}^2$$

$$z' = z\frac{g_2^2}{g^2}$$

An example containing Cu-Ni-Cu (Figure 4), where Eq. 4 reduces to

$$\chi = \frac{N\beta^2}{kT} \cdot \frac{p(g_1+g_2)^2 + 2zg_2^2 + 5(g_1+g_2)^2/p}{p^2 + 3p + 3z + 5/p} \qquad \text{where } p = e^{-2J/kT}$$

The configuration of metal atoms Cu-M-Cu has been found to be linear in some of these complexes, and triangular in others. In each case, there are two equivalent couplings (J) between M and either Cu, and a weaker coupling (J′) between the Cu sites. In other heterotrinuclear complexes, such as {CuTSB}{X-CuTSB}M(H_2O)X, X = Cl, Br (Figure 5), which has two inequivalent copper sites, the M-Cu couplings are unequal in principle, and therefore require a more complicated treatment (2) but Eq. 4 still gives a good representation of the magnetic properties.

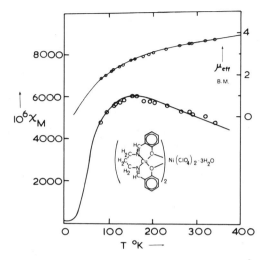

Figure 4. Magnetic properties of the CuNiCu trinuclear complex shown.

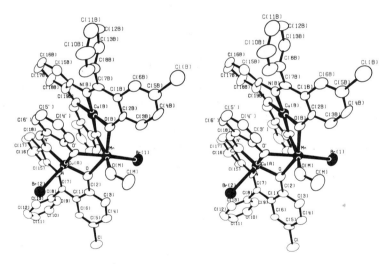

Figure 5. {Cu(TSB)}{X-Cu(TSB)}M(H$_2$O)X, M = Mn, X = Br.

Structural Dependence

Equivalent copper sites can be produced from both bidentate and tridentate Schiff base ligands together with halogen, pseudo-halogen, β-diketone and carboxylate ligands. The coupling between the copper atoms will depend on the efficiency of the superexchange overlap, and if the intermetallic distance is short enough (where here it is not) on the extent of direct orbital overlap. The unpaired electron resides in the d$_{x^2-y^2}$ orbital, which points along the bonds to the bridging atom if these lie within the principal copper plane. The principal factors affecting the efficiency of

Table I

Magnetic Coupling in some Homobinuclear Copper Complexes with Identical Metal Sites

Complex	$-2J/cm^{-1}$	$\tau/°$	Cu-O-Cu	R	R'
$Cu_2Cl_2O_4N_2C_{20}H_{20}$		13.7	103.7	5-Cl	H
$Cu_2O_8N_4C_{20}H_{20}$		9.6	103.5	3-NO_2	H
$Cu_2O_8N_2C_{28}H_{26}$	>1000	10.4	104.0	C_6H_5	H
$Cu_2O_4N_2C_{22}H_{26}$		7.0	104.2	CH_3	H
$Cu_2O_8N_4C_{20}H_{20}$		4.0	106.0	5-NO_2	H
$Cu_2Cl_2O_2N_2C_{18}H_{20}$	560	33.1	103.3	C_2H_5	H
$Cu_2Cl_2Br_2O_2N_2C_{18}H_{20}$	440	35.5	101.2	C_4H_9	C_6H_5
$Cu_2Br_2O_2N_2C_{18}H_{20}$	410	35.7	104.6	C_2H_5	H
$Cu_2Cl_2O_2N_2C_{16}H_{16}$	296	39.3	102.2	CH_3	H
$Cu_2Cl_2O_2C_{20}H_{24}$	290	40.1	103.5	$CH(CH_3)_2$	H

the overlap are summarized in Figure 6. As an example, Table I shows the magnetic coupling for a series of complexes with bi- and tri-dentate ligands, as a function of τ, the dihedral angle which measures distortion towards tetrahedral geometry, ϕ, the Cu-O-Cu angle and the intermetallic distance. In this case, τ predominates, and the coupling can be made quite small by imposing a large tetrahedral distortion. As expected, making compounds fairly flat maximizes the superexchange and produces very strong interactions. In such complexes, the coupling is too strong to measure, and the compounds are fully diamagnetic at room temperature as is also observed in the binuclear copper-containing protein hemocyanin (12). These compounds are good models for this diamagnetism, and demonstrate one criterion for representing the magnetic properties: the copper environment should approximate planarity and the bridging ligands should lie in the principal copper plane.

Inequivalent Metal Sites

Table II gives the couplings of a series of homo- and hetero-binuclear complexes containing copper. All are antiferromagnetic with interactions somewhat though

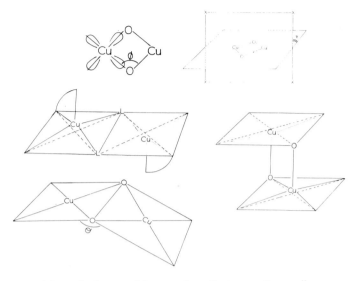

Figure 6. Structural features that affect magnetic coupling.

not dramatically smaller than the interaction required for the Fe-Cu couple in cytochrome oxidase to explain the magnetic properties and the absence of esr for that couple. Some of the complexes, such as CuTSB·M(hfa)$_2$ (M = Cu, Ni, Co, Fe, Mn) (Figure 7) have been characterized by X-ray crystallography. As in cytochrome oxidase, coupling is strong enough to quench the esr in CuTSB·FeCl$_3$·H$_2$O (Figure 8), which contains water and three chlorines that may or may not all be coordinated; a quintet-heptet splitting (−5J) of about 330 cm^{-1} is achieved with this type of complex (Table II) (13). The CuTSB·Cu(hfa)$_2$ complexes are examples of a planar-octahedral coupling, in which the Jahn-Teller distortion axis of the actahedral copper can place its principal plane either coplanar with the Cu$_2$O$_2$ bridge, or approximately orthogonal to it. The former case enhances the exchange overlap, and therefore promotes stronger coupling, while the latter case reduces the overlap and therefore weakens the coupling proportionally.

The CuTSB·M(hfa)$_2$ complexes allow a comparison of magnetic interaction in heterobinuclear, planar Cu-octahedral M complexes. For example, in the CuTSB· Fe(hfa)$_2$ complexes (Figure 7), a decrease in the dihedral angle θ (Figure 6) between the principal metal plane, of about 5° causes the quartet-sextet splitting (−5J) to increase from 30 cm^{-1} to 115 cm^{-1}. This structural effect gives a clue about a possible Fe-Cu couple bridged via oxygen or sulfur (14) in cytochrome oxidase; a large dihedral angle between the principal planes leads to a reduced coupling and therefore a poorer model for the proposed esr-quenching magnetic exchange.

Ferromagnetism vs Antiferromagnetism in Cu-Fe

The quenching of the esr of the Fe-Cu couple in cytochrome oxidase could have

Table II

Magnetic Coupling in some Heterobinuclear and Heterotrinuclear Complexes
with Inequivalent Metal Sites

Binuclear Complex	$-J$	Trinuclear Complex	$-J$
(CuenSal)CuCl$_2$	116	(CuenSal)$_2$Cu(ClO$_4$)$_2$·3H$_2$O	40
(CuprSal)CuCl$_2$·H$_2$O	97	(Cu1,2prSal)$_2$Cu(ClO$_4$)$_2$·2H$_2$O	180
(CuMPSal)CuCl$_2$·H$_2$O	90.5	(CuEHA)$_2$Cu(ClO$_4$)$_2$·2H$_2$O	200
(CuEHA)CuCl$_2$	236	(Cu1,3prSal)$_2$Cu(ClO$_4$)$_2$·2H$_2$O	230
(Cu1,3PHA)CuCl$_2$·H$_2$O	140	(Cu1,3PHA)$_2$Cu(ClO$_4$)$_2$·3H$_2$O	240
(CuprSal)CuBr$_2$·$\frac{1}{2}$H$_2$O	194	(CuenSal)$_2$Ni(ClO$_4$)$_2$·3H$_2$O	22
(CuprSal)CuBr$_2$·H$_2$O	95	(Cu1,3prSal)$_2$Ni(ClO$_4$)$_2$·3H$_2$O	64
(Cu5ClenSal)CuCl$_2$	105	(Cu1,3PHA)$_2$Ni(ClO$_4$)$_2$·3H$_2$O	46
(Cu5,6bzenSal)CuCl$_2$	155	(CuenSal)$_2$Co(ClO$_4$)$_2$·2.5H$_2$O	16
(Cu1,2prSal)CuCl$_2$	106	(Cu1,3PHA)$_2$Co(ClO$_4$)$_2$·2H$_2$O	24
(Cu5Cl1,2prSal)CuCl$_2$	204	(CuenSal)$_2$Fe(ClO$_4$)$_2$·2H$_2$O	9
(Cu5Br1,2prSal)CuCl$_2$	195	(Cu1,3prSal)$_2$Fe(ClO$_4$)$_2$·2H$_2$O	15
(Cu1,2prSal)FeCl$_2$·H$_2$O	55	(CuenSal)$_2$Mn(ClO$_4$)$_2$·3H$_2$O	11
(Cu1,2prSal)MnCl$_2$·2H$_2$O	24	(Cu1,3PHA)$_2$Mn(ClO$_4$)$_2$·2H$_2$O	30
(Cu prp$_2$en)Cu(hfa)$_2$	44.8	[(CuL)(CuLCl)Mn(H$_2$O)$_2$]Cl	8.3
(Cu prp$_2$en)Ni(hfa)$_2$	48.0	[(CuL)(CuLBr)Mn(CH$_3$OH)Br]	12.5
(Cu prp$_2$en)Co(hfa)$_2$	16.3		
(Cu prp$_2$en)Mn(hfa)$_2$	13.2		
(Cu prp$_2$en)Fe(hfa)$_2$	5.5		
(Cu prp$_2$pr)Fe(hfa)$_2$	23		
(Cu prp$_2$pr)Mn(hfa)$_2$	15		
(Cu prp$_2$pr)Co(hfa)$_2$	15		

enSal = N,N′-ethylenebis(salicylaldimine)
prSal = N,N′-o-phenylenebis(salicyaldimine)
MPS = N,N′-4-methyl-o-phenylenebis(salicylaldimine)
EHA = N,N′-ethylenebis(o-hydroxyphenylidenemine)
1,3-PHA = N,N′-1,3-propylenebis(o-hydroxyphenylideneimine)
5ClenSal = N,N′-1,3 ethylenebis(5-chlorsalicylaldimine)
5,6bzenSal - N,N′-ethylenebis (5,6-benzosalicylaldimine)
1,2prSal = N,N′-1,2-propylenebis(salicylaldimine)
1,3prSal = N,N′-1,3-propylenebis(salicylaldimine)
5Cl1,2prSal = N,N′-1,2-propylenebis(5-chlorsalicylaldimine)
L = o-phenylene(N-salicylaldehyde-N′-5-chlorobenzophenyleneimine)
prp$_2$en = N,N′-ethylenebis(o-hydroxypropiophenylideneimine)
prp$_2$pr = N,N′-1,3-propylenebis(o-hydroxypropiophenyleneimine)

been interpreted in terms of a ferromagnetic or antiferromagnetic interaction, but the ferromagnetic case does not need to be considered. Calculations based on planar copper coupling with iron(III) give an energy separation between the $S = 2$ and $S = 3$ state of ΔE, as given in Table III, and the dominant terms in the expression are large and positive (15). This result predicts that ferromagnetic coupling in such heterobinuclears should therefore be relatively rare in general compared to antiferromagnetic cases. Orbital configurations make this particularly true for the Fe-Cu couple, but the result can be generalized to a number of other systems.

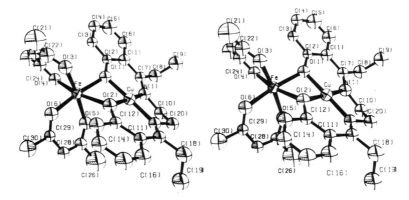

Figure 7. Example of a Cu(TSB)·M(hfa)$_2$ complex.

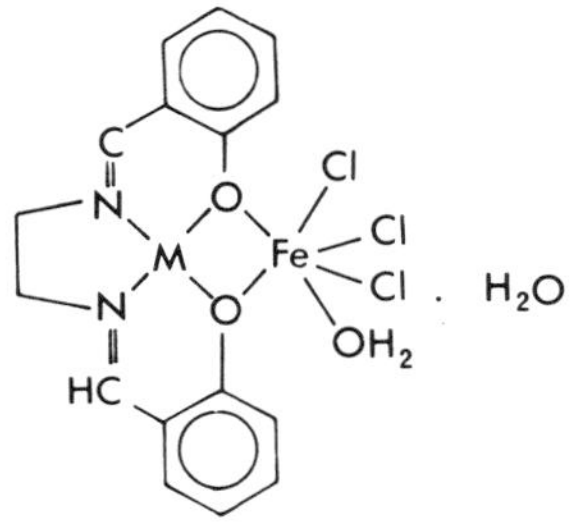

Figure 8. Example of a Cu(II)-Fe(III) heterobinuclear complex [Cu(TSB)·FeCl$_3$(H$_2$O)].

The prospects for heterobinuclear ferromagnets is much better with Cr-Cu and Cu-V couples. Ferromagnetic Cu-V couplings have been reported by Kahn et al (16), although Selbin et al (17) observed either antiferromagnetism or no interaction in Cu-V couples in VO·TSB·Cu complexes, which, however, were not structurally characterized. This discrepancy should be clarified by magnetic studies on structurally characterized complexes.

Bpm Complexes

A different style of heterobinuclear complex (18) [Fe(mac)Bpm·Cu(acac)$_2$]$^{2+}$ was synthesized to model cytochrome c oxidase (19) but it was initially proposed to have the structure shown in Figure 9. Here Bpm was used to model a proposed imidazole bridge in the enzyme, but surprisingly no magnetic coupling was observed between Fe and Cu. When we checked the bridging properties of Bpm in a variety of homobinuclear complexes, we found it to promote antiferromagnetic interactions in each case. Nevertheless, all our experiments either supported or failed to disprove the proposed structure, until we substituted the backside nitrogens of Bpm with CH groups (bpy): the complex formed just as easily, leading us to propose a slightly modified structure of Figure 10 for both the Bpm and bpy complexes, which is in

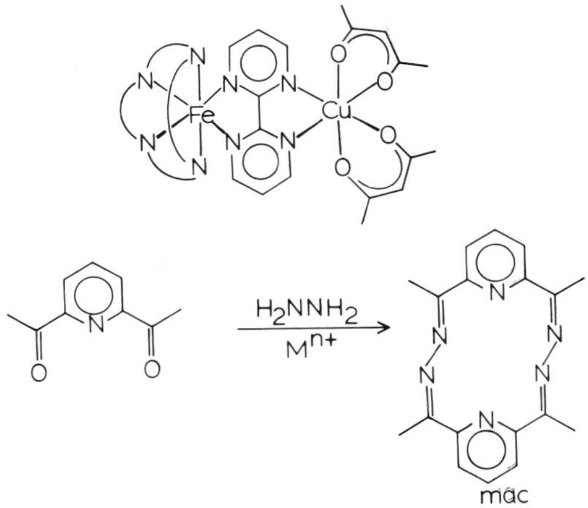

Figure 9. Originally proposed (14) structure for [Fe(mac)BpmCu(acac)$_2$]$^{2+}$. Bpm = bipyrimidine as shown; mac is the macrocyclic ligand shown.

keeping with the absence of antiferromagnetic interactions (20). The earlier electrochemical work on the complex is still valid, but can be interpreted in terms of a mechanism that begins with dissociation of the complex. Key differences from cytochrome oxidase are the absence of magnetic coupling and the fact that the bent mac ligand is no longer a good model for the heme fragment of the enzyme.

Table III

Quintet-Heptet Separation in Fe(III)-Cu(II) Couples

The energy is given by ΔE

$$= E(S=3) - E(S=2)$$

$$= E(S=3) - E_{11}^o + \sum_{2}^{4} \frac{(E_{1i}^o)^2}{(E_{ii}^o - E_{11}^o)}$$

(A positive ΔE signifies antiferromagnetic interaction, $J<0$), where the matrix elements E_{ij} are defined as below for the $S=2$ coupled state.

H	LS1	LS2	LS3	LS4
LS1	E_{11}^o	E_{12}	E_{13}	E_{14}
LS2	E_{21}	E_{22}^o	E_{23}	E_{24}
LS3	E_{31}	E_{32}	E_{33}^o	E_{34}
LS4	E_{41}	E_{42}	E_{43}	E_{44}^o

$$H = \sum h(i) + \sum \frac{2}{r_{ij}}$$

For the Hamiltonian $H = \sum h(i) + \sum \frac{2}{r_{ij}}$, operating on the determinantal wavefunctions

$S=2$
LS1: $|\phi_+^\uparrow \phi_+^\downarrow d_{xy}^\uparrow d_{yz}^\uparrow d_{z^2}^\uparrow|$
LS2: $|\phi_+^\uparrow d_{xy}^\downarrow d_{xy}^\uparrow d_{xz}^\uparrow d_{yz}^\uparrow d_{z^2}^\uparrow|$
LS3: $|\phi_+^\uparrow d_{xy}^\uparrow d_{xz}^\downarrow d_{xz}^\uparrow d_{yz}^\uparrow d_{z^2}^\uparrow|$
LS4: $\phi_+^\uparrow d_{xy}^\uparrow d_{xz}^\uparrow d_{yz}^\downarrow d_{yz}^\uparrow d_{z^2}^\uparrow|$

$S=3$
$|\phi_+^\uparrow d_{xy}^\uparrow d_{xz}^\uparrow d_{yz}^\uparrow d_{z^2}^\uparrow \phi_-^\uparrow|$

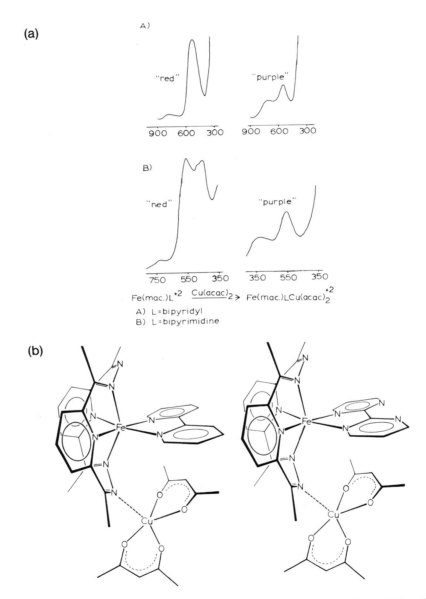

Figure 10. (a) Spectral changes upon adduction of Cu(acac)$_2$ with Fe(mac)bpy^{2+} and Fe(mac)Bpm^{2+}. (b) Plausible structures for [Fe(mac)BpmCu(acac)$_2$]$^{2+}$ and [Fe(mac)bpyCu(acac)$_2$]$^{2+}$.

Imidazole Bridging

Ligands which potentially permit imidazole bridging were frequently found to binucleate in other ways, such as via halogens, or when halogens are made unavailable, via oxygen atoms. As a result, unsymmetrical Schiff base ligands (cbp Im) were designed, including ones with the 4- and 2-aldehydes of imidazole. These ligands are neutral molecules in which the planar coordination geometry readily strips the proton from the imidazole, which otherwise deprotonates with difficulty. The parent complex (Figure 11) has a partial negative charge on the outside nitrogen of the deprotonated imidazole, and the potentially coordinating lone pair pointing away from the sterically restrictive groups of the complex ligand. The approximate planarity of the complex ligand and the fact that with copper, it has the potential Im bridge coplanar with the $d_{x^2-y^2}$ orbital containing the unpaired electron, makes it useful as a magnetic bridge between a variety of paramagnetic metals. In addition, if it cannot produce a suitable model for cytochrome oxidase, due to a probable lack of Im bridging in the enzyme (vide infra), then it can still model other imidazole bridging in a rich diversity of systems. Both these features promote coordination to a further metal atom, thereby opening the way to a wide range of imidazole-bridged complexes. Typical products of this synthesis are the adducts with $M(hfa)_2$ and M(TPP) (Figure 12), all of which are antiferromagnetically coupled in the cases studied to date.

With cbp 4-Im, the parent copper complex is binuclear via weak out-of-plane Cu-O bonds to the phenolic oxygens (Figure 11), further polymerization via the imidazole nitrogen being blocked by a hydrogen-bonded water molecule in the sample used for crystallographic characterization. The $Cu(hfa)_2$ derivative was characterized magnetically ($J = -35cm^{-1}$) and via esr with the observation of a $\Delta M_S = 2$ transition in the triplet state. These features are characteristic of the moderately strong magnetic exchange through the imidazole bridge. Crystallographic characterization shows the retention of the weak binucleating Cu-O bonds between the neighboring tetradentate ligand species (Figure 13). The resulting complex is therefore a centrosymmetric dimer of two $Cu(cbp\ 4-Im)Cu(hfa)_2$ binuclears, i.e. a $[Cu(cbp\ 4-Im)Cu(hfa)_2]_2$ tetranuclear. In each case the coupling through the weak out-of-plane Cu-O bonds is small compared to that of the imidazole.

The Cu(cbp 4-Im) adduct with Co(TPP) was studied because of the ease of establishing the existence of an out-of-plane fifth bond to Co(TPP). At the same time, the cobalt atom has the same occupied orbitals as would an iron atom. The adduct could therefore serve as a starting model for the cytochrome oxidase bridging if this contains an imidazole. The Co(TPP) shows the same spectral changes on adduction of $(Cu\ cbp\ 4-Im)_2$ as it does with N-methyl-Im, indicating formation of a fifth bond to produce the Cu-Im-Co bridge, but the magnetic coupling is relatively weak. This complex eliminates the problems in a Cu-Fe model based on a modified version of the "picket-fence" iron porophyrin which has the proper $d_{x^2-y^2}$ orbital rigorously orthogonal to the porphyrin plane, thereby minimizing the possibility of interaction; in this complex, zero interaction is observed (21). Our Cu-Im-Co structure has the unpaired electron from copper coplanar with the bridging imidazole, to allow maximum magnetic coupling. Failure to observe strong coupling in this optimal geometry suggests that a Cu-Im-porphyrin linkage is not well-suited to provide the strong interactions that are proposed as the quenching mechanism of the esr. The work with the iron analogs (such as Fe(TPP)Cl) is proceeding, but the orbital

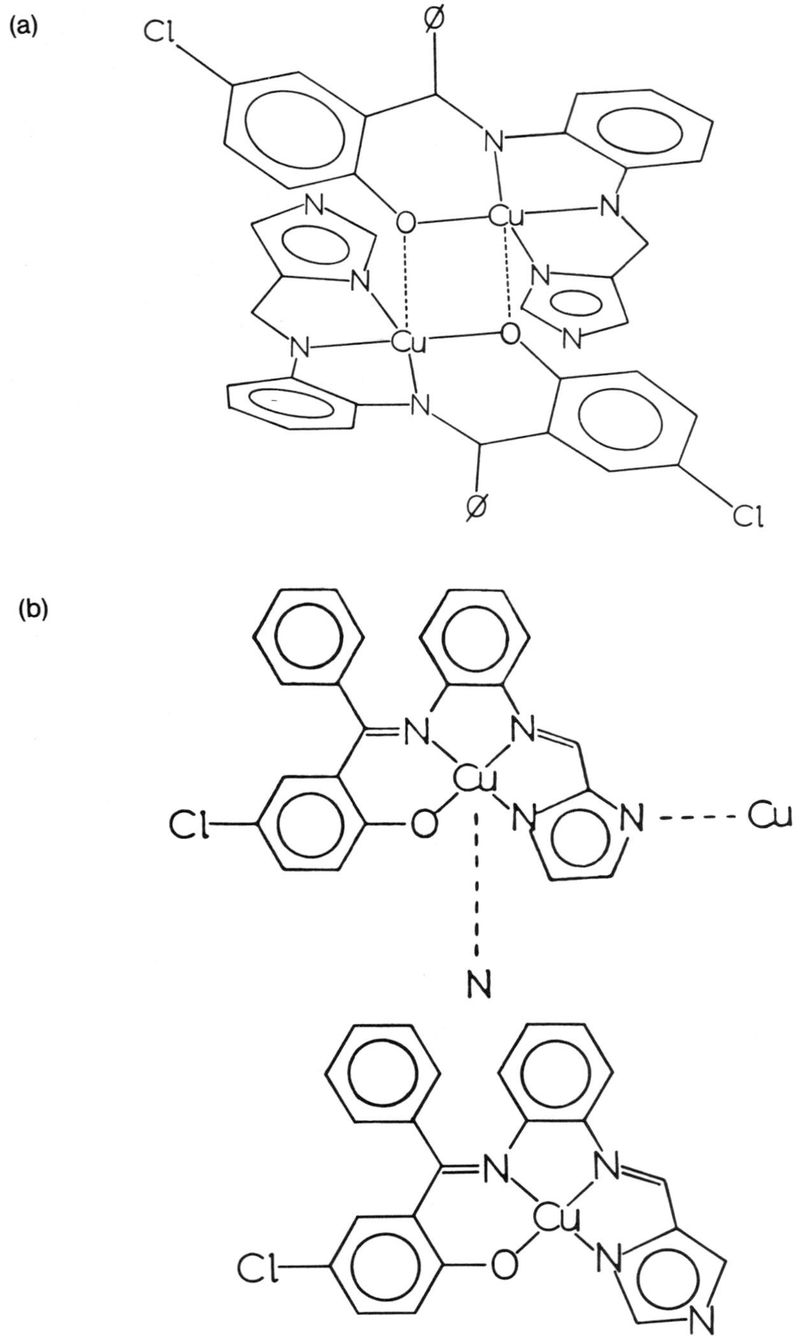

(a)

(b)

Figure 11. (a) The parent complex [Cu(cbp 4-Im)]$_2$ for preparing imidazole bridged heterobinuclear complexes. (b) Proposed polymeric structure of Cu(cbp 2-Im).

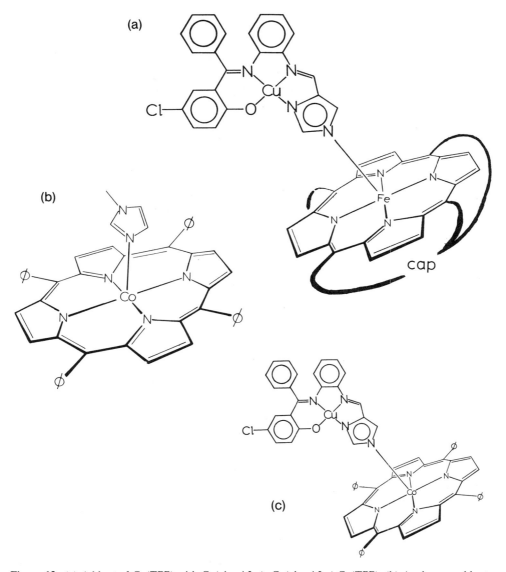

Figure 12. (a) Adduct of Co(TPP) with Cu(cbp 4-Im): Cu(cbp 4-Im)·Co(TPP). (b) Analogous adduct of Co(TPP) with 1-methylimidazole. (c) Adduct of Fe(cap Porph) with Cu(cbp 4-Im): Cu(cbp 4-Im)· Fe(cap Porph).

similarity of the cobalt adduct already studied does not promise a strong Fe-Cu magnetic interaction. Although the Cu Im ·Co(TPP) adduct has not yet been crystallographically characterized, it is presumed to retain the binuclear Cu-O bridge skeleton of complex ligand [Cu(cbp 4-Im)Co(TPP)]$_2$.

The Cu(cbp 2-Im) complex ligand differs only in the shift of the potentially bridging Im nitrogen by one position further from the phenolic oxygen. It is an infinite

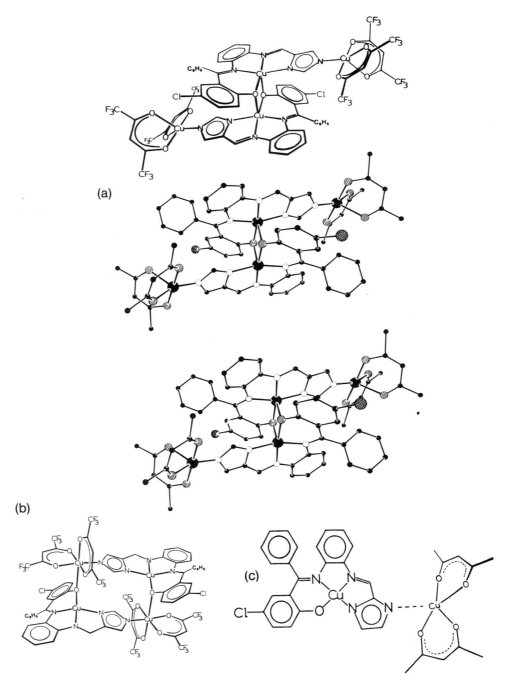

Figure 13. (a) Scale drawing and stereoview of the "normal" [Cu(cbp 4-Im)·Cu(hfa)₂]₂, bridged via the "Schiff base" copper. (b) The other observed isomer of [Cu(cbp 4-Im)·Cu(hfa)₂]₂, bridged via the "hfa" copper. (c) Schematic representation of the Cu(cbp 2-Im) adduct with Cu(hfa)₂.

polymer in the solid state, presumably bridging via the Im nitrogen to the coppers of neighboring complex molecules. Although it appears to be insoluble in all solvents that do not destroy it, it readily dissolves in solutions containing metal ions that can adduct to the Im nitrogen to form $Cu(cbp\ 2\text{-}Im)MX_n$ complexes. The magnetic coupling in $Cu(cbp\ 2\text{-}Im)Cu(hfa)_2$ ($J = -29.8cm^{-1}$) is slightly weaker than in the analog with 4-Im. The 2-Im adducts have not been crystallographically characterized, but the two types of complex ligands are very similar, and there is no reason to exclude a similar Cu-O bridged skeleton in the 2-Im complexes, viz $[Cu(cbp\ 2\text{-}Im)Cu(hfa)_2]_2$.

Cytochrome Oxidase

It appears from our measurements on heterobinuclear complexes that Fe-Im-Cu bridging cannot reproduce the magnetic properties of cytochrome oxidase, while Fe-O-Fe bridging can. Oxygen bridging is therefore considered the most likely. In each of the structurally characterized FeO_2Cu model complexes, the Fe-Cu separation is a little under 3.0 Å. The rigid heme iron group in cytochrome oxidase would not easily accommodate more than a single Fe-O-Cu bridge, in which case, the Fe-Cu distance is expected to open up somewhat. Therefore in the Fe-X-Cu bridge, X is most likely O, while S, Cl and Im are progressively less likely, with a metal-metal separation slightly greater than 3.0Å.

P.I.G.

Iron containing acid phosphatases, such as P.I.G. (progesterone induced glycoprotein) from the allantoic fluid of pregnant pigs, had been postulated to contain one iron atom per molecule (22). However, magnetic measurements indicate the presence of two strongly coupled iron atoms, presumed to be $Fe^{III}\text{-}O\text{-}Fe^{III}$ in the oxidized form and $Fe^{II}\text{-}O\text{-}Fe^{III}$ in the reduced (active) form (23). Replacement of one iron atom with another metal can dramatically change the properties. The Fe-O-Zn form is fully magnetic (Figure 14) and retains most of the phosphatase activity, while Fe-O-Cu is magnetically coupled and retains little enzyme activity. The latter may be considered a kind of non-heme biological cytochrome oxidase model. The ligand field requirements of Cu(II) presumably distorts the iron site sufficiently to minimize the enzyme activity, unlike Zn(II) which has no ligand field requirements.

Unsymmetrical Tetradentate Ligands

Related unsymmetrical TSB ligands with two phenolic oxygens and no Im produce unusual structures such as {Cu(cbp sal)}{Br-Cu(cbp sal)}Mn(H₂O)Br (Figure 5). Like its binuclear analogs with symmetrical TSB Cu(cbp sal) and its analogs produce tetranuclear complexes which are chlorine-bridged dimers of the oxygen-bridged Cu(cbp sal)CuCl₂ binuclears (Figure 15); this bridging is analogous to that in the ferromagnetic $[Cu(BuDP)Cl_2]_2$ (Figure 16). Two of the unsymmetrical Schiff base tetranuclears show unusual magnetic phase changes at very low temperature, which may be an indication of the small rearrangement in the ligand bridge. Instead of

(a)

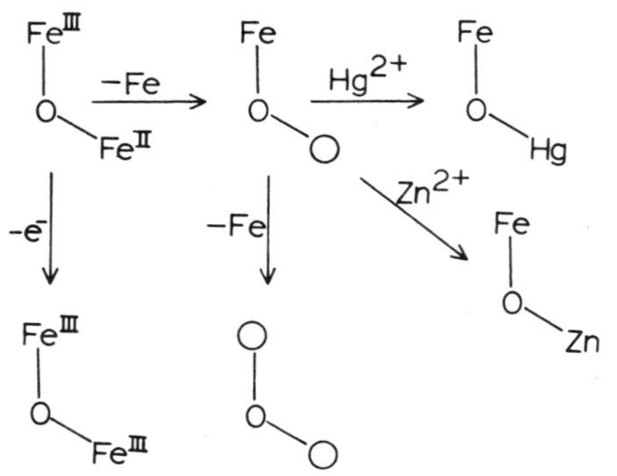

Fe^{III} $\xrightarrow{-Fe}$ Fe $\xrightarrow{Hg^{2+}}$ Fe

$-e^-$ $-Fe$ $\xrightarrow{Zn^{2+}}$ Fe—Zn

Fe^{III}—O—Fe^{III} O   O—O

(b)

$Fe^{III} - O - Fe^{III}$ $\frac{5}{2} - \frac{5}{2} = 0$

$Fe^{III} - O - Fe^{II}$ $\frac{5}{2} - 2 = \frac{1}{2}$

$Fe^{III} - O - Hg^{II}$ $\frac{5}{2} - 0 = \frac{5}{2}$

$Fe^{III} - O - Zn^{II}$ $\frac{5}{2} - 0 = \frac{5}{2}$

$Fe^{III} - O - Cu^{II}$ $\frac{5}{2} - \frac{1}{2} = 2$

Figure 14. (a) Schematic representation of metal replacement and (b) magnetic coupling in P.I.G.

forming a simple binuclear complex (25) with copper nitrate as is known in two structurally characterized examples (Figure 17) Cu(cbp sal) produces an infinite polymer (Figure 18) of binuclears (B) linked via solvent molecules to [Cu(cpb sal)]$_2$ dimers (D$_2$), which are not found in two structurally characterized solid state forms of the parent Cu(cbp sal) complex (26). The magnetic properties of this complex are shown in Figure 19.

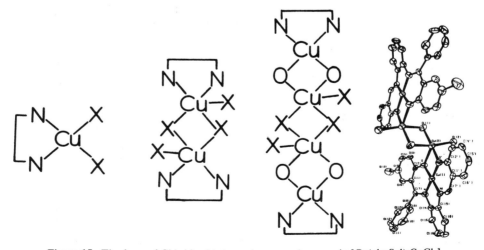

Figure 15. The form of Cl-bridged tetranuclear complexes, as in [Cu(cbpSal)·CuCl$_2$]$_2$.

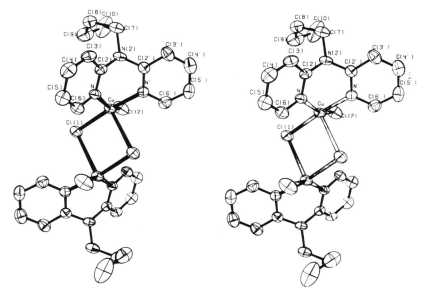

Figure 16. [Cu(BuDP)Cl$_2$]$_2$, a ferromagnetic Cl-bridged binuclear complex; BuDP = N-n-butyldipyridyl-amine.

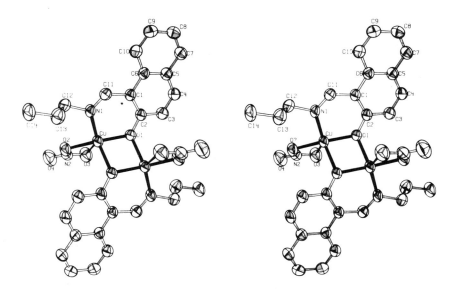

Figure 17. Stereoview of the binuclear complex [Cu(n-PropSal)(NO$_3$)]$_2$.

Pentadentate Complexes

We and many other workers have used a variety of ligands to distort copper

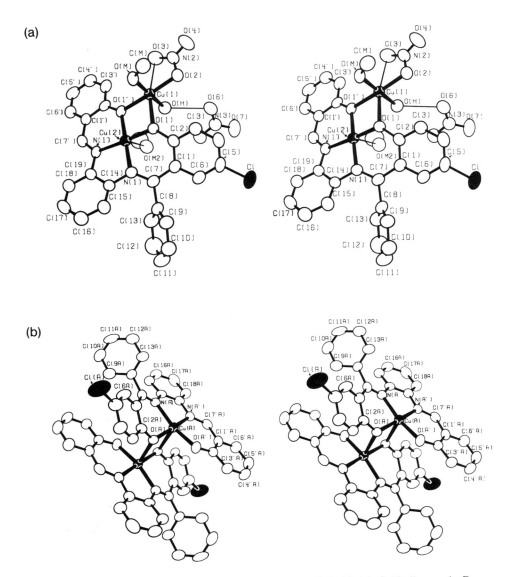

Figure 18. (a) Binuclear units Cu(cbpSal)Cu(NO$_3$) units B (b) [Cu(cbpSal)]$_2$ dimer units D$_2$.

geometries to simulate geometries in copper-containing biomolecules (27). For example, in a structure between planar and tetrahedral, the distortion from planarity towards tetrahedral destabilizes copper(II) and the distortion from tetrahedral towards planar destabilizes copper(I), to bring the free energies of both oxidation states close to the activation barrier between them, by facilitating Cu(I)/Cu(II) electron kinetics. One of our early strategies included complexes with a weak fifth donor atom built into the ligand as in Cu(cbpS) (28) (Figure 20). These pentadentate

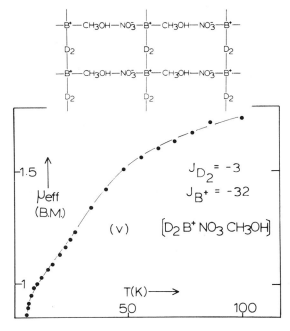

Figure 19. Magnetic properties of B·D$_2$ polymer.

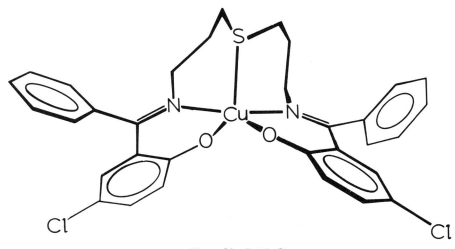

Figure 20. Cu(cbpS).

ligands can also produce unusual tetrameric structures such as that in Figure 21 which contains both phenoxide and alkyl bridges between coppers as well as two adjacent Cu$_3$O bridges. The two Cu$_3$O units are equivalent to two Cu-O-Cu bridges linked to each other by external Cu-O bonds.

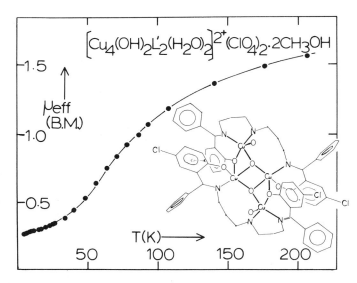

Figure 21. Tetramer structure and magnetic properties of complex from pentadentate ligand.

Complexes with hydroxyalkyl substituted ligands of the type in Figure 22 can be monomeric, approximately planar, neutral copper(II) complexes, or with the aid of an additional ligand, X^-, can be binuclears containing alkanolic oxygen. A typical Cu-Cu separation is 3.6A, which closely matches that proposed for hemocyanin from EXAFS data. Despite the identical nature of the two coordination environments offered by the binucleating ligand, the copper sites are invariably dissimilar when X is a carboxylate, due to solvent coordination to one of the two coppers. The coordination site left vacant by the absence of a solvent molecule in the X = benzoate complex, permits an out-of-plane dimerizing Cu-O bridging between the binuclear units to form the tetranuclear complex in Figure 24. Somewhat related to this structure is the tetranuclear shown in Figure 25, which is the result of a successfully designed tetranuclear synthesis: complexes with bidentate ligands form salicylaldehyde derivatives and propanolamine are known to be binuclear, (CuPr-OSal)$_2$, while copper-bis(salicylidine) complexes, Cu(sal)$_2$, form binuclears with Cu(hfa)$_2$. Therefore substitution of the Cu(sal)$_2$ complexes in the latter reaction with the already binuclear Cu(PrOsal)$_2$ species forms a Cu(hfa)$_2$ derivative which is tetranuclear. The complex is made neutral by the inclusion of an ethoxide bridging ligand.

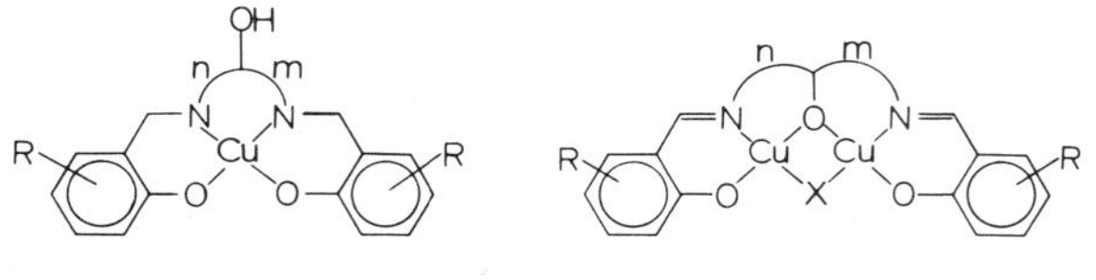

Figure 22. Monomeric and binuclear complexes of hydroxydiaminesalicylidenes.

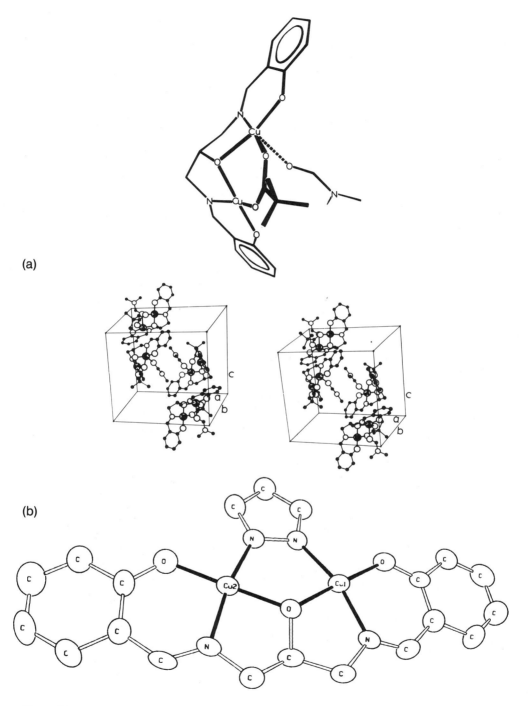

Figure 23. (a) Scale drawing and stereoview of the "bent" binuclear [Cu₂(PrOSal₂)t-BuCOO]DMF. (b) Pyrazole analog.

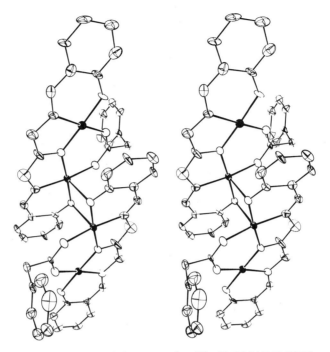

Figure 24. Stereoview of the tetranuclear $[Cu_2(PrOSal_2)C_6H_5COO]_2$.

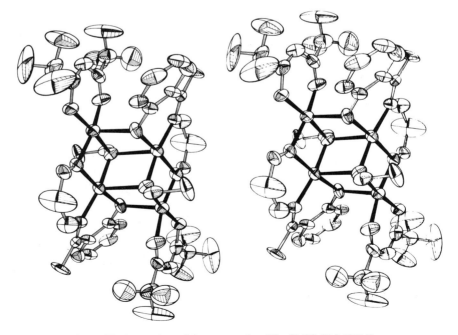

Figure 25. Stereoview of the tetranuclear $[Cu_2(PrOSal)hfa(OEt)]_2$.

$Cu_2(Ligand)X$ Complexes

The geometry around the individual copper atoms is most readily varied by modifying the length of the alkyl chain, but the series of complexes required to quantify this structural control has not been crystallographically characterized. The angle between the principal planes of the two coppers is most easily affected by steric constraints at the ligand X and the effect of changing the interplanar angle has been examined. Any Cu-O-Cu bridging raises the possibility of coupling so strong (29) as to make the complexes essentially diamagnetic, which would make comparison between slightly different compounds difficult. The case where X is a carboxylate is useful because it prevents the coupling from being too strong to enable accurate magnetic measurements. When X is dichloroacetate, the angle is $7°$ and the coupling relatively strong ($J = -50$ cm^{-1}), while the complex with X = tBu·COO$^-$ (Figure 23), has the interplanar angle $\theta = 60°$ and the coupling J is negligible. Further studies on these complexes and their thiol analogs, Cu-S-Cu, are under way.

Acknowledgements

The assistance of many coworkers and support under NSF grants CHE83-00516 and CHE83-11449 is gratefully acknowledged.

References and Footnotes

1. E. Sinn and C. M. Harris, *Coord. Chem. Rev. 4*, 391 (1969) and references cited.
2. E. Sinn, *Coord. Chem. Rev. 5*, 313 (1970) and references cited.
3. D. J. Hodgson, *Progr. Inorg. Chem. 19*, 173 (1975) and references cited.
4. R.J. Butcher and E. Sinn, *Inorg. Chem. 15*, 1604 (1976) and references cited.
5. B. Bleaney and K. D. Bowers, *Proc. Roy. Soc. 214*, 451 (1952).
6. C. M. Harris, H. R. H. Patil and E. Sinn, *Inorg. Chem. 6*, 1102 (1967).
7. C. J. O'Connor, D. P. Freyberg and E. Sinn, *Inorg. Chem. 18*, 1077 (1979); G. A. Brewer and E. Sinn, unpublished work.
8. S. J. Gruber, C. M. Harris and E. Sinn, *J. Chem. Phys. 49*, 2183 (1968); *J. Inorg. Nucl. Chem. 30*, 2723 (1968).
9. J. S. Richardson, K.A. Thomas, B. H. Rubin and D. C. Richardson, *Proc. Natl Acad. Sci. U.S.A., 72*, 1349 (1975).
10. K. M. Beem, D. C. Richardson, R. B. Rajagopalan, *Biochem. 16*, 1930 (1977); J. A. Fee and R.G. Briggs, *Biophys. Acta, 400*, 435 (1975).
11. A. Disideri, M. Cerdonio, F. Mogno, S. Vitale, L. Calabrese, D. Cocco and G. Rotilio, *FEBS Lett., 89*, 83 (1978).
12. J. M. Brown, L. Powers, B. Kincaid, J. A. Larrabee and T. G. Spiro, *J. Am. Chem. Soc. 102*, 4210 (1980); G.L. Woolery, L. Powers, M. Winkler, E.I. Solomon and T. G. Spiro, *J. Am. Chem. Soc. 106*, 86 (1984).
13. S. Kokot, C. M. Harris and E. Sinn, *Australian J. Chem. 25*, 45 (1972).
14. L. Powers, B. Chance, Y. Ching and P. Angioliollo, *J. Biophys. 34*, 465 (1981).
15. G. A. Brewer and E. Sinn, paper presented at A. C. S. Central/Great Lakes Regional Meeting, Dayton, OH, May 20-22 1981 (INOR 177); paper presented at A.C.S. 182nd National Meeting, New York, August 23-28 1981 (INOR 297).
16. O. Kahn, P. Tola, J. Galy and H. Coudanne, *J. Am. Chem. Soc. 100*, 3933 (1978); M. Julve, M. Verdaguer, M. Charlot and O. Kahn, *Inorg. Chim. Acta 82*, 5 (1984).

17. J. Selbin and L. Ganguly, *Inorg. Nucl. Chem. Lett. 8,* 815 (1969).
18. R.H. Petty, B.R. Welsh, L.J. Wilson, L.A. Bottomley and K.M. Kaddish, *J. Am. Chem. Soc. 102,* 611 (1980).
19. G. Palmer, G.T. Babcock and L.E. Vickery, *Proc. Nat. Acad. Sci. USA 23,* 2206 (1976).
20. G. A. Brewer and E. Sinn, *Inorg. Chem. 23,* 2532 (1984).
21. M. J. Gunter, L. N. Mander, G. M. McLaughlin, K. S. Murray, K. J. Berry, P. E. Clark and D. A. Buckingham, *J. Am. Chem. Soc. 102,* 1470 (1980).
22. B. C. Antanaitis and P. Aisen, *J. Biol. Chem. 257,* 1885, 5330 (1982); B.C. Antanaitis, T. Stekas and P. Aisen, *J. Biol. Chem. 257,* 3766 (1982).
23. E. Sinn, C. J. O'Connor, J. deJersey and B. Zerner, *Inorg. Chim. Acta L13,* 78 (1983); G.M. Mockler, C.J. O'Connor, J. deJersey, B. Zerner and E. Sinn, *J. Am. Chem. Soc. 105,* 1891 (1983).
24. E. Sinn, G. M. Mockler, G. A. Brewer, J. deJersey and B. Zerner, paper presented at A.C.S. 185th National Meeting, Seattle, March 20-25 1983 (INOR 60); E. Sinn, C.J. O'Connor, J. deJersey, G.M. Mockler and B. Zerner, paper presented at 29th I.U.P.A.C. Congress, Cologne FDR, June 5-10 1983.
25. E. Sinn, *Inorg. Chem. 15,* 366 (1976).
26. R.J. Butcher, C.J. O'Connor, G.M. Mockler and E. Sinn, paper presented at A.C.S. 179th National Meeting, Houston, March 24-28 1980 (INOR 100).
27. A.W. Addison and E. Sinn, *Inorg. Chem. 22,* 1225 (1983); A. W. Addison, T.N. Rao and E. Sinn, *Inorg. Chem. 23,* 1957 (1984); C.E. Baxter, O.R. Rodig, R.K. Schlatzer and E. Sinn, *Inorg. Chem. 18,* 1918 (1979); E. M. Gouge, J.F. Geldard and E. Sinn, *Inorg. Chem. 19,* 3356 (1980); M.S. Haddad, S.R. Wilson, K.O. Hodgson and D.N. Hendrickson, *J. Am. Chem. Soc. 103,* 384 (1981).
28. D. P. Freyberg, G. M. Mockler and E. Sinn, *Inorg. Chem. 16,* 1660 (1977).
29. R. J. Butcher, C. J. O'Connor and E. Sinn, *Inorg. Chem. 18,* 1913 (1979); *Inorg. Chem. 20,* 537 (1981).

Biological & Inorganic Copper Chemistry,
ISBN 0-940030-11-X, Eds., K. D. Karlin & J. Zubieta, Adenine Press, ©Adenine Press, 1985

Synthesis, Redox and Structural Properties of Copper Complexes with Tridentate Ligands

J. M. Latour[a], G. A. Leonard[b], D. Limosin[a], D. C. Povey[b] and S. S. Tandon[a]

a) Laboratoires de Chimie, Département de Recherche Fondamentale,
Centre d'Etudes Nucléaires de Grenoble, 85 X, F.38041
GRENOBLE CEDEX, FRANCE
b) Department of Chemistry, University of Surrey,
GUILDFORD GU2 5XH, UK

Abstract

A series of copper complexes with tridentate ligands has been synthesized and their structural, spectroscopic and redox properties investigated in the hope of getting a deeper insight into the active site of monocopper enzymes. The structure of two complexes has been solved by X-ray diffraction techniques and shows that they possess a square planar geometry. A tetragonal geometry is retained in solution although anionic ligands are replaced by solvent molecules. Disproportionation of the cuprous complexes is observed for most mononuclear species. On the other hand, upon electrochemical reduction multinuclear complexes give rise to mixed valence $Cu^{II}Cu^{I}$ compounds. These properties are compared to the behavior of the enzyme galactose oxidase.

Introduction

Copper complexes of ligands formed from salicylaldehyde and N-substituted salicylaldehyde have been widely studied over the past three decades (1,2). However, considerably less attention has been devoted to copper complexes of tridentate Schiff-bases, especially those involving a diamine in addition to the salicyl moiety. This is rather surprising since copper complexes of such ligands can be envisaged as valuable models for the so-called type II copper found in galactose oxidase (3) or dopamine hydroxylase (4) and the mononuclear copper site of metapohemocyanin (5).

Copper complexes of ligands formed from salicylaldehyde and N-substituted ethylenediamines were first reported by Sacconi and Bertini (6). More recently, Muto (7) and Elias (8) have extended these studies. On the other hand, ligands involving only imine nitrogens to more closely mimic histidine coordination have been developed only in the past few years by Nakahara (9) and Walker (10) who used imidazole, and Coleman (11) who used pyridine as nitrogeneous base.

In order to get a deeper insight into the properties of biological monocopper sites, we started investigating systematically copper complexes of the ligands depicted in figure 1. These ligands were chosen for their ability to provide the metal with a N_2O environment as found in the enzymes and also because their easy synthesis allows structural and electronic properties to be varied almost at will. In this paper, we describe the synthesis and spectroscopic, redox and structural properties of several copper(II) complexes of these ligands and emphasize some striking features that evolved from these studies.

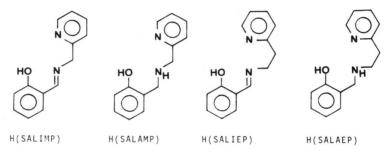

H(SALIMP)   H(SALAMP)   H(SALIEP)   H(SALAEP)

Figure 1. Ligands used in this work.

Materials and Methods

Instrumentation

UV-visible and IR spectra were recorded with Beckman Acta VI and Beckman IR 4250 spectrophotometers, respectively. NMR and ESR spectra were obtained with Varian EM390 and Varian E9 instruments. Conductance measurements were performed with a Metrohm E518 conductometer. Magnetic susceptibilities were determined through the use of an SHE Corp. variable temperature superconducting magnetometer at a field of 5 kG.

The X-ray data was collected on an Enraf Nonius CAD4 single crystal diffractometer using graphite monochromated MoKα radiation.

Electrochemical studies have been done in dimethylformamide solutions 10^{-1} M in tetrabutylammonium tetrafluoroborate using a conventional three electrode cell with a saturated calomel reference electrode and a platinum working electrode. Electrochemical apparatus consisted in a PAR 173 potentiostat/galvanostat driven by a PAR 175 Universal Programmer, a PAR 179 coulometer and a Sefram TGM 164 XY recorder.

Syntheses

Chemicals and solvents were of reagent grade quality and have been used as received, except dimethylformamide for electrochemistry which was vacuum distilled and stored over 4 Å molecular sieves. Tetrabutylammonium tetrafluoroborate was prepared according to a published procedure (12).

The cupric complexes are prepared upon reaction of the ligand with one equivalent of the chosen copper salt in ethanol. Upon concentration of the solution, the complex precipitates out. It is filtered, thoroughly washed and dried in vacuum at 60°C for 24 hours. Satisfactory elemental analyses have been obtained for all compounds and IR spectra were consistent with the proposed formulation.

The Schiff-base ligands H(SALIMP) and H(SALIEP) are obtained upon reaction of salicylaldehyde and the corresponding aminoalkylpyridine in refluxing absolute ethanol for 15 mn. They must be used immediately to avoid noticeable degradation to occur. Reduction of the imine linkage is effected with sodium borohydride in 50:50 ethanol-water, and subsequent hydrolysis with hydrochloric acid. This procedure furnished the reduced ligands H(SALAMP) and H(SALAEP) quantitatively. All ligands have been characterized through NMR spectroscopy.

Results and Discussion

Syntheses of the complexes

Table I summarizes spectroscopic and conductance data of the complexes prepared in this study, together with their room temperature magnetic moment. Examination of this table reveals two unexpected features. Firstly, upon reaction of the reduced ligands with cupric chloride, the ligand is not deprotonated and the complex retains two chloride counter anions. This behavior can be explained if one considers that in these ligands ortho-substitution by an electron donating substituent decreases the acidity of the phenolic proton. Thus rose the possibility of copper coordination by a phenol oxygen, a situation which had not been observed so far. In order to probe it, we have determined the structure of $Cu[H(SALAMP)]Cl_2*C_2H_5OH$ by X-ray diffraction (see below).

Secondly, it appears that with H(SALIMP) chloride and acetate copper complexes are mononuclear while with H(SALIEP), which has one additional carbon in the chain, dinuclear and trinuclear complexes are formed. The structures of the latter compounds have not been determined yet, but their redox and magnetic properties are fully consistent with the assumed multinuclear formulations. In agreement with Coleman's observation (11), $[Cu(SALIEP)Cl]_2$ exhibits a reduced room temperature magnetic moment (Table I). Analysis of the temperature dependence of its magnetic properties indicates that they can be roughly accounted for on the basis of a dimer formulation with a coupling constant 2J of about -350 cm^{-1}. On the other hand, magnetism of the acetate derivative $Cu_3(SALIEP)_2(AcO)_4$ can be interpreted by assuming that it is a linear trinuclear complex. The "distal" coupling is negligible while the "proximal" one amounts to $J = -32$ cm^{-1} from simulation of the data.

Table I

Analytical data

	Λ^a	$\lambda_{dd}{}^e$	$\lambda_{CT}{}^e$	$g_{\parallel}$	$g_{\perp}$	$A_{\parallel}$	μ^g	$-Ep_c{}^i$
Cu(SALIMP)(NO₃)	80[b]	635 (140)	378 (5250)	2.243	2.059	180	1.86	0.56
Cu(SALIMP)Cl*1/2H₂O	15[c]	650 (200)	380 (5750)	2.272	2.057	180	1.88	0.27
Cu(SALIMP)(AcO)*1/2H₂O	29[b]	635 (130)	373 (4475)	f			1.91	0.95
Cu(SALIEP)(NO₃)	77[c]	647 (101)	372 (4805)	2.285	2.086	170	1.89	0.36
[Cu(SALIEP)Cl]₂	24[c,d]	~650	375 (~9600)	2.260	2.062	150	2.43 0.41[h]	0.44 1.25
Cu₃(SALIEP)₂(AcO)₄	13[c]	670 (379)	375 (11650)	2.252	2.066	175	3.14 1.86[h]	0.50 0.92
Cu(SALAMP)(AcO)*3H₂O	37[b]	648 (137)	398 (753)	2.270	2.068	170	2.03	0.73
Cu(SALAEP)(NO₃)	68[c]	652 (153)	407 (1247)	2.259	2.063	173		0.38
Cu(SALAEP)(AcO)*2H₂O	36[b]	663 (167)	402 (1071)	2.295	2.085	165		0.70
Cu[H(SALAMP)]Cl₂*C₂H₅OH	73[b] 22[c]	730 (52)	362 (840)	2.433	2.091	145	1.87	0.08
Cu[H(SALAEP)]Cl₂*3/2H₂O	104[b]	660 (70)	375 (840)	2.299	2.093	200		
Cu(SALIEP)₂	51[c]	600 (98)	365 (9300)	2.241	2.064	170	1.94	1.06

a: in $\mu s \cdot cm^{-1}$ for a 10^{-3} M solution; b: in methanol; c: in dimethylformamide; d: for a 5.10^{-4} M solution; e: in the solvent indicated for conductance measurements; f: unresolved spectrum; g: in Bohr magnetons at 300 K; h: at 6 K; i: in demethylformamide 10^{-1} M in $N(C_4H_9)_4(BF_4)$; potentials in V_{sce} for the reduction of Cu^{II} to Cu^I.

Structural properties

Figure 2 presents a view of the coordination sphere of Cu(SALIMP)(NO₃) and summarizes important bond lengths and angles around the copper atom. Relevant crystallographic data are collected in table II. The compound possesses a pseudo square-planar geometry with the ligand holding three coordination positions. The fourth coordination site is occupied by the nitrate ion. In methanol solution however, the complex behaves as a 1:1 electrolyte indicating that the nitrate ion is not bound anymore. The copper coordination sphere is thus probably completed by one or possibly two solvent molecules.

The structure of Cu[H(SALAMP)]Cl₂*C₂H₅OH is depicted in figure 3 and corresponding crystallographic data are gathered in table II. The copper coordination sphere is constituted by two nitrogen atoms from the ligand and two chloride

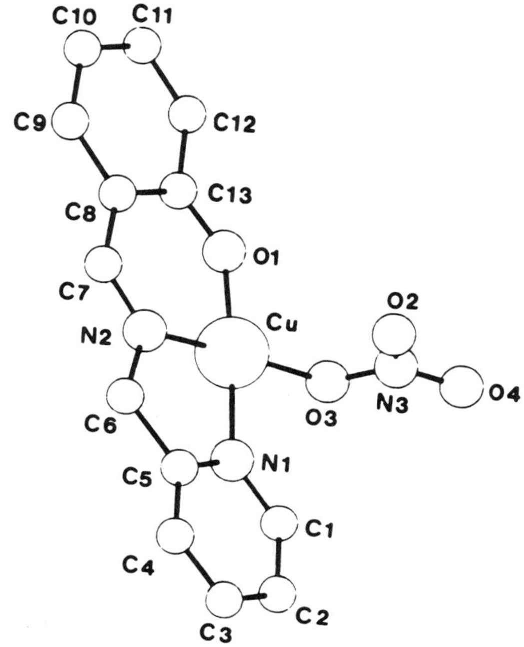

Figure 2. View of the coordination geometry of Cu(SALIMP)(NO$_3$). Bond lengths (A): CuO$_1$: 1.875(4); CuN$_1$: 1.985(4); CuN$_2$: 1.936(4); CuO$_3$: 2.012(4). Bond angles($°$): O$_1$CuN$_2$: 94.1(2); N$_1$CuN$_2$: 83.5(2); N$_1$CuO$_3$: 92.4(2); O$_1$CuO$_3$: 90.1(2); O$_1$CuN$_1$: 176.3(2); O$_3$CuN$_2$: 174.7(2).

assembled in a pseudo square-planar array. Our main interest in this structure was concerned with the possibility of the phenol oxygen coordination. Although phenol

Table II
Crystallographic data

	Cu(SALIMP)NO$_3$	Cu[H(SALAMP)]Cl$_2$*C$_2$H$_5$OH
Molecular formula	C$_{13}$H$_{11}$N$_3$O$_4$Cu	C$_{13}$H$_{13}$N$_2$OCl$_2$Cu·C$_2$H$_5$OH
Crystal system	monoclinic	monoclinic
Space group	P$_n$	P2$_{1/c}$
Cell constants a(A)	7.769(1)	9.959(1)
b(A)	5.958(1)	9.924(1)
c(A)	14.403(2)	18.197(2)
β($°$)	101.99(2)	103.20(2)
V$_c$(A^3)	652(1)	1751(1)
Formula units/unit cell	2	4
Calculated density (g·cm^{-3})	1.72	1.49
Linear absorption coefficient (cm^{-1})	17.1	15.6
Number of reflexions collected	1144	3075
Reflexions with F > 5 (F)	1099	684
R	0.023	0.050

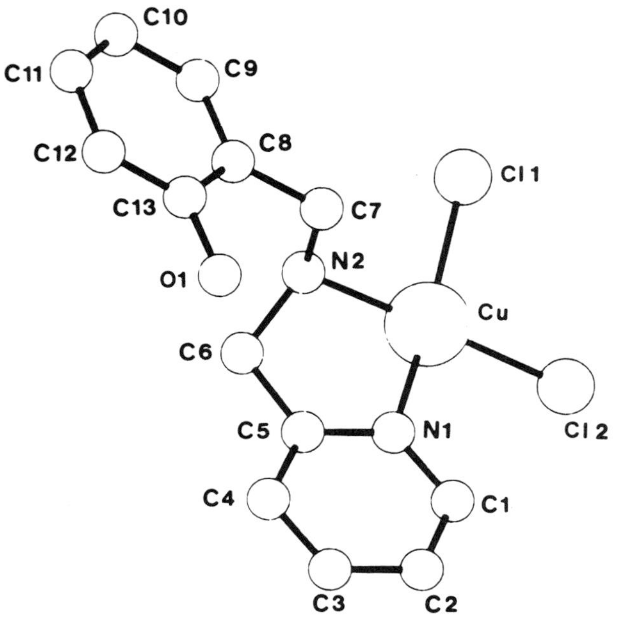

Figure 3. View of the coordination geometry of Cu[H(SALAMP)]Cl$_2$*C$_2$H$_5$OH. Bond lengths (A): CuN$_1$: 2.001(3); CuN$_2$: 2.030(3); CuCl$_1$: 2.287(1); CuCl$_2$: 2.260(1). Bond angles ($^\circ$): N$_1$CuN$_2$: 81.4(1); N$_1$CuCl$_2$: 96.2(1); N$_2$CuCl$_1$: 89.2(1); Cl$_1$CuCl$_2$: 93.06(4); N$_1$CuCl$_1$: 164.4(1); N$_2$CuCl$_2$: 177.5(1).

to copper coordination has never been observed, one might have expected it to occur in the present case where chelate effect would provide an additional stabilization. X-ray data undoubtedly show that the phenol oxygen is not coordinated even as an apical fifth ligand. This finding emphasizes the very poor coordination ability of phenol oxygen.

Spectroscopic properties

Examination of table I that lists the products spectroscopic properties, shows that all compounds possess in solution a tetragonal symmetry close probably to square pyramidal (13), as judged from ESR measurements. UV-visible spectra on the other hand exhibit two transitions: one of low intensity at about 650 nm and a more intense one near 380 nm. The first one clearly corresponds to the d-d transitions of the cupric ion. It is not very sensitive to ligand changes although it seems that in complexes of aminoethylpyridine derived ligands this transition occurs at slightly lower energy when compared to complexes of aminomethylpyridine derived ligands.

The most intense absorption deserves more comment. Both its location and its intensity suggest that it is a charge transfer transition. According to Bosnich (14) it can be attributed to a charge transfer from the filled d orbitals of copper(II) to antibonding (π*) orbitals of the phenolic residue. From table I it can be seen that complexes of Schiff-base ligands differ from complexes of the reduced ligands both in the location and the intensity of this band. In the former compounds, the band is in the range 370-380 nm with an extinction coefficient of 5-6 10^3 cm·mole^{-1}. Closely similar values are noted by Elias (8) for complexes of dimethylaminoethyl-salicylaldimine, thus proving that this band is associated with the copper-salicyl-aldimine moiety. An analogous absorption is present in copper complexes of the reduced ligands, but it is red-shifted by about 20 nm and its intensity amounts to only about 10^3 cm·mole^{-1}. So both the energy and the intensity of the charge transfer transition are strongly influenced by substitution of the phenol residue.

Redox properties

Mononuclear complexes of the tridentate ligands behave as described in detail for Cu(SALIEP)(NO$_3$). They have been studied extensively in dimethylformamide solution, but changing the solvent to dimethylsulfoxide or acetonitrile does not change the electrochemical processes although some minor changes are observed in the peak potentials.

In cyclic voltammetry Cu(SALIEP)NO$_3$) presents a one electron reduction at Ep$_c$ $= -0.36$ V$_{sce}$ which is at best quasi-reversible. But exhaustive electrolysis at -0.6 V$_{sce}$ requires about 1.5 electron·mole^{-1} and is accompanied by copper deposition. These findings seem to indicate that the one electron reduction of [Cu^{II}(SALIEP)]$^+$ to Cu^I(SALIEP) is followed by disproportionation of the latter to copper metal and [Cu^{II}(SALIEP)]$^+$. But such a process would give a coulometric analysis of 2 electrons·mole^{-1} instead of 1.5 electron·mole^{-1} as observed. Spectroscopic (ESR and UV-visible) and electrochemical analyses of the electrolyzed solution show that it contains Cu^{II}(SALIEP)$_2$. Formation of the latter compound can be accounted for by assuming that SALIEP$^-$ formed in the disproportionation combines with [Cu^{II}(SALIEP)]$^+$. So, part of the starting compound is trapped as Cu(SALIEP)$_2$ which gives rise to a lower coulometric result since the bis-ligand complex is reduced only at Ep$_c$ $= -1.06$ V$_{sce}$. Its reduction is also followed by disproportionation. The overall mechanism is depicted in Scheme I.

Scheme I: (L$^-$ = SALIEP$^-$)
$$[Cu^{II}L]^+ + e^- \Rightarrow Cu^I L$$
$$2Cu^I L \Rightarrow [Cu^{II}L]^+ + L^- + Cu^\circ$$
$$[Cu^{II}L]^+ + L^- \Rightarrow Cu^{II}L_2$$
$$Cu^{II}L_2 + e^- \Rightarrow [Cu^I L_2]^-$$
$$2[Cu^I L_2]^- \Rightarrow Cu^{II}L_2 + 2L^- + Cu^\circ$$

[Cu(SALIEP)Cl]$_2$ exhibits a quite different behavior since it presents two reduction peaks at Ep$_c^1$ $= -0.41$ V$_{sce}$ and Ep$_c^2$ $= -1.25$ V$_{sce}$. The first process is chemically reversible but electrochemically irreversible (Ep$_a$ $= 0.50$ V$_{sce}$). Electrolysis at -0.5 V$_{sce}$ consumes 0.5 electron·mole^{-1}, so one electron per copper, and accordingly produces a mixed-valence complex [Cu^{I}Cu^{II}(SALIEP)$_2$Cl$_2$]$^-$. Formation of this complex is accompanied by an important structural change as shown by the large difference in peak potentials ΔEp = 0.9 V for the Cu^I/Cu^{II} couple. The mixed-valence compound has an axial ESR spectrum ($g_\parallel$ = 2.246 $A_\parallel$ = 178 G, $g_\perp$ = 2.057) which shows small deviations from the one of the starting bis-copper(II) complex (Table I). This difference can be attributed to a distortion of the cupric site induced by the neighbouring cuprous ion. The resulting spectrum still presents four lines even at room temperature which indicates that the odd electron is localized on only one copper site and accordingly the compound is a class I mixed valence species (15). The second reduction process is followed by disproportionation as in the preceding case.

The redox properties of $Cu_3(SALIEP)_2(AcO)_4$ resemble those of the chloro dimer. Its first reduction is chemically reversible but electrochemically irreversible (Ep_c^1 = −0.50 V_{sce}, Ep_a^1 = ~0.6 V_{sce}) and electrolysis at −0.45 V_{sce} consumes about one electron per copper. In this case, also a class I mixed valence compound is formed $[Cu^ICu^{II}_2(SALIEP)_2(AcO)_4]^-$. Again the second reduction leads to the breaking of the complex, copper deposition and $Cu(SALIEP)_2$ formation.

Redox properties of copper salicylaldimine complexes of the type $Cu(SAL-R)_2$ (where $SAL-R$ is the condensation product of salicylaldehyde with an amine RNH_2) have been studied by Paterson and Holm (16). These authors observed one electron reversible processes for all compounds in the range −0.6 to −0.9 V_{sce} depending on R. The products studied in this work depart from this simple behavior since the cuprous species are formed at markedly higher potentials and are not stable toward disproportionation. The reason for this discrepancy lies undoubtedly in the difference in copper ligation. In the bis-salicylaldimine complexes, the copper in bound to two nitrogens and two phenoxide oxygens. Due to charge effects (or the hard nature of anionic oxygens) such an environment stabilized Cu^{II} *vs* Cu^I, as reflected by the low potential of the Cu^I/Cu^{II} couple. Ligands used in our work are only monoanionic and the corresonding cuprous species are neutral, accordingly formation of the latter occurs at less negative potentials. The difference in reversibility could be attributed to the different ligands structures. In $Cu(SAL-R)_2$ the two ligands are independent from each other and can accommodate tetragonal as well as tetrahedral geometries around copper. Such an easy geometrical change is not possible for a tridentate ligand and the ligand deformation surely imposes a barrier and is responsible for the electrochemical irreversibility of the reduction process.

Since the electron transfers involved in the reduction of the present complexes are not reversible, the associated potentials are not, strictly speaking, thermodynamically meaningful. However, the quasi-reversibility observed at high sweep rates (60 V·mn^{-1}) and the uniqueness of the electrochemical process allow valuable comparisons to be made. Examination of the nitrates reduction potentials (Table I) shows that the amino *vs* imino nature of the inner nitrogen has little influence if any, while the chain length (two vs three carbon atoms) between the two nitrogens is decisive in fixing the redox potential of the cupric ion. A longer chain allows a better accommodation of the tetrahedral structure required by the cuprous ion. Such a preeminence of steric factors has been previously noted (16).

Another interesting finding is the unstability of most cuprous species obtained in this work toward disproportionation. Although disproportionation of cuprous compounds is very often observed, in the present case it is rather surprising for it does not occur for simple copper bis-salicylaldiminates (16) and moreover a bis(phenoxocopper(I)) complex has been recently characterized (17). In the latter compound, the cuprous ions possess tetrahedral symmetry, a situation which is probably attained in the bis-salicylaldiminates. It thus seems reasonable that the reluctance of the tridentate ligand to accommodate the required tetrahedral geometry is responsible for the disproportionation of their complexes.

Biological relevance

Even though they have been extensively studied for years, copper salicylaldiminates still attract much interest as convenient materials to design synthetic models for protein centers (9,10,18). In this respect, the present study has revealed several points of interest.

As stated by Bereman (19), galactose oxidase can be viewed as the prototype for type II copper enzymes since it does not contain any other prosthetic group. Extensive spectroscopic studies have led this author to propose that galactose oxidase active site is constituted by two histidine imidazoles, a negatively charged oxygen donor and two labile ligands arranged as a tetragonal environment. Together with other compounds described in this work, $Cu(SALIMP)(NO_3)$ incorporates some features of the proposed enzyme active site. X-ray diffraction data have shown a pseudo-square planar arrangement of the ligands in solid state. However, conductance measurements indicated that in methanol solution, the nitrate ion is dissociated and is probably replaced with one or two solvent molecules. Moreover, this compound also exhibits ESR spectral properties close to those of the enzyme ($g_{\parallel} = 2.277$, $A_{\parallel} = 175$ G) (19). Nevertheless, "static" spectral comparisons are far from being sufficient to draw conclusions about the structure of enzyme active sites. Azide binding capability has been demonstrated for $Cu(SALIEP)(NO_3)$ and such complexation studies are being extended to other similar ligands as a preliminary basis to understanding ligand induced spectral changes of galactose oxidase.

References and Footnotes

1. R. H. Holm, G. W. Everett and A. Chakravorty, *Progr. Inorg. Chem. 7*, 83 (1966).
2. E. Sinn and C. M. Harris, *Coord. Chem. Rev. 4*, 391 (1969).
3. M. J. Ettinger and D. J. Kosman, in *Metal Ions in Biology*, Ed. T. G. Spiro Wiley, *vol. 3*, chap. 6, p. 219 (1981).
4. J. J. Villafranca, *ibid*, chap. 7, p. 263.
5. R. S. Himmelwright, N. C. Eickman and E. I. Solomon, *J. Amer. Chem. Soc. 101*, 1576 (1979).
6. L. Sacconi and I. Bertini, *Inorg. Chem. 5*, 1520 (1966).
7. Y. Muto and T. Tokoo, *Bull. Chem. Soc. Jpn 51*, 139 (1978).
8. H. Elias, E. Hilms and H. Paulus, *Z. Naturforsch. 37b*, 1266 (1982).
9. Y. Nakao, W. Mori, N. Okuda and A. Nakahara, *Inorg. Chim. Acta 33*, 1 (1979).
10. M. R. Wagner and F. A. Walker, *Inorg. Chem. 22*, 3021 (1983).
11. L. T. Taylor and W. M. Coleman, *Inorg. Chim. Acta. 63*, 183 (1982).

12. L. C. Portis, J. C. Roberson and C. K. Mann, *Anal. Chem. 44,* 294 (1972).

13. B. J. Hathaway and D. E. Billing, *Coord. Chem. Rev. 5,* 143 (1970).

14. A. R. Amundsen, J. Whelan and B. Bosnich, *J. Amer. Chem. Soc. 99,* 6730 (1977).

15. M. B. Robin and P. Day, *Adv. Inorg. Chem. Radiochem. 10,* 247 (1967).

16. G. S. Paterson and R. H. Holm, *Bioinorg. Chem. 4,* 257 (1975).

17. M. Pasquali, P. Fiaschi, C. Floriani and A. Gaetani-Manfredotti, *J. Chem. Soc., Chem. Comm.,* 197 (1983).

18. R. C. Alder, E. A. Glubauch, W. R. Heinemann, P. J. Burke and D. R. McMillin, *Inorg. Chem. 22,* 2777 (1983).

19. R. D. Bereman, G. D. Shields, J. R. Dorfman and J. Bordner, *J. Inorg. Biochem. 19,* 75 (1983).

Biological & Inorganic Copper Chemistry,
ISBN 0-940030-11-X, Eds., K. D. Karlin & J. Zubieta, Adenine Press, ©Adenine Press, 1985

Biomimetic Systems for the "Visible" Copper-site Cu_A in Cytochrome c Oxidase

Hans Toftlund and Jan Becher
Department of Chemistry, University of Odense,
DK-5230 Odense M, Denmark

Abstract

Two copper(II) complexes of Schiff-base ligands derived from 4-formyl-1,3-dimethyl-pyrazol-5-thiolate and 2,2'-diaminobiphenyls have been prepared and characterized. The electronic spectra show intense $Cu \Leftarrow S$ charge-transfer bands, and the ESR spectra exhibit small $A_{\parallel}$ (Cu) values indicative of pseudotetrahedral CuN_2S_2 coordination.

The parameters obtained are discussed in relation to the parameters of the Cu_A site in cytochrome c oxidase.

Introduction

Cytochrome c oxidase, found in the mitochondria of the cells of all aerobic organisms, is the terminal enzyme in the respiratory electron transfer system effecting the reduction of oxygen to water.

Cytochrome c oxidase contains two heme a's and two copper-sites, none of which are equivalent. Cytochrome a_3 and Cu_B form the oxygen reduction site, while cytochrome a and Cu_A participate in electron transfer.

Cu_B is ESR silent even in its oxidized form, probably through its antiferromagnetic coupling to a_3 (1). Cu_A, on the other hand, is ESR visible in the oxidized form, although with spectral properties very atypical of a Cu(II) site (2). It has been assumed that the Cu_A site is similar to the Type 1 copper systems, the so-called "Blue Copper" sites, which are generally involved in electron transfer. However, as described in a recent review (3), Cu_A differs considerably from the Type 1 sites.

It now seems to be established that the coordinating groups are two histidine imidazoles and two cysteine thiolates (2,3). The description of the electronic ground state of the oxidized Cu_A is still controversial, but S. I. Chan *et al.* (2) have presented several experiments, strongly supporting the veiwpoint that the unpaired electron spin density is mainly situated at the cysteinyl sulfurs.

The goal of the present work has been to synthesize copper complexes which duplicate the spectral and physico-chemical properties of the Cu$_A$ site of cytochrome c oxidase.

Preparation and characterization

An extensive literature is available on the copper(II) complexes with sulfur and nitrogen containing chelate ligands (3,4,5). Many of these systems contain thioether sulfurs and will not be considered as models for the Cu$_A$ site. Systems containing two imine nitrogens and two thiolate sulfurs have been reviewed by Toftlund *et al.* (3). In a few cases, where the ligands are designed to give a tetrahedral distorted environment around the copper central ion, systems with some resemblance to the Type 1 sites have been obtained (6,7,8).

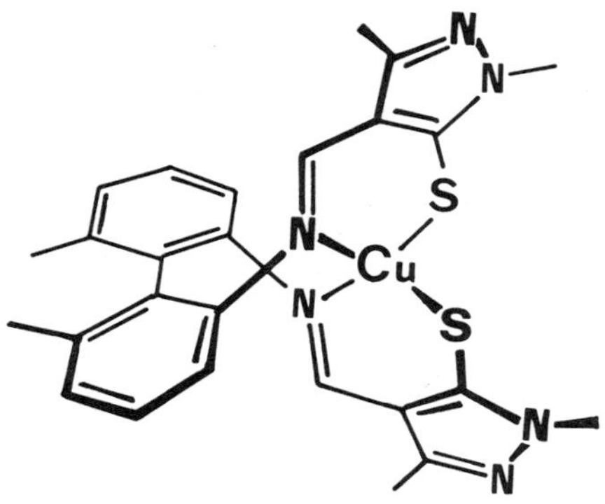

Figure 1. The geometry of the Schiff-base Cu(II) complex. The non-planar geometry is caused by the non-planarity of the biphenyl part of the molecule.

The preparation of these complexes is often impeded by the formation of undesired condensation and oxidation products of the thiolate ligands. These synthetic problems can be solved if the thiol function is protected prior to the metallation. We have demonstrated (7) that *t*-butylsulfides are convenient sources of copper(II) thiolato complexes, because Cu(II) is a sufficiently strong Lewis acid to cleave the sulfur *t*-butyl bond. Thus, preparation of the complex in Figure 1 was accomplished from the corresponding bis-*t*-butyl sulfide and copper(II) trifluoroacetate by refluxing in 2-methoxyethanol solution for one hour. The rationale behind the choice of 2,2'-diaminobiphenyls as the backbone in the ligands is that because of the large distance between the two donor nitrogens, the NCuN angle will be opened, and a tetrahedral geometry will be favoured. Cheeseman *et al.* have solved the crystal structure of a similar phenolato complex and found a dihedral angle ϕ of 37° (9). Because of the larger radius of sulfur compared to oxygen, this value must be considered as a lower limit of ϕ in our complexes. The Cu(II) complex derived from 2,2'-diamino-biphenyl as well as the Cu(II) complex derived from 6,6'-dimethyl-2,2'diaminobiphenyl are intensely blue violet coloured. Both are quite stable compounds; heating at the m.p. did not lead to decomposition. Thus, the mass spectra could be obtained at the m.p. of each compound with the molecular ion as the dominating peak. This is in marked contrast to what has been found for the bis bidentate β-iminothione Cu(II) complexes (8), which are stable only at low temperature.

Electronic spectra

The electronic spectra of both the systems are nearly identical. Figure 2 shows the spectrum of the 6,6'-dimethyl system dissolved in 2-methoxyethanol.

The band maxima occur at 1240 (86), 656 (1663), 535 (2820), 346 (16150), and 287 nm (31220) (the figures in the brackets are extinction coefficients ϵ in 1 mol^{-1} cm^{-1}).

The weak band at 1240 nm is assigned to the d-d transitions, and its low energy in comparison with similar complexes (800-1000 nm) is indicative of substantial distortion from square-planar toward tetrahedral co-ordination geometry (3,7). The bands at

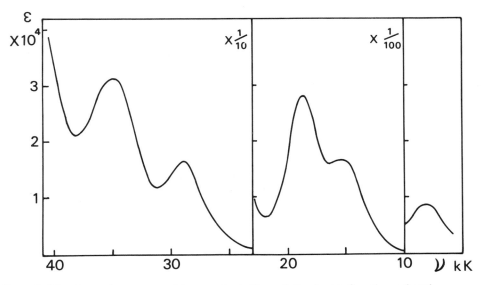

Figure 2. The electronic spectrum of the complex in Figure 1 dissolved in 2-methoxyethanol.

656 and 535 nm are assigned as Cu^{II} $\Leftarrow$ RS (π and σ) ligand to metal charge transfer (LMCT) bands due to their high intensity. Type 1, blue copper protein centres, shows bands of similar origin in the range 550-790 nm, with the most intense blue band at 600-630 nm (10).

ESR Spectra

In the characterization of Cu(II) complexes ESR spectroscopy has been a most useful tool. The Cu hyperfine splitting A$_{||}$ and the g$_{||}$ value can be estimated readily from the low field feature of the cryogenic solution spectra. Such a spectrum of the 6,6'-dimethylsubstituted Cu(II) complex in a DMF, H_2O, CH_3OH (1:1:5) glass at 113 K is shown in Figure 3a. From this spectrum the following parameters are obtained: $A_{||}$ = 14.1 mK (1 mK = 10^{-3} cm^{-1}), $g_{||}$ = 2.158, and $g_\perp$ = 2.026. The unsubstituted complex gave practically the same spectrum. Compared with $A_{||}$ = 18.4 mK, $g_{||}$ = 2.139, and $g_\perp$ = 2.020 for the essentially planar analogue complex derived from 1,2-diaminoethane (3) the reduced magnitude of $A_{||}$ in the present complexes is indicative of their anticipated distortion toward tetrahedral geometry. When doped into the analogous zinc complex, the Cu complex shows a spectrum characteristic of further twisting towards a tetrahedral geometry. Figure 3b, with $A_{||}$ = 11.7mK, $g_{||}$ = 2.164, and $g_\perp$ = 2.031. These latter parameters approach those of the Type 1 centres, but are still markedly different from the values found for Cu$_A$ $A_{||}$ < 3mK, g_z = 2.18, g_x = 1.99, and g_y = 2.03 (2).

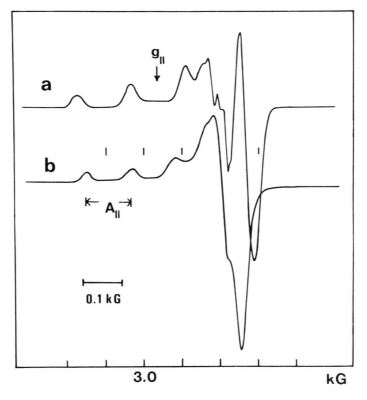

Figure 3. a. The frozen glass ESR spectrum of the complex in Figure 1. b. The ESR spectrum of the same compound diluted into the corresponding zinc complex.

Discussion

Ligand field models such as AOM (11), are convenient tools for predicting the geometrical variation of the d-orbital state energies. The result of such a calculation for a CuX$_4$ chromophore is shown in Figure 4. It is seen from the figure that a tetrahedral twist away from the square planar configuration will result in a red shift of the d-d transitions. In the calculation we have used radial parameters, which are the average between typical sulfur and nitrogen values. The d-d excitation energy of about 8 kK found for the present compounds is the lowest ever found for a CuN$_2$S$_2$ model compound. From the calculation a $\theta = 64°$ corresponding to a dihedral angle ϕ of 69° is predicted.

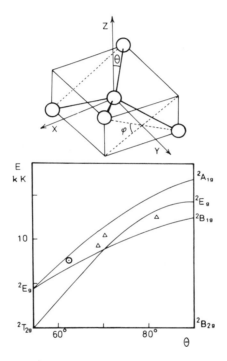

Figure 4. Top: Reference coordinate system for a twisted CuX$_4$ chromophore. Below: The angular dependences of the ligand field state energies as a function of θ for a d^9 ion. $\triangle$ are values from ref. 6. $\odot$ is the value for the complex in Figure 1.

The angular variation of the position of the charge transfer bands is less well understood. Toftlund *et al.* (3) have suggested a model based on the angular variation of the optical electronegativities of the central ion.

Although it is established (6) that a tetrahedral twist of the CuN$_2$S$_2$ chromophore results in a decrease of A$_{\parallel}$, an extrapolation to the value found for Cu$_A$ is hardly justified. Even for a ϕ of 90° the real geometry is C$_{2v}$ and the ligand field is far from being of T$_d$ symmetry. We believe that the spectrum in Figure 3b corresponds to a situation where ϕ is near to 90°, so we shall not expect to find A$_{\parallel}$ much lower than 10 mK for a Cu^{II}N$_2$S$_2$ complex. The only alternative then is the previously mentioned model, in which the unpaired electron spends most of its time at the sulfur atom and therefore exerts a very weak coupling to the copper nucleus (2). Toftlund *et al.* (3) have discussed the ESR properties of Cu_A within a $Cu(I)-Cu(II)$ chemical exchange model, which might account for the actual values.

Conclusion

The electronic parameters of Cu_A are so different to those obtained from analogous synthetic systems that a similar electronic structure can be excluded.

The synthesis of a realistic model system for the Cu_A site probably requires that the chromophore be built into a large molecule so that a stable thiyl radical $Cu(I)$ pair can be obtained.

Acknowledgements

The authors wish to express their gratitutde to Dr. S. I. Chan for stimulating discussions.

References and Footnotes

1. G. Palmer, G. T. Babcock, and L. E. Vickery, *Proc. Natl. Acad. Sci. USA 73* 2206 (1976).
2. D. F. Blair, C. T. Martin, J. Gelles, H. Wang, G. W. Brudvig, T. H. Stevens, and S. I. Chan, *Chemica Scripta 21* 43 (1983).
3. H. Toftlund, J. Becher, and P. H. Olesen, *Israel J. Chem. 25,* 56 (1985).
4. K. D. Karlin and J. Zubieta, *Inorg. Persp. Biol. Med. 2* 127 (1979).
5. K. D. Karlin and J. Zubieta (Ed.), *Copper Coord. Chem: Biochemical & Inorganic Perspectives,* Adenine Press, New York (1983).
6. R. D. Bereman et al. in ref. 5.
7. J. Becher, H. Toftlund, and P. H. Olesen, *J. Chem. Soc. Chem. Commun.* 740 (1983).
8. P. Beardwood and J. F. Gibson, *J. Chem. Soc. Chem. Commun.,* 1099 (1983).
9. T. P. Cheeseman, D. Hall, and T. N. Waters, *J. Chem. Soc. A,* 1396 (1966).
10. E. I. Solomon, J. W. Hare, D. M. Dooley, J. H. Dawson, P. J. Stephens, and H. B. Gray, *J. Am. Chem. Soc. 102,* 168 (1980).
11. C. K. Jørgensen, *Modern Aspects of Ligand Field Theory,* North-Holland, Amsterdam (1971).

Biological & Inorganic Copper Chemistry,
ISBN 0-940030-11-X, Eds., K. D. Karlin & J. Zubieta, Adenine Press, ©Adenine Press, 1985

Transmetalation of Tetranuclear Copper(II) Complexes

by **G.-Z. Cai, G. Davies, M.A. El-Sayed*, A. El-Toukhy*,**
T.R. Gilbert, M. Henary, K.D. Onan and M. Veidis
Department of Chemistry
Northeastern University
Boston, MA 02115

Abstract

Partial and complete metal exchange with core structure retention occurs in reactions of tetranuclear copper(II) complexes with Ni(NS)$_2$ reagents (NS is a nitrogen-sulfur ligand) in aprotic solvents. These transmetalation reactions are rapid and quantitative at room temperature and the products are easily separated. Some properties of new tetranuclear products are discussed.

Introduction

What was originally intended to be an investigation of some aprotic Lewis acid-base chemistry has resulted in the discovery of *direct transmetalation* (1-3).

The bases are the oxo groups in structures *I* and *II* resulting from aprotic oxidation of tetranuclear copper(I) complexes by dioxygen (4,5).

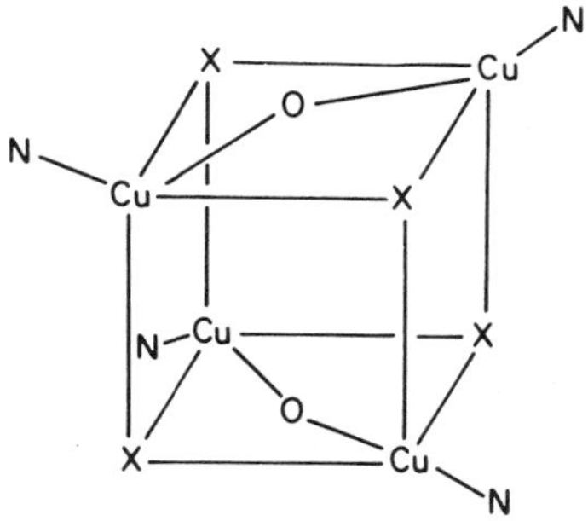

I 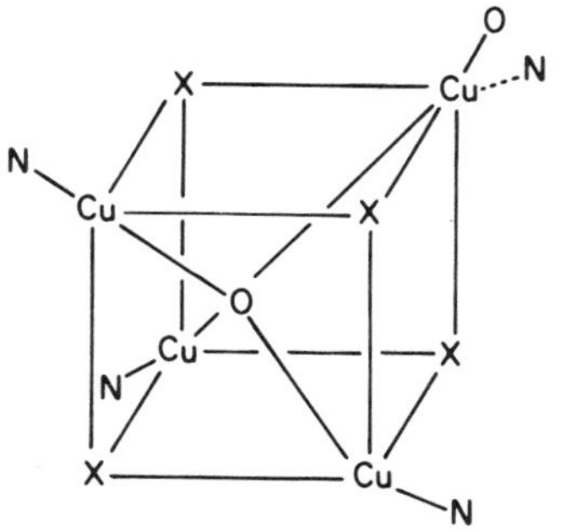   *II*

*On leave of absence from Department of Chemistry, Faculty of Science, Alexandria University, Egypt.

The acids are complexes like ***III*(a-c)** (6,7). Dimer ***IIIa*** is a strong Lewis acid because each half contains geometrically unfavorable square planar zinc(II). Eq 1 is typical of these complexes (8).

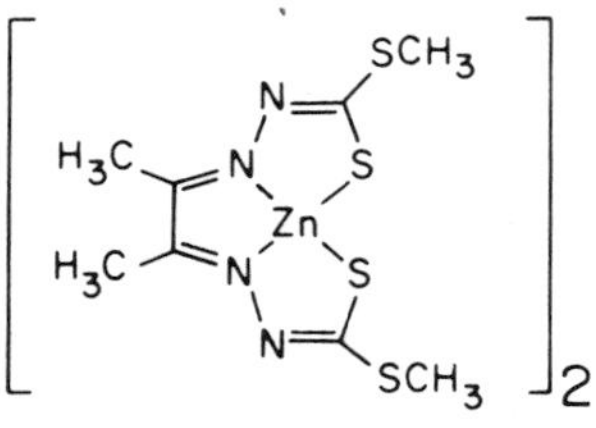

$$\underset{\underset{\widetilde{}}{III\,a}}{}$$

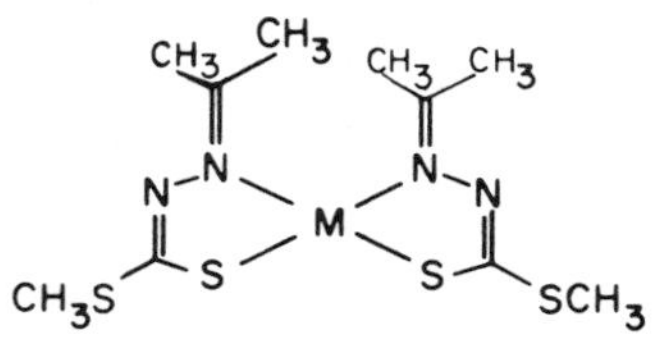

$$\underset{\underset{\widetilde{}}{III\,b}}{} \qquad\qquad \underset{\underset{\widetilde{}}{III\,c}}{}$$

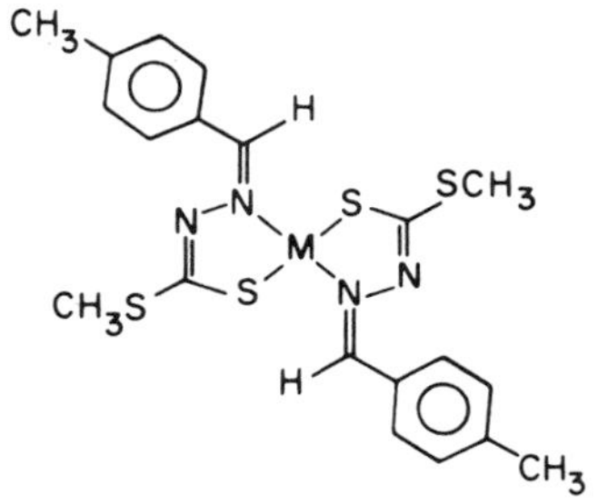

$$[\text{Zn}(\text{N}_2\text{S}_2)]_2 + 2\text{B} \rightleftharpoons 2\text{Zn}(\text{N}_2\text{S}_2)\cdot\text{B} \tag{1}$$

Transmetalation

Instead of the anticipated reactions 2 and 3, we observed complete exchange of zinc for copper on mixing 2 mols of ***IIIa*** or 4 mols of ***IIIb,c*** (M=Zn) with 1 mol of ***I*** or ***II***. Two isolated and structurally characterized (1) products are (½ ***IIIa***)·DENC and Cl$_2$Zn(DENC)$_2$ZnCl$_2$ (DENC = N,N-di-ethylnicotinamide). That is, the original tetranuclear structure is lost on metal exchange with zinc(II), presumably because 20-electron centers are created (1). The driving force for exchange is the high thermodyanmic stability of the M(NS)$_2$ coproducts (***III***; M = Cu).

$$[\text{Zn}(\text{N}_2\text{S}_2)]_2 + 2\textit{II} \rightleftharpoons 2\text{Zn}(\text{N}_2\text{S}_2)\cdot\textit{II} \tag{2}$$

$$[\text{Zn}(\text{N}_2\text{S}_2)]_2 + \textit{I} \rightleftharpoons \text{Zn}(\text{N}_2\text{S}_2)\cdot\textit{I}\cdot(\text{N}_2\text{S}_2)\text{Zn} \tag{3}$$

When the original core structure of a polymetallic complex is maintained on metal exchange we call the phenomenon *direct transmetalation.*

Because nickel(II) has fewer electrons than zinc(II), tetranuclear products were expected and found in reactions of *I, IV, IX,* and *X* with *IIIb,c* (M=Ni, Scheme I). The reactions are rapid and quantitative at room temperature and the products typified by eq 4 are easily separated by gel permeation chromatography (2,3). With M=Ni, one water molecule is incorporated with each new nickel center during product isolation. Intermolecular hydrogen-bonding causes association of species *V* and *VI* in aprotic solvents but none of the other products are associated (2,3).

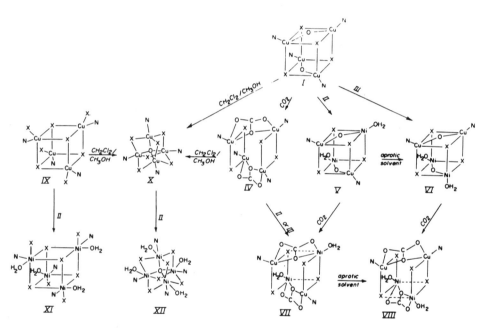

Scheme I. Transmetalation reactions of tetranuclear copper(II) complexes. Key: N = DENC or ethylnicotinate; X = Cl or Br, except for *IX,* which is restricted to N = DENC.

$$[NCuX]_4X_4 + 4Ni(NS)_2 \overset{H_2O}{\Rightarrow} [NNi(H_2O)X]_4X_4 + 4Cu(NS)_2 \qquad (4)$$

Scheme I includes complete and partial (substoichiometric) transmetalation reactions. The formation of species *V-VIII* even in the presence of a large excess of Ni(NS)$_2$ is due to the influence of μ_2-oxo and μ_2-carbonato bridges, which also control co-ordination numbers and ligand substitution behavior (2,3). We know that even complete transmetalation systems are stepwise, stoichiometric processes (9).

In families containing Cu_xM_{4-x} metal cores only x = 2 with μ_2-bridges can give rise to geometrical isomeric pairs *V, VI* and *VII, VIII.* Species *V* and *VII* are racemic. Efforts to resolve them are complicated by the spontaneous isomerization of *V* to *VI* and of *VII* to *VIII* in aprotic solvents (2,3).

The kinetics of isomerization help to explain why reactions of *I* with *IIIb* and *IIIc* give *V* and *VI,* respectively, while *IV* gives *VII* with both reagents (3). Catalysis of isomerization of *V* to *VI* by the acidic (10) coproduct *IIIc* (M=Cu) occurs with *V* but not with *VII* because *V* is the more basic. Coproduct *IIIb* (M=Cu) (11) is too weak an acid to be an effective catalyst for isomerization.

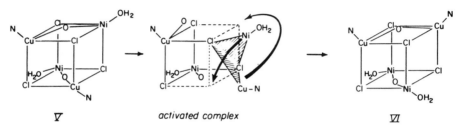

Figure 1. Model for isomerization via metal exchange between tetrahedral holes in an X_4 core structure (2).

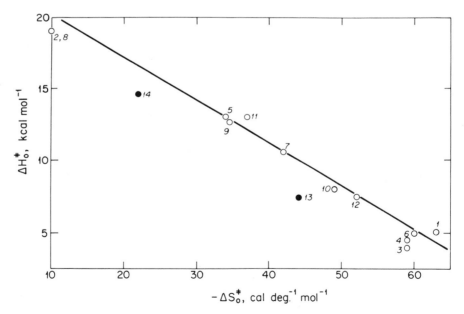

Figure 2. Plot of $\Delta H_o^{\ddagger}$ *vs.* $\Delta S_o^{\ddagger}$ for isomerization of complexes *V* and *VII* in methylene chloride, M, and nitrobenzene, NB. Key: for *V,* N = DENC, X = Cl (1), Br (2) in M, X = Cl (4), Br (5) in NB; N = ENCA, X = Cl (3) in M, X = Cl (6) in NB; for *VII,* N = DENC, X = Cl (7), Br (8) in M, X = Cl (10), Br (11) in NB; N = ENCA, X = Cl (9) in M, X = Cl (12) in NB. Also included are activation parameters for catalyzed isomerization of *V,* L = DENC, X = Cl (13) and X = Br (14) in NB. The catalyst is *IIIc* (M = Cu) (3).

The acid-base interaction in $Cu(NS)_2$ catalysis locks the μ_2-oxo groups in position and this is one of several reasons for preferring isomerization *via* metal exchange in *V* and *VII* (Figure 1). The results for 12 isomerization systems (Figure 2) suggest that this mechanism is general (3).

Transmetalation of Structure II

Structure *II* is an initiator of phenolic oxidative coupling by dioxygen (4). Although *II* is completely transmetalated by *IIIb,c* (M = Ni) we cannot separate the products, which have time-dependent properties (2). Complete transmetalation prevents the initiation and catalysis of phenolic oxidative coupling by dioxygen (2).

Based on this and other work (9) we can be confident that transmetalation of other polynuclear complexes will give a large number of new polymetallic products. The basic requirements are favorable thermodynamics, convenient rates under mild conditions and easy product separation.

Acknowledgements

This work was supported financially by the Department of Health and Human Services (Biomedical Research Support Grant RR07143), by Northeastern University (Faculty Research Grant 7590) and by the Egyptian Government. We are very grateful for this support.

References and Footnotes

1. G. Davies, A. El-Toukhy, K.D. Onan and M. Veidis, *Inorg. Chim. Acta, 84,* 41 (1984).
2. A. El-Toukhy, G.-Z. Cai, G. Davies, T.R. Gilbert, K.D. Onan and M. Veidis, *J. Amer. Chem. Soc., 106,* 4596 (1984).
3. G.-Z. Cai, G. Davies, A. El-Toukhy, T.R. Gilbert and M. Henary, *Inorg. Chem.,* in press.
4. G. Davies and M.A. El-Sayed, *Inorg. Chem., 22,* 1257 (1983).
5. G. Davies and M.A. El-Sayed, in *Inorganic and Biochemical Perspectives in Copper Coordination Chemistry,* K. D. Karlin, J. A. Zubieta, Eds., Adenine Press, Guilderland, NY, p. 281 (1983).
6. M. F. Iskander, A. El-Toukhy and M. M. Mishrikey, *J. Inorg. Nucl. Chem., 42,* 361 (1980).
7. A. El-Toukhy, M. El-Essawi, M. Tawfik, L. El-Sayed and M.F. Iskander, *Transition Met. Chem., 8,* 116 (1983).
8. L. El-Sayed, A. El-Toukhy, M.F. Iskander and M. Tawfik, *Inorg. Chim. Acta.,* in press.
9. G.-Z. Cai, G. Davies, M.A. El-Sayed, A. El-Toukhy, T.R. Gilbert and K.D. Onan, work in progress.
10. A. El-Toukhy, M.S. Thesis, Alexandria University, (1973).
11. L. El-Sayed, M.F. Iskander and A. El-Toukhy, *J. Inorg. Nucl. Chem., 36,* 1739 (1974).

Biological & Inorganic Copper Chemistry,
ISBN 0-940030-11-X, Eds., K. D. Karlin & J. Zubieta, Adenine Press, ©Adenine Press, 1985

Binuclear Complexes and Higher Order Clusters Containing Copper

G. Doyle, K. A. Eriksen and D. Van Engen

Corporate Research Laboratories and Analytical Division
Exxon Research and Engineering Company
Annandale, New Jersey 08801

Abstract

The reaction of phosphine or amine substituted copper(I) halides with a variety of transition metal carbonyl monoanions leads to the formation of a number of interesting bimetallic complexes. Infrared measurements and subsequent x-ray diffraction studies reveal a wide range of Cu-metal and Cu-CO interactions. The complex $(tmed)CuCo(CO_4)$ possesses a very short Cu-Co bond (2.38 Å) and a single semi-bridging CO while $[(C_6H_5)_3P]_3CuV(CO)_6$ exists as separate $[(C_6H_5)_3P]_3Cu^+$ and $V(CO)_6^-$ ions with no Cu-V interaction. Many of the other complexes prepared, such as $(tmed)CuMo(CO)_3(C_5H_5)$ and $[(C_6H_5)_3P]_2CuMn(CO)_5$ appear to have structures which fall between these two extremes.

The reaction of $Fe(CO)_4^{2-}$ with copper(I) halides or various substituted copper(I) halides has lead to several novel bimetallic Cu-Fe clusters. $(diphos)CuCl$ undergoes an interesting reaction with $Fe(CO)_4^{2-}$ yielding an ionic complex with the composition $[(diphos)_2Cu]_2$-$Cu_6Fe_4(CO)_{16}$. The copper atoms are approximately tetrahedrally coordinated by the two diphos ligands in the cations while the structure of the anions consists of an octrahedron of copper atoms capped on four faces with an $Fe(CO)_4$ group. Similar complexes are formed from $[(C_6H_5)_3P]_nCuCl$ complexes but under certain conditions a $\{[(C_6H_5)_3P]_2Cu\}_2Fe(CO)_4$ complex with a nearly linear Cu-Fe-Cu arrangement results.

The reaction of unsubstituted copper(I) halides with $Fe(CO)_4^{2-}$ in a 1:1 molar ratio yields the planar six atom cluster anion $Cu_3Fe_3(CO)_{12}^{3-}$ which has a triangular arrangement of the metal atoms. The addition of one equivalent of CuBr to a solution of the $Cu_3Fe_3(CO)_{12}^{3-}$ anion results in the formation of an even larger planar cluster anion with the composition $Cu_5Fe_4(CO)_{16}^{3-}$. The nine metal atoms are arranged in a rhombus with $Fe(CO)_4$ groups occupying the corner positions. Further addition of CuBr to $Cu_3Fe_3(CO)_{12}^{3-}$ or $Cu_5Fe_4(CO)_{16}^{3-}$ forms the $Cu_6Fe_4(CO)_{16}^{2-}$ species. All three cluster anions can be interconverted by the addition of CuBr or $Fe(CO)_4^{2-}$ in the proper proportions.

Introduction

In the past few years the structural details of a number of binuclear (1,2) and larger clusters (3-8) containing copper have been reported. This information has shed new light on the way copper bonds to transition metal carbonyl species. In particular it has been shown that semi-bridging carbonyl interactions between the copper and one or more of the carbonyl groups on the other metal may play a significant role in the bonding of the complexes. In the earlier work (9-12) it was generally believed that the copper was covalently bound to the other metal with no mention of copper-CO interactions. An x-ray crystal structure study carried out on (o-triars)CuMn(CO)$_5$, which showed this simple type of bonding, lent support to this notion (13).

Our recent work (14) and the work of Floriani (15) and coworkers on homo-binuclear copper complexes suggested that further investigations of the heteronuclear complexes could lead to interesting structural features and reaction chemistry especially in cases where copper atoms are coordinately unsaturated.

Binuclear Complexes

By employing the simple reaction of a ligand substituted copper halide and a sodium salt of a metal carbonyl anion, Nyholm's group was able to prepare a number of copper-transition metal derivatives (9-12).

$$L_nCuCl + NaM(CO)_xL'_y \Rightarrow L_nCuM(CO)_xL'_y + NaCl \qquad (1)$$

We have found that this procedure is quite satisfactory for the preparation of copper-cobalt complexes in which a chelating diamine or diphosine ligand is bound to the copper. This procedure is not as satisfactory for the preparation of complexes with monodentate ligands because of the lability of the ligands and the tendency to form product mixtures in which the number of ligands bound to copper varies. By suitable modifications however, both *bis* and *tris*-monodentate phosphine complexes can be prepared.

With the exception of the (tmed)CuCo(CO)$_4$ (tmed = N,N,N',N',tetramethylethylenediamine) complex, the infrared spectra of all the Cu-Co complexes, including those prepared previously (11,16), are quite similar (Table I). The spectrum of the tmed complex, as a nujol mull, displays a band at 1820 cm^{-1} which is considerably lower in frequency indicating a somewhat different environment for the carbonyl groups in this complex. A single crystal x-ray diffraction study was carried out on this complex and a perspective view showing its structure is shown in Fig. 1. The two most notable features of structures are the very short Cu-Co bond (2.378Å) and the very close approach of one of the carbonyl groups to the Cu atom in what appears to be a semi-bridging interaction.

Although bond length is not a reliable indicator of bond strength or bond order, the short Cu-Co bond in the (tmed)CuCo(CO)$_4$ complex does suggest a strong bond between the metals. The short Cu-Co distance may be due in part to the presence of the semibridging CO group. The distance btween the Cu and the C atom of the carbonyl group is considerably longer than the Cu-C distance observed for the symmetrically bridging carbonyl groups in the homonuclear complexes (14,15) but

Table I

Infrared Spectral Data for Some Cu-Co Complexes

Complex	Solvent	Frequencies, cm^{-1}[a]			
(tmed)CuCo(CO)$_4$	Ch$_2$Cl$_2$	2028(m)	1946(s)	1926(s)	1860(s)
	mull	2020(m)	1930(vs)	1820(m)	
(o-triars)CuCo(CO$_4$)[b]	CHCl$_3$	2033	1945	1919	
[(phen)CuCo(CO)$_4$]$_n$[c]	mull	2017	1936	1900	1842
[(bipy)CuCo(CO)$_4$]$_n$[c]	mull	2020	1938	1926	1857
(Ph$_3$P)$_2$CuCo(CO)$_4$	mull	2023(m)	1945(s)	1905(s)	1868(s)
(Ph$_3$P)$_3$CuCo(CO)$_4$	mull	2028(m)	1948(s)	1910(s)	1871(s)
[(CH$_3$)$_2$P(CH$_2$)$_2$P(CH$_3$)$_2$]CuCo(CO)$_4$	mull	2025(m)	1935(vs,bd)	1890(s)	
(Ph$_2$P(CH$_2$)$_2$PPh$_2$)CuCo(CO)$_4$	mull	2028(m)	1940(vs)	1912(vs)	1880(sh)
(Ph$_2$P(CH$_2$)$_4$PPH$_2$)CuCo(CO)$_4$	mull	2030(m)	1933(s)	1907(s)	1874(vs,bd)
(Ph$_2$PCH$_2$PPh$_2$)CuCo(CO)$_4$	mull	2032(m)	1974(m)	1935(vs)	1890(sh)
[Ph$_2$(CH$_3$)P]$_2$CuCo(CO)$_4$	mull	2020(m)	1930(s)	1905(s)	1873(s)
[(n-C$_4$H$_9$)$_3$P]$_2$CuCo(CO)$_4$	Ch$_2$Cl$_2$	2020(m)	1940(s)	1908(s)	1880(s)

[a] w = weak, m = medium, s = strong, v = very, bd = broad, sh = shoulder
[b] ref. 11
[c] ref. 16

it is by far the shortest Cu-C distance (see Table II) found in any of the hetero-nuclear complexes where semi-bridging CO bonding is possible. The semi-bridging CO group is presumably responsible for the low frequency CO band in the infrared spectrum of the (tmed)CuCo(CO)$_4$ complex in the solid state. The absence of this band in solution indicates that the semi-bridging interactions do not persist in solution and is restricted to the solid complex.

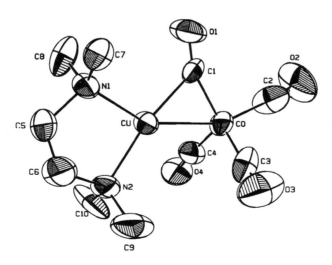

Figure 1. Perspective Ortep drawing of the (tmed)CuCo(CO)$_4$ complex. All non-hydrogen atoms are represented by thermal vibration ellipsoids drawn to encompass 50% of their electron density.

The preparation of copper-vanadium binuclear complexes has proven to be somewhat more difficult since many of the substituted copper halides, such as (tmed)CuCl, are reduced to copper metal by $V(CO)_6^-$. Phosphine substituted copper halides generally give complex product mixtures of which $(R_3P)_3CuV(CO)_6$ complexes are the dominant component. $[(C_6H_5)_3P]_3CuV(CO)_6$ can be prepared in relatively high yield from $[(C_6H_5)_3P]CuCl$ and $V(CO)_6^-$ but complexes containing fewer phosphine ligands per copper have not been observed. The $[(C_6H_5)_3P]_3CuV(CO)_6$ complex exhibits an infrared spectrum quite similar to that reported for (o-triars)CuV(CO)$_6$ (9) which was assumed to possess a Cu-V bond and as a consequence seven-coordinate vanadium. An Au-V complex, $(C_6H_5)_3PAuV(CO)_6$ (17) does have this type of coordination but an x-ray structure determination of $[(C_6H_5)_3P]_3CuV(CO)_6$ showed it to consist of discrete $[(C_6H_5)_3P]_3Cu^+$ cations and $V(CO)_6^-$ anions (see Fig. 2). The $V(CO)_6^-$ anion has an almost ideal octahedral geometry. The three phosphine atoms are arranged in a trigonal plane about the copper and there is obviously no bonding interaction between the metals or between the copper atom and any of the carbonyl groups.

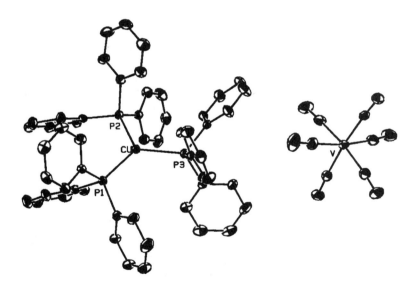

Figure 2. Perspective Ortep drawing of the $[(C_6H_5)_3P]_3CuV(CO)_6$ molecule showing the independent $[(C_6H_5)_3P]_3Cu^+$ cations and $V(CO)_6^-$ anion. Only the Cu, V, and P atoms are labeled for clarity.

The Cu-Co and the Cu-V complexes appear to represent two extremes in the degree of Cu-M and Cu-CO interaction with the Cu-Co representing a very strong interaction and the Cu-V complex showing no interaction at all. The Cu-Mn complex prepared by Nyholm's group (10) and similar complexes such as (tmed)CuMn(CO)$_5$ and $[(C_6H_5)_3P]_3CuMn(CO)_5$ prepared by us are intermediate cases with a "normal" Cu-Mn bond but no Cu-CO bonding. The $(C_5H_5)M(CO)_3^-$ (M=Cr,Mo,W) derivatives of Cu also appear to have Cu-M bonds but in these complexes some semi-bridging

CO bonding is evident. We and Carlton and coworkers (1) have succeeded in preparing a number of (tmed)Cu- and $[(C_6H_5)_3P]_2CuM(CO)_3(C_5H_5)$ complexes all of which are characterized by an infrared spectrum with three strong CO stretching bands; one at approximately 1900 cm^{-1} and two bands below 1800 cm^{-1} (Table II). A structural determination of (tmed)CuMo(CO)$_3$(C$_5$H$_5$) (Fig. 3) revealed a Cu-Mo bond and three distinctly different carbonyl groups bound to the molybdenum. One CO group is a typical terminal CO whereas the two other CO groups show differing degrees of semibridging interaction. The Cu-C distance is fairly short (2.19Å) for one of these CO groups but is considerably longer (2.41Å) for the other although the Mo-C-O angle deviates only slightly from linear for all three carbonyl groups. Similar structural features were found for the two $[(C_6H_5)_3P]_2CuW(CO)_3(C_5H_5)$ isomers and also for the unusual $(4CH_3C_5H_4N)Cu(CH_3CO_2)_2Mo(CO)_2(C_5H_5)$ complex prepared by Werner (2).

Table II
Infrared Spectra Data for Some L$_2$CuM(CO)$_3$(C$_5$H$_5$) Complexes

Compound	CO Stretching Frequencies, cm^{-1}[a]		
$[(C_6H_5)_3P]_2CuCr(CO)_3(C_5H_5)$	1902	1796	1753
(tmed)CuCr(CO)$_3$(C$_5$H$_5$)	1886	1795	1769
$[(C_6H_5)_3P]_2CuMo(CO)_3(C_5H_5)$	1896	1795	1776
(tmed)CuMo(CO)$_3$(C$_5$H$_5$)	1891	1795	1768
$[(C_6H_5)_3P]_2CuW(CO)_3(C_5H_5)$[b]	1890	1790	1769
	1890	1786	1731
(tmed)CuW(CO)$_3$(C$_5$H$_5$)	1894	1786	1759

[a]Nujol mulls
[b]Ref. 1

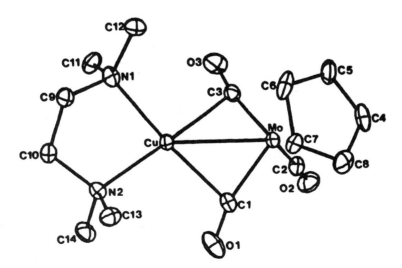

Figure 3. Perspective Ortep drawing of the (tmed)CuMo(CO)$_3$(C$_5$H$_5$) complex. All non-hydrogen atoms are represented by thermal vibration ellipsoids drawn to encompass 50% of their electron density.

It is apparent that copper is capable of forming bimetallic complexes with a number of transition metals and that the manner in which the bonding takes place in these complexes is quite varied. The data given in Table III summarizes the important Cu-M and Cu-CO distances observed in the binuclear complexes for which data is available.

Copper-Iron Clusters

Our success in preparing binuclear complexes containing copper as one of the metals and the interesting structural properties of these complexes suggested that analogous tri- and tetranuclear complexes might also be synthesized by the reaction of substituted copper halides with metal carbonyl dianions such as $Fe(CO)_4^{2-}$ and $Fe_2(CO)_8^{2-}$. At least one such complex [(o-triars)Cu]$_2$Fe(CO)$_4$, had been previously synthesized (11) but very little is known of its properties or structure.

The reaction of Na$_2$Fe(CO)$_4$ with a number of phosphine substituted copper halides was carried out in an attempt to prepare Cu$_2$Fe complexes similar to the [(o-triars)-Cu]$_2$Fe(CO)$_4$ complex but with one or more coordination sites on the copper unoccupied. It was found that (diphos)CuCl (diphos = 1,2-bis-diphenylposphino-ethane) reacts readily at room temperature with Na$_2$Fe(CO)$_4$ to form a complex with the stoichiometry (diphos)Cu$_2$Fe(CO)$_4$ in quantitative yields (equation 2).

$$2(\text{diphos})\text{CuCl} + \text{Na}_2\text{Fe(CO)}_4 \Rightarrow (\text{diphos})\text{Cu}_2\text{Fe(CO)}_4 + \text{diphos} + 2\,\text{NaCl} \quad (2)$$

It was also found that (dmpe)CuCl (dmpe = 1,2-bis-dimethylphosphinoethane) reacts in a similar manner. The liberation of the free chelating diphosphine ligand seemed quite unusual although not unprecedented (18). It was later found that one could carry out the same type of reaction using (diphos)Cu$_2$Cl$_2$ or (dmpe)Cu$_2$Cl$_2$ which avoids the separation of the diphosphine from the product. The (diphos)Cu$_2$Fe(CO)$_4$ and (dmpe)Cu$_2$Fe(CO)$_4$ complexes, both in solution and in the solid state, have infrared spectra which resemble, but are not identical to, that reported for [(o-triars)Cu]$_2$Fe(CO)$_4$. The phosphine complexes have two carbonyl stretching bands at approximately 1970 and 1870 cm^{-1} whereas the arsine derivative has two bands at 1942 and 1852 cm^{-1}. These differences seemed too large to be accounted for by the change in ligands and coordination number on copper. It also seemed that there were no compelling steric or electronic arguments for the loss of the diphosphine ligands if the resulting complexes were to have the same structure as the [o-triars)Cu]$_2$Fe(CO)$_4$ complex. A single crystal x-ray diffraction study of (diphos)Cu$_2$Fe(CO)$_4$ was undertaken. The results of this study revealed the complex to be a salt consisting of (diphos)$_2$Cu$^+$ cations and Cu$_6$Fe$_4$(CO)$_{16}^{2-}$ anions, the overall composition being [(diphos)$_2$Cu]$_2$Cu$_6$Fe$_4$(CO)$_{16}$. The structure of the cations (an Ortep diagram of one of the two crystallographically independent cations is shown in Figure 4) shows distorted tetrahedral geometry for the four phosphorous atoms coordinated to the copper, similar to that reported by Leoni and coworkers (19). All important bond angles and bond lengths seem ordinary for a cation of this type.

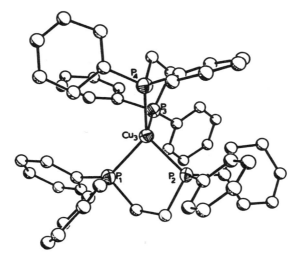

Figure 4. Perspective Ortep drawing of one of the two crystallographically-independent (diphos)$_2$Cu$^+$ cations present in [(disphos)$_2$Cu]$_2$Cu$_6$Fe$_4$(CO)$_{16}$. Cu and P atoms are represented by thermal vibration ellipsoids drawn to encompass 50% of their electron density; carbon atoms are represented by arbitrary-sized spheres and are unlabeled for clarity.

The structure of the anion is exceptionally interesting; consisting of an octahedron of copper atoms capped on four faces by a Fe(CO)$_4$ group. (See Figure 5 for an Ortep drawing of one of the three crystallographically independent Cu$_6$Fe$_4$(CO)$_{16}$$^{2-}$

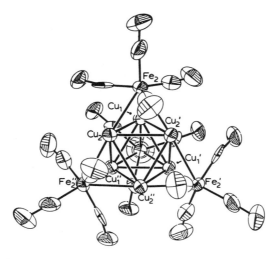

Figure 5. Perspective Ortep drawing of one of the three crystallographically-independent Cu$_6$Fe$_4$(CO)$_{16}$$^{2-}$ anions present in [(diphos)$_2$Cu]$_2$Cu$_6$Fe$_4$(CO)$_{16}$ with thermal vibration ellipsoids drawn at the 50% probability level. This drawing shows Anion I viewed down the crystallographic C$_3$-axis. Carbonyl groups are unlabeled for clarity.

anions.) The structure can also be described as a ν_2-tetrahedron and the arrangement of the metal atoms is similar to that reported for $Os_{10}C(CO)_{24}$ (20). Although a number of octahedral copper clusters have previously been prepared (21-23) this is the first in which no bridging ligands are present and is the largest bimetallic carbonyl cluster containing copper which has been synthesized. The average Cu-Cu distance (Table IV) is 2.64 Å which is about the same distance observed in other hexanuclear copper clusters and slightly longer than the Cu-Cu distance found in Cu metal (24). The average Cu-Fe distance of 2.46 Å is somewhat shorter than that predicted by summing the atomic radii but is in line with the Cu-M distances determined for other copper-metal complexes (1-5) (see Table III).

Table III
Summary of Cu-M and Cu-CO Bonding in Binuclear Copper Complexes

Complex	Cu-M Dist.	Cu-CO Dist.
$(Ph_3P)_3CuV(CO)_6$	6.92	
$(tmed)CuMo(CO_3)(C_5H_5)$	2.59	2.19, 2.41
$(Me-py)CuMo(CO)_3(OAc)_2(C_5H_5)$	2.56	2.14, 2.45
$(Ph_3P)_2CuW(CO)_3(C_5H_5)$ A	2.72	2.31, 2.41
$(Ph_3P)_2CuW(CO)_3(C_5H_5)$ B	2.71	2.20, 2.26
$(triars)CuMn(CO)_5$	2.56	>2.5
$(tmed)CuCo(CO)_4$	2.38	2.03
$(tmed)_2Cu_2(CO)(C_4O_4)$	2.42	1.84, 1.86

The arrangement of the carbonyl groups about the iron can best be described as trigonal bipyramidal with carbonyl groups occupying one of the apical and the three equitorial positions. The remaining apical position of the trigonal bipyramid is taken by a Cu_3 face of the Cu_6 octahedron with the apical CO located on a three-fold axis. The carbon atoms of the three equitorial carbonyls are located quite close to a copper atom (avg. Cu-C distance ~ 2.3 Å) indicating a weak semi-bridging interaction.

The ease of formation of the Cu_6Fe_4 cluster anion under such mild conditions seems remarkable since the reaction involves an extensive rearrangement of the ligands and copper atoms yet proceeds in high yields. One is accustomed to thinking of cluster formation as requiring robust conditions and often yielding small amounts of products or, commonly, product mixtures requiring lengthy separations.

The reaction of $[C_6H_5)_3P]_2CuCl$ with $Na_2Fe(CO)_4$ at first glance appears to proceed in the same manner as the analogous reaction using (diphos)CuCl. A quantitative yield of NaCl is produced and the IR spectrum of the reaction solution has two CO stretching bands at positions nearly identical to those of the diphos derivative (1970 and 1880 cm^{-1}). On evaporation of the solvent, the yellow crystals which form display an entirely different infrared spectrum with three bands of approximately

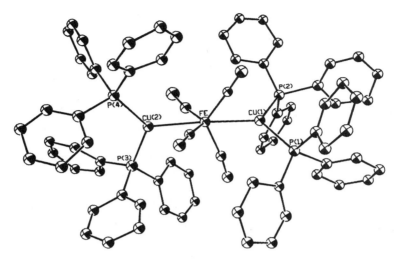

Figure 6. A perspective Ortep drawing of the {[(C$_6$H$_5$)$_3$P]$_2$Cu}$_2$Fe(CO)$_4$ molecule. Only the Cu, Fe, and P atoms are labeled for clarity.

equal intensity at 1820, 1799 and 1780 cm^{-1}. No triphenylphosphine can be extracted from the solid indicating that all the phosphine is complexed to the copper and elemental analyses confirmed the composition [(C$_6$H$_5$)$_3$P]$_4$Cu$_2$Fe(CO)$_4$. When redissolved in THF, the spectrum of the complex reverts to the two band pattern typical of the Cu$_6$Fe$_4$(CO)$_{16}^{2-}$ dianion. Crystals obtained by slow evaporation of the solvent were subjected to an x-ray diffraction study. An Ortep representation of this complex is shown in Figure 6. This complex consists of a nearly linear three metal atom Cu-Fe-Cu grouping. The Cu-Fe distances are slightly longer than those seen in the Cu$_6$Fe$_4$ dianion. The coordination of the carbonyl group about the central iron atom is approximately tetrahedral with the copper-iron bond bisecting opposite edges of the tetrahedron. The four carbonyl groups are bent toward the copper atoms and each copper atom appears to interact with two carbonyl groups. The Cu-C distances are approximately 2.25 and 2.4 Å. Disregarding the carbonyl groups, the other groups are arranged in a trigonal plane about the copper atom.

Although the pattern observed for the carbonyl stretching modes in the infrared spectrum of {[(C$_6$H$_5$)$_3$P]$_2$Cu}$_2$Fe(CO)$_4$ is quite unusual, the frequencies of the bands are about what one would expect for a simple Cu$_2$Fe complex. In most of the Cu-M complexes prepared thus far, modest shifts to higher frequency are observed when one goes from the free anion to the Cu-M complex. If the four carbonyl groups in the complex were rigidly tetrahedral one would expect to see a single infrared active carbonyl band. The deviation from this geometry is evidently sufficient to split the band into the three band pattern which is observed.

Attempts to prepare simple four atom Cu$_2$Fe$_2$ complexes by the reaction of substituted copper halides and Na$_2$Fe$_2$(CO)$_8$ were not successful. In most cases the Fe$_2$(CO)$_8^{2-}$

dianion undergoes a disproportionation reaction leading to $Fe_3(CO)_{12}$ and a complex derived from $Fe(CO)_4^{2-}$ such as $Cu_6Fe_4(CO)_{16}^{2-}$ (equation 3).

$$24(diphos)_2CuCl + 12\,Na_2Fe_2(CO)_8 \rightleftharpoons [(diphos)_2Cu]_2Cu_6Fe_4(CO)_{16} + $$
$$4\,Fe_3(CO)_{12} + 24\,NaCl + 12\,diphos \quad (3)$$

The ability to prepare such vastly different complexes such as the Cu_6Fe_4 dianion and the Cu_2Fe compound by making just a minor change in the ligands and the ease in which the two materials can be interconverted is very interesting. Based on the infrared data, it would appear that the Cu_6Fe_4 cluster is the dominant species but is in equilibrium with the Cu_2Fe complex. Depending on the phosphine chosen and the particular reaction conditions, it is possible to obtain either product. In the case of the diphos complexes, the $[(diphos)_2Cu]_2Cu_6Fe_4(CO)_{16}$ salt is the least soluble and is the product obtained. With the reaction of $[(C_6H_5)_3P]_2CuCl$, the $\{[(C_6H_5)_3P]_2-Cu\}_2Fe(CO)_4$ compound is the least soluble material and, as it precipitates, the equilibrium is driven in the direction of its formation. It is interesting to note that if one adds free diphos to a solution prepared by dissolving the Cu_2Fe complex, the product obtained on crystallization is the $(diphos)_2Cu^+$ salt of the $Cu_6Fe_4(CO)_{16}^{2-}$ dianion. It is also interesting to note that if instead of starting with $[(C_6H_5)_3P]_2CuCl$, one uses $[(C_6H_5)_3P]CuCl$ the product obtained is $\{[(C_6H_5)_3P]_3Cu\}_2Cu_6Fe_4(CO)_{16}$ (equation 4) and no evidence of the formation of $\{[(C_6H_5)_3P]_2Cu\}_2Fe(CO)_4$ is seen.

$$8[(C_6H_5)_3P]CuCl + 4Na_2Fe(CO)_4 \rightleftharpoons \{[(C_6H_5)_3P]_3Cu\}_2Cu_6Fe_4(CO)_{16} + $$
$$8\,NaCl + 2\,(C_6H_5)_3P \quad (4)$$

The unusual reactions observed with substituted copper halides and the $Fe(CO)_4^{2-}$ anion prompted us to examine the same type of reaction with the unsubstituted halides in a manner similar to that used by Chini to prepare the $Cu[Co(CO)_4]_2^-$ anion (25). These reactions are very sensitive to the solvent and the particular halide chosen, but under the proper conditions a 1:1 mixture of CuCl or CuBr and $Na_2Fe(CO)_4$ react to form a complex with the composition $NaCuFe(CO)_4 \cdot 2THF$ as the major product. Unsolvated salts can be obtained by precipitation with tetraalkylammonium ions. These salts, both in solution and as mulls, have infrared spectra very similar to the $Cu_6Fe_4(CO)_{16}^{2-}$ salts, but with the bands shifted down to ~ 1930 and 1800 cm^{-1} which clearly is not the spectra expected for a simple $CuFe(CO)_4^-$ anion.

A crystal structure of the tetraethylammonium salt was carried out which revealed the anion to be a trimer, $Cu_3Fe_3(CO)_{12}^{3-}$. The six metal atoms are all planar and are arranged in the form of a triangle (see Figure 7 for an Ortep diagram). The three copper atoms form an equilateral triangle and each edge is bridged by a $Fe(CO)_4$ group. The average Cu-Cu bond distances (2.60 Å) and Cu-Fe bond distances (2.42 Å) are somewhat shorter than those observed in the $Cu_6Fe_4(CO)_{16}^{2-}$ dianion. The $Cu_3Fe_3(CO)_{12}^{3-}$ cluster can be envisioned as being one of the large triangular faces of the Cu_6Fe_4 cluster. The arrangement of the CO groups around the iron atoms is similar to that of the Cu_6Fe_4 cluster and in this case there also seems to be a

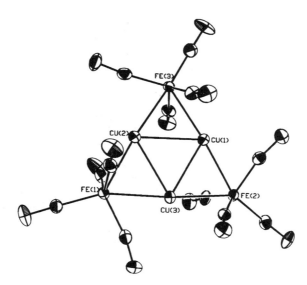

Figure 7. A perspective Ortep drawing of the $Cu_3Fe_3(CO)_{12}^{3-}$ anion in crystalline $[(C_2H_5)_4N]_3Cu_3Fe_3(CO)_{12}$ viewed perpendicular to the plane containing the six metal atoms with thermal vibration ellipsoids drawn at the 50% probability level. Carbonyl groups are unlabeled for clarity.

semi-bridging interaction between the carbonyl groups and the copper atoms. (See Table IV for typical bond lengths). This type of close-packed planar array of metal atoms is unusual for a transition metal carbonyl cluster of this size, although a nonplanar Pt_3Fe_3 complex with a similar structure has been reported (26).

The structural relationship between the $Cu_3Fe_3(CO)_{12}^{3-}$ and the $Cu_6Fe_4(CO)_{16}^{2-}$ complexes suggests that there may be a chemical relationship also. To some extent this has proven true. The addition of diphos to a solution of $Na_3Cu_3Fe_3(CO)_{12}$ and subsequent crystallization results in the formation of $[(diphos)_2Cu]_2Cu_6Fe_4(CO)_{16}$ in moderate yields. More interestingly, if one adds three equivalents of CuCl and one equivalent of $Na_2Fe(CO)_4$ to a solution of $Na_3Cu_3Fe_3(CO)_{12}$ then one forms in nearly quantitative yields, $Na_2Cu_6Fe_4(CO)_{16}$ (equation 5).

$$Na_3Cu_3Fe_3(CO)_{12} + 3CuCl + Na_2Fe(CO)_4 \Rightarrow Na_2Cu_6Fe_4(CO)_{16} + 3\,NaCl \quad (5)$$

Although this appears to be a rational construction of the larger cluster from the smaller one, it is not clear if this is indeed the process taking place. The $Cu_3Fe_3(CO)_{12}^{3-}$ species seems to be quite stable in solution but it is possible for some dissociation to take place and for the large cluster to be built up from the new fragments. The addition of one equivalent of CuCl to a solution of $Cu_3Fe_3(CO)_{12}^{3-}$ causes a clean stepwise change in the infrared spectrum resulting in two new bands at 1950 and 1850 cm^{-1}. Further addition of CuCl results in progressive changes in the spectra, and at a Cu:Fe ratio of 1.5:1 the spectrum of the $Cu_6Fe_4(CO)_{16}^{2-}$ ion is observed as expected.

From the reaction of $Na_3Cu_3Fe_3(CO)_{12}$ and one equivalent of CuBr a yellow crystalline solid has been isolated which can be readily converted to a tetraalkylammonium salt having the composition of $[R_4N]_3Cu_5Fe_4(CO)_{16}$. The composition of this product has a number of implications among which is the fact that the $Cu_3Fe_3(CO)_{12}{}^{3-}$ ion must undergo some dissociation in solution. A Cu_5Fe_4 species could not be formed from a Cu_3Fe_3 fragment by the simple addition of CuBr. The additional Fe needed to form the Cu_5Fe_4 cluster could only have come from the dissociation of $Cu_3Fe_3(CO)_{12}{}^{3-}$. Since the formation of the Cu_6Fe_4 cluster from $Cu_3Fe_3(CO)_{12}{}^{3-}$ takes place under similar conditions, it is quite feasible that a prior dissociation step may have taken place in this instance also. If this is the case, then it should be possible to form the $Cu_6Fe_4(CO)_{16}{}^{2-}$ cluster directly from $Fe(CO)_4{}^{2-}$ and a copper(I) halide. This has recently been confirmed. We have also found that the $Cu_6Fe_4(CO)_{16}{}^{2-}$ cluster can be formed by the addition of a single equivalent of CuBr to the $Cu_5Fe_4(CO)_{16}{}^{2-}$ anion. The ability to form the simple salts of these cluster anions in high yields by these direct routes has important synthetic implications. In the case of the $Cu_6Fe_4(CO)_{16}{}^{2-}$ anion, only phosphine substituted Cu(I) salts were previously available but cations of this type introduce a number of complications and are detrimental to studies of simple reactions which we wished to carry out on the anion.

The $Cu_5Fe_4(CO)_{16}{}^{3-}$ anion has a very unusual composition and, although a few nine atom carbonyl clusters are known (28), none of the observed arrangements for nine atom clusters seemed to be likely possibilities for the structure of this cluster. An x-ray diffraction study of this material showed the metal atoms to be arranged in a nearly perfect 3×3 rhombus. $Fe(CO)_4$ groups occupy the four corners and copper atoms are located in the remaining positions (see Figures 8 and 9). The metal atoms thus form a small section of a close packed surface. To the best of our knowledge this is the largest planar carbonyl cluster which has been synthesized. As can be readily seen, there are two different types of iron atoms and copper atoms in the cluster, the central Cu atom having six nearest neighbors in the plane. The central Cu atom is 2.53 Å from the edge lying Cu atoms whereas the edge lying coppers are 2.69 Å from the copper atom on the adjacent edge. The two Fe atoms which define the short diagonal of the rhombus bridge three coppers and are located 2.43 Å from the copper atoms on the edge and 2.49 Å from the central copper atom. The remaining two iron atoms bridge two coppers with a Fe-Cu distance of 2.39 Å. The average metal-metal distances (see Table IV) are thus similar to those observed in the Cu_3Fe_3 and Cu_6Fe_6 cluster anions.

The arrangement of the carbonyl groups around the iron atoms is quite different from that found in the Cu_6Fe_4 cluster anion. In the Cu_5Fe_4 cluster anion, two of the carbonyls on each of the irons lie in the plane of the metal atoms. The other two carbonyls are bent over the metal-containing plane, one above and one below. These two carbonyl groups and the iron atom to which they are attached lie in a plane which also contains the central copper atom and the iron atom with its two carbonyl groups on the opposite corner of the rhombus. These two planes are perpendicular to the metal-containing plane. The $Fe(CO)_4$ groups therefore appear as somewhat flattened tetrahedra similar to that seen in the Cu_2Fe complex. Although

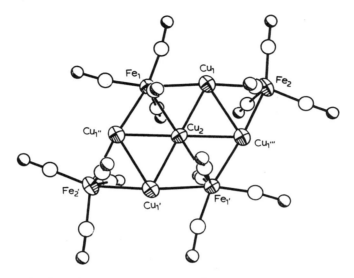

Figure 8. A perspective Ortep drawing of the $Cu_5Fe_4(CO)_{16}^{3-}$ anion in crystalline $[(C_2H_5)_4N]_3Cu_5Fe_4(CO)_{16}$ with the atoms represented by thermal vibration ellipsoids drawn to encompass 50% of their electron density viewed perpendicular to the plane of the nine metal atoms.

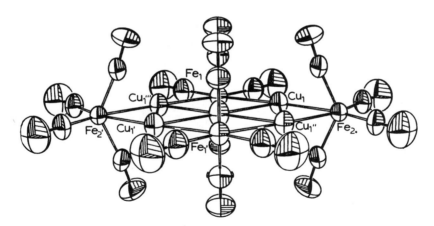

Figure 9. A perspective Ortep drawing of the $Cu_5Fe_4(CO)_{16}^{3-}$ anion in crystalline $[(C_2H_5)_4N]_3Cu_5Fe_4(CO)_{16}$ with nonhydrogen atoms represented by thermal vibration ellipsoids drawn at the 50% probability level viewed nearly parallel to the plane of the nine metals.

there seems to be some interaction between the carbonyl groups and the copper atoms, it is apparently somewhat weaker than in the other three complexes, if the Cu-C distances are a good indicator of the strength of this interaction. The closest Cu-C distance for the copper atoms lying on the edge is 2.40 Å while the shortest Cu-C distance for the central copper atom is even longer at 2.50 Å, both considerably longer than those observed in the other Cu-Fe clusters.

The structural relationship between the $Cu_5Fe_4(CO)_{16}^{3-}$ and $Cu_3Fe_3(CO)_{12}^{3-}$ anions is obvious but what we find more interesting is the relationship between the $Cu_5Fe_4(CO)_{16}^{3-}$ and the $Cu_6Fe_4(CO)_{16}^{2-}$ anions. If one folds the Cu_5Fe_4 plane along the short diagonal containing atoms Fe(1), Cu(2) and Fe(1) forming a compressed butterfly arrangement, the resulting figure is very similar to the $Cu_6Fe_4(CO)_{16}^{2-}$ anion except for a vacancy in one of the Cu positions. This structural relationship suggests a number of experiments in which the vacant Cu position could be filled, the simplest of which would involve the addition of a single Cu(I) species to the $Cu_5Fe_4(CO)_{16}^{3-}$ anion. We have found that the addition of CuBr to $Na_3Cu_5Fe_4(CO)_{16}$ gives a high yield of $Na_2Cu_6Fe_4(CO)_{16}$ under very mild conditions. In a formal sense, the added Cu(I) ion has filled the vacant site closing the butterfly and forming the ν_2-tetrahedron although it is uncertain whether the reaction proceeds in this straightforward manner.

The chemistry of Cu-Fe bimetallic complexes is proving to be a rich synthetic area. The products obtained from seemingly simple metathesis reactions are often complex and completely unpredictable. The ease of interconversion of some of these complexes also lends interest and may provide clues to how the larger clusters are formed. The reactions of these materials are just now being exploited and hopefully will also be fruitful and lead to interesting new chemistry.

Table IV
Summary of Important Bond Distances in Cu-Fe Clusters

Complex	Cu-Cu Distance, Å	Cu-Fe Distance, Å	Shortest Cu-C Distance, Å
$[(Ph_3P)_2Cu]_2Fe(CO)_4$	—	2.509	2.24
$Cu_3Fe_3(CO)_{12}^{3-}$	2.602	2.421	2.20
$Cu_5Fe_4(CO)_{16}^{3-}$	2.527	2.426	2.40
	2.691	2.491	
		2.394	
$Cu_6Fe_4(CO)_{16}^{3-}$	2.616	2.466	2.26

References and Footnotes

1. L. Carlton, W. E. Lindsell, K. J. McCullough, P. N. Preston, *J. Chem. Soc. Chem. Commun.* 216, 1983.
2. H. Werner, H. Roll, K. Linse, M. L. Zeigler, *Angew. Chem. 95*, 1023, 1983.
3. G. R. Clark, C. M. Cochrane, W. R. Roper, L. J. Wright, *J. Organometal, Chem., 199*, C35, 1980.
4. J. S. Bradley, R. L. Pruett, E. R. Hill, G. B. Ansell, M. E. Leonowicz, M. A. Modrick, *Organometallics 1*, 748, 1982.
5. L. F. Rhodes, J. C. Huffman, K. G. Caulton, *J. Am. Chem. Soc. 105*, 5137, 1983.
6. D. Braga, K. Henrick, B. F. G. Johnson, J. Lewis, M. McPartlin, W. J. H. Nelson, A. Sironi, M. D. Vargas, *J. Chem. Soc. Chem. Commum.* 1131, 1983.
7. P. Braunstein, J. Rose, *J. Organometal. Chem. 262*, 223, 1984.
8. P. Klufers, *Angew. Chemie Int. Ed. Eng. 23*, 307, 1984.
9. A. S. Kasenally, R. S. Nyholm, R. J. O'Brien, M. H. B. Stiddard, *Nature, 204*, 871, 1964.
10. A. S. Kasenally, R. S. Nyholm, M. H. B. Stiddard, *J. Am. Chem. Soc., 86*, 1884, 1964.
11. A. S. Kasenally, R. S. Nyholm, M. H. B. Stiddard, *J. Chem. Soc.* 5343, 1965.

12. R. J. Haines, R. S. Nyholm, M. H. B. Stiddard, *J. Chem. Soc. A*, 46, 1968.
13. B. T. Kilbourn, T. L. Blundell, H. M. Powell, *J. Chem. Soc. Chem. Commun.*, 444, 1965.
14. G. Doyle, K. A. Eriksen, M. Modrick, G. Ansell, *Organometallics, 1,* 1613, 1982.
15. M. Pasquali, C. Floriani, G. Venturi, A. Gaetani-Manfredotti, A. Chiesi-Villa, *J. Am. Chem. Soc., 104,* 4092, 1982.
16. P. Hackett, A. R. Manning, *J. Chem. Soc. Dalton Trans.,* 1606, 1975.
17. H. M. Powell, unpublished results.
18. C. E. Briant, R. G. Smith, D. M. P . Mingos, *J. Chem. Soc. Chem. Commun.*, 586, 1984.
19. P. Leoni, M. Pasquali, C. A. Ghilardi, *J. Chem. Soc. Chem. Commun.,* 240, 1983.
20. P. F. Jackson, B. F. G. Johnson, J. Lewis, W. J. H. Nelson, M. McPartlin, *J. Chem. Soc. Dalton Trans.* 2099, 1982.
21. S. A. Bezman, M. R. Churchill, J. A. Osborne, J. Wormald, *J. Am. Chem. Soc. 93,* 2063, 1971.
22. G. van Koten, J. G. Noltes, *J. Organometal. Chem. 102,* 551, 1975.
23. R. W. M. ten Hoedt, J. G. Noltes, G. van Koten, *J. Chem. Soc. Dalton Trans.,* 1800, 1979.
24. A. F. Wells, *Structural Inorganic Chemistry,* Oxford University Press, Oxford, England, p.985, 1962.
25. P. Chini, S. Martinengo, G. Longoni, *Gazz. Chim. Ital., 105,* 203, 1975.
26. G. Longoni, M. Manassero, M. Sansonis, *J. Am. Chem. Soc. 102,* 7974, 1980.
27. See B. K. Teo, G. Longoni and F. R. K. Chung, Inorg. Chem., 23, 1257 and references cited therein, 1984.

Biological & Inorganic Copper Chemistry,
ISBN 0-940030-11-X, Eds., K. D. Karlin & J. Zubieta, Adenine Press, ©Adenine Press, 1985

Rational Syntheses of Copper Polyhydride Complexes

Kenneth G. Caulton, Gary V. Goeden, Timothy H. Lemmen, Larry F. Rhodes and John C. Huffman

Department of Chemistry
Indiana University
Bloomington, Indiana 47405

Abstract

Synthetic routes to and properties of compounds containing Cu-H bonds are reviewed. One general method involves hydrogenation of the products of phosphine addition to $(CuO^tBu)_4$; monodentate phosphorus ligands yield hexameric $(HCuPR_3)_6$ species, for which structural data suggests at most very weak Cu/Cu bonding. Heterometallic copper hydride complexes are also available by condensation of $Cu(NCMe)_4PF_6$ with the polyhydrides $ReH_5(PMePh_2)_3$, *fac*- and *mer*-$IrH_3(PMe_2Ph)_3$, and Cp_2MH_2 (M = Mo, W). These latter complexes are suggested to be inner sphere electron transfer intermediates analogous to those operative in Ag^+ oxidation of transition metal polyhydrides.

Copper Hydride Complexes

Our initial interest in copper hydride complexes evolved from an interest in exploring factors involved in the synthesis of methanol from CO/H_2, heterogeneously catalyzed by oxides of copper together with zinc (1). We reasoned that an understanding of the reactivity of soluble copper hydride complexes would represent a useful first step in this quest, and might simultaneously yield reagents of broader utility in hydrogenation reactions.

Our synthetic quest had little precedent (2,3). Our own approach was to employ a synthetic method closely related to a possible step in the methanol synthesis (eq. 1). This procedure

$$L_nCu\text{-}OR + H_2 \Rightarrow L_nCuH + HOR \qquad (1)$$

simultaneously generates a ligated copper hydride and an alcohol, a reaction which is formally the heterolytic splitting of H_2 into H^- (on Cu^I) and H^+ (on OR^-). In the interest of employing a soluble copper (I) alkoxide, we selected copper t-butoxide, shown by the group of Weiss (4) to be a planar tetramer (Figure 1). Although this compound is unreactive towards 1 atm H_2 at 25°, the addition of phosphine ligands to the reaction solution gives prompt conversion to red to orange hydride complexes,

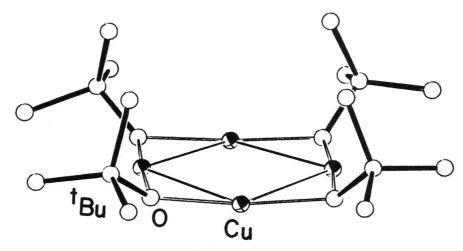

Figure 1. (CuO^{t}Bu)$_4$

along with ^{t}BuOH. The reaction is quite general for a variety of phosphorus ligands, including PPh$_3$, P(p-tolyl)$_3$, P(O^{i}Pr)$_3$, P(NMe$_2$)$_3$, and several mixed aryl/alkyl phosphines. All of these complexes have been structurally characterized, but it is

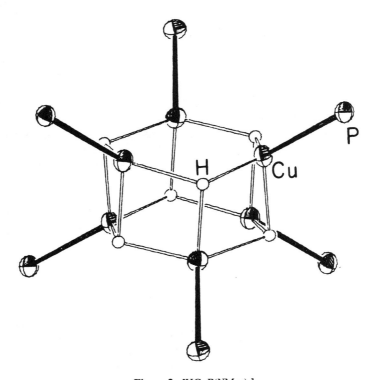

Figure 2. [HCuP(NMe$_2$)$_3$]$_6$

only recently that we have collected X-ray diffraction data of sufficient quality to allow location and refinement of the hydride positions. As shown in Figure 2, $[HCuP(NMe_2)_3]_6$ has six μ_3-hydride bridges.

A striking result of the structural studies carried out on several of these hexameric $(HCuPR_3)_6$ species is the pattern of metal-metal separations (Table I). The first point to be observed is that corresponding Cu/Cu separations in these trigonal antiprismatic aggregates are influenced by the phosphine incorporated by as much as 0.23 Å. Such effects are quite rare. The second point is that the equilateral triangles in the $P(O^iPr)_3$ derivative involve the *shorter* Cu/Cu separation, while the other three complexes have the equilateral triangle bounded by the *longer* separation. Taken together, we feel that these results bear on the provocative question of the strength of metal-metal bonding in these $3d^{10}/3d^{10}$ systems. Specifically, we feel that such flexible, plastic "bonds" are at best very weak, at worst nonexistent. The force which is altering the Cu/Cu separations in this series of complexes is, we judge, repulsions between phosphine ligands within the equilateral triangle. As shown above, this triangle is stretched to its largest in the derivative of $P(NMe_2)_3$, a ligand which our work (examination of space filling models (6)) shows to be much larger than previously recognized.

Table I
Structural Parameters for $(HCuPR_3)_6$ Complexes

	$P(O^iPr)_3$	PPh_3 (3)	$P(p\text{-tolyl})_3$ (5)	$P(NMe_2)_3$
			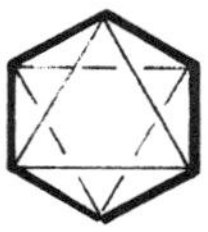	
Long (light):	2.67 Å	2.66	2.66	2.80
Short (bold):	2.57	2.54	2.54	2.51
Ligand Cone Angle	130°	145°	145°	~170°

Heterobimetallic Copper Hydrides

Additional progress on the properties of the copper-hydride bond derives from work which initially appears wholly unrelated to this topic. We have been pursuing for some time the conversion of 18-valence electron polyhydride complexes into odd-electron species, in the hope that such derived species will display enhanced reactivity in comparison to their saturated analogs. Such a conversion could in principle be achieved either by one electron oxidation or by one electron reduction. We reported our initial results in the former area (7, eq. 2), which demonstrated a) a rapid second one electron oxidation follows

$$MoH_4P_4 + 2\,Ag^+ + \overset{MeCN}{\Rightarrow} MoH_2(MeCN)_2P_4{}^{2+} + H_2 + 2\,Ag^\circ \qquad (2)$$

the initial oxidation (employing silver as oxidant in acetonitrile) and b) evolution of H_2, a two electron reduction, to return molybdenum to its initial oxidation state. Silver metal is formed. In an effort to understand the mechanism of these oxidations (Ag(I) had not been previously established to be inner sphere, outer sphere, etc.), we moved to the less aggressive Group IB oxidant, Cu(I), which reveals itself to be quite a cooperative electrophile.

Reaction of Cu(I) with ReH$_5$(PMePh$_2$)$_3$

This reaction (note that this rhenium complex is isoelectronic with MoH$_4$P$_4$), executed in THF at and below 25°, was encouraging to us in that there is neither hydrogen evolution nor copper metal deposition. Surprisingly, however, ^{31}P NMR "spectral titrations" showed that the reaction proceeds with a 2 Cu:1 Re stoichiometry, in spite of the fact that Cu(I) is at most a one-electron oxidant. The crystal structure of the resulting product (8), Re$_2$CuH$_{10}$(PMePh$_2$)$_6{}^+$PF$_6{}^+$, shows a linear trimetal array with three μ_2-hydride ligands flanking each of the two Re-Cu vectors (Figure 3). Each rhenium center retains the original three phosphine ligands, and also two

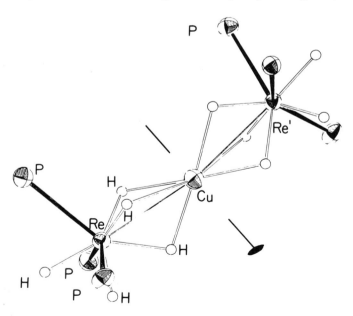

Figure 3. Cu[H$_5$Re(PMePh$_2$)$_3$]$_2{}^+$

hydrides as terminal ligands. We now have the structure of $ReH_5(PMePh_2)_3$, available from a neutron diffraction study (9), and it is significant that the ReP_3 skeleton there duplicates that found in $Cu[ReH_5(PMePh_2)_3]_2^+$; there is thus little distortion of the heavy atom coordination polyhedron on binding the Cu(I) electrophile to three of the five hydrides in ReH_5P_3. The most remarkable feature of our spectroscopic characterization of $Cu[ReH_5(PMePh_2)_3]_2^+$ is the discovery that, while hydride ligands scramble between terminal and bridging sites, they do so only locally, about one or the other rhenium; hydride ligands do not undergo facile (NMR time scale) migration past copper. This result is significant with respect to the energetics of hydride migration on metal alloy surfaces.

Other Hydride Donors

Similar Cu(I) adducts have been isolated and characterized for both the *fac* and *mer*-isomers of $IrH_3(PMe_2Ph)_3$ (10). Moreover, the oxidative stability of these iridium complexes in THF allows the isolation of a corresponding adduct with the more aggressive oxidant Ag(I). Surprisingly (in the light of our results with $ReH_5(PMePh_2)_3$) the polyhydride $Cu[fac\text{-}IrH_3(PMe_2Ph)_3]_2^+$ has only two of the three hydride ligands of each iridium center bridging to copper.

Redox Reactions

An electrochemical study of the one-electron oxidation of Cp_2WH_2 has been carried out (11) and reveals the transient character of the species $Cp_2WH_2^+$. We find that Cp_2MH_2 (M = Mo and W) reacts with $Cu(NCMe)_4^+$ in THF to give $Cu(H_2MCp_2)_2^+$. A single-crystal X-ray diffraction determination of the structure of this compound (as the PF_6^- salt) reveals a linear trimetallic array in the cation with four μ_2-hydride ligands. The crystal contains two crystallographically independent cations, and these show distinctly different dihedral angles between the two $Mo(\mu\text{-}H)_2Cu$ planes (31° and 51°). This is diagnostic of a copper center which has no strong preference for tetrahedral vs. planar coordination geometry (in the CuH_4 unit).

It is possible to tie together the above inner sphere electron transfer preredox intermediates with authentic redox chemistry by returning to Ag(I), in its reactions with Cp_2WH_2. We have established the following reaction (Scheme I), by NMR titrations and by resolving coupling constants between hydride and silver centers. While the 2:1 (W:Ag) complex is redox-stable,

$$AgH_2WCp_2^+ + Cp_2WH_2$$
$$\Uparrow \Downarrow THF$$
$$\quad\quad THF$$
$$2\,Cp_2WH_2 + Ag^+ \;\Rightarrow\; Ag(H_2WCp_2)_2^+$$
$$MeCN \Downarrow Ag^+$$
$$2\,Ag^\circ + Cp_2WH_3^+ + Cp_2WH(NCMe)^+$$

Scheme I

addition of additional Ag^+ in MeCN leads to immediate deposition of Ag°. Thus, when the stoichiometry appropriate for 1-electron oxidation (1 Ag^+:1 W) is achieved in acetonitrile, this electron transfer does indeed occur, but the product detected is not $Cp_2W^VH_2{}^+$, but rather its disproportionation products $Cp_2W^{VI}H_3{}^+$ and $Cp_2W^{IV}H(NCMe)^+$. These products are not those found upon electrochemical oxidation (11), a result which may speak for mechanistic differences. Indeed, a recent structural report (12) of the dichloride adduct of $(CpMoH_2Cu)_2{}^{2+}$ suggests that the second equivalent of Ag^+ may add to $Ag(H_2WCp_2)_2{}^+$ to give an adduct of structure $\underset{\sim}{I}$, and electron transfer and geminate proton transfer

$$2+$$

$$\underset{\sim}{I}$$

in such an aggregate may be responsible for the different products seen from electrochemical and chemical oxidation. The polyhydride cluster character of these species is thus manifest in the reaction products.

Conclusion

Group IB electrophiles (oxidants), when coordinated to acetonitrile (an apparent good leaving group) and accompanied only by "non-coordinating" counterions ($PF_6{}^-$, $BF_4{}^-$) seem to provide an effective "glue" about which cluster polyhydrides can be constructed. These, together with the phosphine hydride clusters of copper alone, offer new reagents whose hydride transfer capabilities are currently under study.

Acknowledgement

This work was supported by the National Science Foundation (Grant CHE 83-05281), Johnson, Matthey Company, Cleveland Refractory Metals, and the Gulf Oil Foundation.

References and Footnotes

1. H. L. Kung, *Catal. Rev., 22,* 235 (1980).
2. J. Goedkoop and A. Andresen, *Acta Cryst., 8,* 118 (1955).
3. M. R. Churchill, S. A. Bezman, J. A. Osborn and J. Wormald, *Inorg. Chem., 11,* 1818 (1972).
4. T. Greiser and E. Weiss, *Chem. Ber., 109,* 3142 (1976).
5. D. M. Ho and R. Bau, *Inorg. Chim. Acta, 84,* 213 (1984).
6. T. H. Lemmen, to be published.

7. L. F. Rhodes, J. D. Zubkowski, K. Folting, J. C. Huffman and K. G. Caulton, *Inorg. Chem., 21,* 4185 (1982).
8. L. F. Rhodes, J. C. Huffman and K. G. Caulton, *J. Am. Chem. Soc., 105,* 5137 (1983).
9. T. J. Emge, T. F. Koetzle, J. W. Bruno and K. G. Caulton, *Inorg. Chem., 23,* 4012 (1984).
10. L. G. Rhodes, J. C. Huffman and K. G. Caulton *J. Am. Chem. Soc., 106,* 6874 (1984).
11. R. J. Klingler, J. C. Huffman and J. K. Kochi, *J. Am. Chem. Soc., 102,* 208 (1980).
12. E. B. Lobkovskii, A. B. Aripovskii, V. K. Bel'skii and B. M. Bulychev, *Koord. Khim,. 8,* 104 (1982).

Biological & Inorganic Copper Chemistry,
ISBN 0-940030-11-X, Eds., K. D. Karlin & J. Zubieta, Adenine Press, ©Adenine Press, 1985

Some Synthetic and Structural Aspects of Neutral Organocuprate Reagents $Cu_nLi_mR_{n+m}$: The Asymmetric Bonding Configuration of the Bridging Organo Group

Gerard van Koten(1)[a]**, Johann T.B.H. Jastrzebski**[a]**,**
Casper H. Stam[b] **and Christian Brevard**[c]**,**
[a]Anorganisch Chemisch Laboratorium, [b]Laboratorium voor Kristallografie,
University of Amsterdam, The Netherlands and
[c]SADIS Bruker Spectrospin, 67160
Wissembourg, France

Abstract

The number of synthetic applications of organocuprates is growing rapidly but the mechanistic understanding only slowly. Development of the latter aspect requires knowledge concerning the structural features (in the solid and solution) of these reagents which to date is still very limited. Recent studies in our laboratory have provided information concerning the structures in the solid of the unique series R_4Li_4 (*1a*), $R_4Cu_2Li_2$ (*2a*), and $R_4Au_2Li_2$ (*4a*) where R is $C_6H_4CH_2NMe_2-2$.

These structures encompass for the first time: i, the change in the metal core going from an organolithium to a cuprate (or aurate) species and ii, the change of the aryl-metal bonding from a purely symmetrical two electron-four center $(2e-4c)$ $R-Li_3$ bonding in the aryllithium *1a*, via an asymmetric $2e-3c$ $R-CuLi$ bonding in the cuprate *2a* to a $R-AuLi$ bonding with an almost pure $2e-2c$ $R-Au$ bond in the aurate *4a*.

Information concerning the solution structure of *1a*, *2a* and *4a*, that is also pertinent to the interpretation of the reactivity of cuprates, comprises: i the ^{109}Ag and ^7Li NMR spectra of analogous $R_4Ag_2Li_2$ that establish the retention of the neutral M_2Li_2 core in non-coordinating solvents and ii, the influence of the solvent on the structure, e.g. the R_4Li_4 structure of *1a* in Et_2O breaks down to a R_2Li_2·4THF structure in THF.

Based on this new information an analysis will be presented of the factors influencing the bonding of organo groups in organocuprate species.

Introduction

The number of synthetic applications of organocuprates is growing rapidly (2a) but the mechanistic understanding (2b) of organocuprate reactions only slowly. Development of the latter aspect requires knowledge concerning the structural features of these reagents both in the solid and in solution. To date the available information is still limited (3). The main application of organocuprates is their use in C−C bond forming reactions as is outlined schematically in Scheme 1:

$$R-M \xrightarrow{\text{Cu}^I X} \text{Organocopper reagent} \xrightarrow[\text{substrate}]{} \text{C-C coupling products}$$

M=Li or Mg   "RCu","R$_2$Cu$^-$M$^+$" or "RCu.MX"

Reactivity of the organocopper reagent depends on:
1. **Method of preparation**
2. **Presence of metal salts**
3. **Type of solvent used**
4. **Presence of additional ligands.**

The organolithium or -magnesium reagent is made in situ and converted by addition of the appropriate equivalents of a copper(I) salt or compound (e.g. CuCN, CuC≡CR, etc.) into an organocopper (cuprate) reagent. Accordingly, the resulting mixture comprises a complex get-together of various metals (Li,Mg,Cu), anions (halides, CN,BF$_4$) and even in many cases of organo groups also (i.e., organo groups that form a stable bond to the copper lithium core, vide infra, and those that are transferrable to the substrate) (3). Furthermore, the reactivity as well as the reproducibility of these reagents have been found to be, sometimes critically, dependent on a series of factors (see Scheme 1: 1-4). It is obvious, therefore, that labelling these cuprate reagents as "RCu", "RR'CuM", "R$_2$Cu$^-$" etc. is a serious oversimplification. This is misleading as to the nature of the organocuprate species present in solution and in particular hampers the mechanistic understanding of the cuprate reactions.

A more systematic study of the structural and bonding aspects of the cuprate reagents seems appropriate. However, so far almost all structural studies of organocuprates *in solution* using NMR spectroscopy have been carried out on mixtures of the type described above. For example, reports have appeared for alkyl-copperlithium and -coppermagnesium salt mixtures (4). In another case an elegant study was carried out on methylsilver lithium species by ^{1}H, ^{13}C, ^{31}P and ^{7}Li NMR spectroscopy using the propitious magnetic properties of silver (vide infra) for detection of the connectivity of the various groups to silver and lithium (5). Even this study, however, lacked detailed structural information to warrant sensible speculation as to both the nature of the species present in solution and the exchange reactions in which they are involved.

The general stability of cuprate species is low; they are extremely sensitive towards hydrolysis and oxidation while the thermal stability increases in the series alkyl<alkenyl~aryl<alkynyl (3). For the more stable aryl species some structural information is available (3,6,7). Actually, one of the compounds which is also a subject of this paper (*2a,* Figure 1) was the first and seems still to be the only pure cuprate reagent of which the structure *in solution* is known with certainty (6). This species has in solution and solid state (vide infra) a $Cu_2Li_2R_4$ stoichiometry and three center, two electron aryl-to-CuLi bonding.

In this paper we present a rather detailed picture of the structural and reactivity aspects of the interesting series of aryl-lithium, -copper and -copper lithium compounds as well as corresponding silver and gold species shown in Figure 1. The choice of these particular species for more detailed investigation is not accidental. It exemplifies the strategy we have been following in our study of the structure-reactivity relationship of cuprates, i.e. the chosen series fulfills a number of important criteria:

Series A, $R=$ [structure: phenyl ring with R" CHNMe$_2$ substituent at top, M substituent, and R' substituent at bottom]

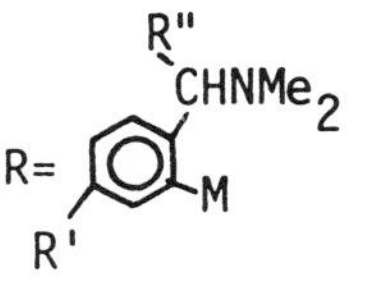

a $R'=H$ and b $R'=Me$.

$M=Li$, 1; $\frac{1}{2}CuLi$, 2; $\frac{1}{2}$ AgLi, 3;

$\frac{1}{2}$ AuLi, $\underset{\sim}{4}$; Cu, 5, Ag, 6, Au, 7;

$AuPPh_3$,8,

Series B, $R=$ Me—[phenyl ring]—M

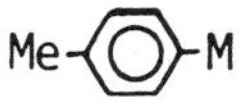

$M=Li$, 9; $\frac{1}{2}CuLi(OEt_2)$, 10;

$\frac{1}{2}AuLi(OEt_2)$, 11; Cu, 12.

i. the series comprises all stages encountered during preparation of the cuprate reagents.

ii. The compounds are formed in high yields, i.e. they are not minor products such as are encountered in the reactions of, for example, RLi with CuBr to form "RCu" or "R$_2$CuLi";

iii. They can be isolated pure thus allowing careful structural characterizations (X-ray, NMR, mol. wt. determinations);

iv. The compounds have sufficient thermal stability in solution to enable multinuclear NMR spectroscopic study over a sensible temperature range, i.e. not only the structure but also the dynamic behaviour in solution of these compounds can be studied;

v.   The compounds have acceptable solubilities in different solvents, e.g. in Et_2O and C_6H_6, which allows study of the effects of the different preferences of Li and Cu towards ether coordination on the stability of the cuprate species.

vi. Comparison of series A and B (Figure 1) may provide insight into the effect that a potentially coordinating substituent in the ortho-position of the C—M bond has on the structural and bonding features of cuprates. This information is relevant, because the cuprates used in organic synthesis often contain such coordinating substitutents (8). In the following sections some recent results of our studies in this area will be discussed in the broader context of the understanding of the structure and reactivity of cuprates.

Synthetic Aspects

Since the isolation of *pure* aryllithium, -metal IB and -ate complexes thereof seems not to be a trivial affair (9) a short outline of the synthetic routes we are following will be given below.

A. Aryllithium Compounds (12)

Pure, i.e. lithium salt-free (9), aryllithium compounds of the series B have been obtained by using the iodide-lithium exchange reaction 1 in apolar solvents (13).

$$nArI \ + \ \tfrac{n}{4}(Bu^n_4Li_4) \ \xrightarrow{\text{Hexane}} \ (ArLi)_n \ + \ nBu^nI \qquad (1)$$

$$\tfrac{1}{n}(ArLi)_n \ + \ RI \ \longrightarrow \ ArR \ + \ LiI \qquad (2)$$

$$R=Bu^n \ \text{or} \ Ar \qquad Ar=o\text{-},m\text{-},\text{or} \ p\text{-tolyl} \quad 9$$

The aryllithium compound crystallizes out from the reaction solution while secondary products (Bu^nI) remain dissolved. The cross-coupling reaction 2, which is a potential source of LiI, is blocked in hexane.

Reaction 1 is specific for aryl iodides. The corresponding aryl bromides only metallate in ether solvents but then reaction 2 also takes place and formation of LiBr interferes with the isolation of the pure, salt free, aryllithium compounds (vide infra).

The aryllithium compounds with the $CH(R'')NMe_2$ ortho-substituent (series A) are synthesized via the hydrogen-lithium exchange route 3 (11,12). This reaction, which in the case of $R''=H$ takes about 19 h for completion when Bu^nLi is used, is extremely clean (only butane is formed).

$$\text{R'}=\text{H(a) or Me(b)}$$
$$\text{R''}=\text{H,Me,Et,Pr}^i \text{ or Bu}^t$$

Reaction times:
For $\text{R''}=\text{H}$: Bu^nLi 19 h
   Bu^tLi 5 min.

When using arenes, RH, containing a benzylic substituent R'' of increasing size (see eqn. 3) we have recently found that the reaction slows down in the series $R''=\text{H}\gg\text{Me}\gg\text{Et}$ while no metallation is observed for $R''=\text{Pr}^i$ or Bu^t (14).

Furthermore, in the case of $R''=\text{Me}$ we have found evidence that mixed $(\text{aryl})_{4-n}$-$(\text{butyl})_n\text{Li}_4\cdot\text{RH}_n$ intermediates are present in solution which leads to a mixture of inseparable aryllithium compounds. The latter problem can be solved by using the more basic tert.-butyllithium reagent. For $R''=\text{H,Me}$ or Et solutions of the pure aryllithium compounds were obtained in extremely short reaction times (5 minutes) (14).

B. Arylmetal IB Compounds (3)

General requirements for the successful synthesis and isolation of pure, uncomplexed, arylmetal IB compounds of both series A and B are:

  i. the use of pure aryllithium compounds which may contain lithium halides but must be free from other metal halides or other ligands,

 ii. the correct order of addition of the metal IB halides or complexes and the aryllithium compounds and

iii. the use of exact 1/1 molar ratios of the reagents as well as the appropriate reaction temperatures.

There is ample evidence that most of the arylmetal IB compounds can react with metal halide salts (3,15,16). The latter salts may be present as a result of the applied transmetallation reaction (when Grignard or organozinc reagents are used) or because excess of metal halide is applied.

These metal salts are often not present as separable contaminants but instead are integral parts of the polynuclear structures of these arylmetal IB compounds: e.g. in $\text{Cu}_6\text{Br}_2(\text{C}_6\text{H}_4\text{NMe}_2\text{-}2)_4$ (16) or in $\text{Cu}_4\text{Br}_2\{(Z)\text{-}(2\text{-Me}_2\text{NC}_6\text{H}_4)\text{C}=\text{C(Me)-}(\text{C}_6\text{H}_4\text{Me}\text{-}4)\}_2$ (17).

The presence of additional ligands (cf. i) may lead to ionic compounds: e.g. $[(\text{mesityl})_2\text{Cu}]^-[\text{CuDiphos}_2]^+$ (18) or to secondary cleavage reactions, see eqn. *4* (19).

$$\text{(structure: } C_6H_4\text{-}CH_2NMe_2\text{-Cu)} + 2 \text{ Diphos} \xrightarrow[RT]{C_6H_6} CuPPh_2(\text{Diphos}) + Ph_2PCH=CH_2$$

$$+ \text{(structure: } C_6H_4\text{-}CH_2NMe_2\text{-H)} \qquad (4)$$

A synthesis in which the order of addition of the reagents is important is given in eqn. *5* (15):

$$\text{(structure with } R'', CHNMe_2, R', Li) \xrightarrow[-\frac{1}{2}LiBr]{\frac{1}{2}CuBr} \frac{1}{2}\text{(structure with } R'', CHNMe_2, R', CuLi)_2 \xrightarrow[-\frac{1}{2}LiBr]{\frac{1}{2}CuBr} \text{(structure with } R'', CHNMe_2, R', Cu)$$

e.g. *2*   solvent: Et_2O (5)

For the synthesis of the arylcopper compounds of series A it is necessary to add the ether insoluble CuBr to the aryllithium solution or suspension. The reactions for R″=H or Me proceed via the ether soluble copper lithium complexes, e.g. *2*, to give finally the less soluble arylcopper compounds when the Li/Cu ratio reaches unity. In contrast, reversed addition leads to direct formation of insoluble, stable aryl-copper-copper bromide coordination polymers, e.g. $Cu(C_6H_4CH_2NMe_2-2)\cdot nCuBr$ (15), from which the pure arylcopper species can not be isolated.

The synthesis of the arylgold(I) compounds *7* is interesting because here we take advantage of our knowledge that the arylgold lithium compounds of type *4* do not react with, for example, phosphines (20). Accordingly, to prepare pure *7a*, *4a* is isolated first and then reacted with Me_3SnBr to give the ligand free arylgold species *7a*; see eqn. *6* (20):

$$\text{(structure: } CH_2NMe_2, Li) \xrightarrow[-LiBr:PPh_3]{\frac{1}{2}AuBr(PPh_3)} \frac{1}{2}\text{(structure: } CH_2NMe_2, AuLi)_2 \xrightarrow[\substack{-LiBr;\\-Me_3ArSn}]{Me_3SnBr} \text{(structure: } CH_2NMe_2, Au) \qquad (6)$$

4a   *7a*

Detailed experimental descriptions for the preparations of the other compounds can be found in the papers cited in reference 3.

C. Bis(aryl)metal IB lithium (-ate) Complexes

The ate complexes *2-4* (11,20,21), *10* (22) and *11* (22) can be formed directly from the 2/1 reaction of the aryllithium complexes and the appropriate metal IB salts (cf. eqns. 5 and 6). However, the preferred route leading directly to solutions of the pure ate complexes is the 1/1 reaction of the pure aryllithium and arylmetal IB complexes. For example, mixing p-tolyllithium (vide infra) and -copper in a 1/1 molar ratio in benzene leads to the formation of the insoluble ate complex CuLi(p-tolyl)$_2$. On addition of exactly one equivalent of diethyl ether the latter complex dissolves completely in benzene forming *10* (22):

$$4\text{Li}(p\text{-tol}) + \text{Cu}_4(p\text{-tol})_4 \xrightarrow{\text{C}_6\text{H}_6} 4\text{CuLi}(p\text{-tol})_2 \xrightarrow{4\text{Et}_2\text{O}} 2\text{Cu}_2\text{Li}_2(p\text{-tol})_4 2\text{Et}_2\text{O} \quad (7)$$

insoluble   soluble   insoluble   10,soluble

Similar observations were made during the synthesis of the corresponding gold(I) lithium species *11*.

The ate complexes *2-4* have likewise been prepared by the 1/1 reaction of the tetranuclear aryllithium and arylmetal IB compounds in benzene or toluene. These ate complexes are very soluble in both ether and aromatic solvents.

Structural Aspects

A. Aryllithium Compounds

Until recently little was known concerning the structures of aryllithium compounds (9b,23). For Li(C$_6$H$_3$CH$_2$NMe$_2$−2−Me−5), *1b,* a tetranuclear structure in benezene was proposed based on cryoscopic molecular weight measurements (10,11). This proposal is now supported by the crystal structure (10) of *1a* shown schematically in Figure 2. The similarities of this structure with those of a subsequently reported unsubstituted phenyllithium-etherate, *13* (9b), are striking. (see Figure 2). In both compounds the aryl groups are four center, two electron bonded to a Li$_3$ face of the central Li$_4$ tetrahedron. Accordingly each Li atom takes part in three electron-deficient Li−C interactions using orbitals which are in a trigonal planar arrangement. Additional electron donation of a nitrogen lone pair of the well-positioned intramolecular ligand in *1a,* occurs to an empty Li orbital perpendicular to the

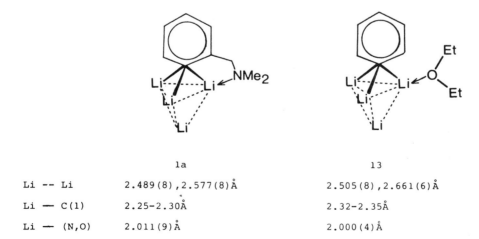

	1a	*13*
Li -- Li	2.489(8),2.577(8)Å	2.505(8),2.661(6)Å
Li — C(1)	2.25-2.30Å	2.32-2.35Å
Li — (N,O)	2.011(9)Å	2.000(4)Å

Figure 2. Schematic structures of *1a* (10) (involving intramolecular N donor coordination) and of the unsubstituted phenyllithium-etherate *13* (9b) (with O donor coordination of the diethyl ether molecule). Only the occupation of one triangular Li$_3$ face by the aryl ring is shown.

latter trigonal plane. In the unsubstituted phenyllithium structure the role of this N donor atom is taken over by an oxygen lone pair of the coordinated ether molecule. Power showed that LiBr can be incorporated into the polynuclear structure of phenyllithium. In (PhLi·OEt$_2$)$_3$LiBr one bridging phenyl group has been replaced by a four center bonded Br anion (9b).

Table I

Some Natural Abundance ^{13}C and ^{6}Li NMR Data of Some Aryllithium Compounds in Toluene-d$_8$[a]

Compounds	Pure[c]	Et$_2$O		THF[d]		TMEDA
		1 eq.	excess	1 eq.	excess	
i. A series						
1b (structure: CH$_2$NMe$_2$, Li, Me)	176.0(12)[e] [3.58] Tetramer	N.C.[f]	N.C.[g]	189.2(20)[h,i] [2.74] Dimer	j	189.4(20) — Dimer
15 (structure: CH$_2$NMe$_2$, Li, CH$_2$NMe$_2$)	189.3(20)[h] [2.41] Dimer	N.C.	N.C.	N.C.	N.C.	N.C.
ii. B series						
13 (structure: Li)	Insol.	174.6(~11)[e] [1.93] Tetramer	174.7(~11)[e] [1.90]	175.9(~11)[e] [2.01] Tetramer	188.7(19.5)[h] [1.47] Dimer	186.8(19.5)[h] [1.47] Dimer
9 (structure: Me, Li)	Insol	170.2(~11)[e] [1.80] Tetramer	170.9(~11)[e] [1.90]	171.3(11)[e] [2.17] Tetramer	178.7(20)[h] Dimer	182.8(20)[h] [1.89] Dimer
(structure: Li, Me)	Insol.	Insol.	182.8 [1.98]	185.5 [1.70]	188.1(20)[h] [1.38] Dimer	189.3(20)[h] [1.72] Dimer

[a]Chemical shift data: on first line δ^{13}C with J(^{13}C(1), ^{7}Li)[b] between brackets, on second line δ^6Li (ppm relative to 70% LiCl in D$_2$O external) and on third line assignment of these data in terms of a structure. Spectra unless otherwise indicated recorded at 293 K.

[b]Expected multiplicity for ^{13}C(1) in a two center, two electron bond, four equidistant lines (~40 Hz) of equal intensity; in a three center, two electron bond (*dimer*), seven lines (~20Hz) with 1:2:3:4:3:2:1 intensities and in a four center, two electron bond (*tetramer*), ten lines (11 Hz) with 1:3:6:10:12:12:10:6:3:1 intensities.

[c]Pure in toluene-d$_8$.

[d]Added to the toluene-d$_8$ solutions as THF-d$_8$. Excess is up to three equivalents.

[e]Linewidth of 110 Hz which points to a J(^{13}C(1), ^{7}Li) of about 11 Hz, i.e. with four center, two electron bonding.

[f]N.C. no change of the NMR data reported in the previous column: i.e. no change of the structural features.

[g]Also in pure Et$_2$O.

[h]Seven line pattern, see footnote b.

[i]Only one half of *1* has been converted into the dinuclear species *14*, see eqn. (8). Data of the dimer *14* are given.

[j]*1* has been completely converted into *14* after addition of two equivalents of THF-d$_8$.

In a ^{13}C and Li NMR spectroscopic study we are currently comparing the solution features of lithium halide free aryllithium compounds of the A and B series. The preliminary results, which are presented in Table 1, are pertinent to the question of the role of the N-donors in the structures of the A series compounds. The multiplicity of the ^{13}C(1) resonance as well as the size (25) of J(^{13}C(1),^{7}Li) provides conclusive evidence concerning the number of C(1)...Li interactions and thus to the size of the Li core (cf. footnote b in Table 1), i.e., characterization of the solution structures can be based on these data. (The present discussion will be restricted to the situations observed in the slow exchange limit; i.e., when inter- and intramolecular exchange processes are slow on the NMR time scales).

A most important observation concerning the compounds of the A and B series is their different solubility in toluene-d$_8$. Unlike the readily soluble A series, methyl substituted and unsubstituted phenyllithium compounds are only soluble when one equivalent of Et$_2$O or THF (per Li) is added. The NMR data indicate that these latter compounds are dissolved as tetrameric species with a structure similar to that of Ph$_4$Li$_4$·(OEt$_2$)$_4$ shown in Figure 2. This reveals that apart from its role in the metallation reaction (14) shown in eqn. 3, the N donor substituent functions as a well-positioned "intramolecular solvent" molecule (27).

The tetrameric structures of both *1b* and *13* (*9*) are retained when excess Et$_2$O is added to their toluene solutions. However, the data in Table 1 also show that addition of THF to *1* results in a break-down of its tetranuclear structure into a dimeric one, see *14* in eqn. *8*:

$$R_4Li_4 \xrightarrow{\text{8THF}} 2 \qquad \qquad \text{(8)}$$

1

14

The structural features of *14* are similar to those of well-documented Ph$_2$Li$_2$·2−TMEDA, *15* (28). The δ^{13}C and J(^{13}C(1), ^{7}Li) data of *14* and *15* support this view. ^{13}C NMR data of the CH$_2$NMe$_2$ substituent in *14* indicated that the N-atoms are not coordinating to Li.

The latter observation is important in that it reveals the role of the N−Li coordination in *1* and explains the effects of coordinating substituents in aryllithium clusters in general. Since an uncoordinated CH$_2$NMe$_2$ ortho substituent can clearly be seen to produce a very bulky aryl group a tetrameric aggregate would in the first instance be anticipated to be less favoured than a dinuclear unit. Indeed, the structure of *1a* shows that N−Li coordination compensates for the steric bulk a free CH$_2$NMe$_2$ group otherwise would represent. In contrast, the structure of *14* shows that in case the solvent molecules take over from N coordination, the dinuclear structures (with three center, two electron bonded aryl groups) have bridging configurations that provide room for the free CH$_2$NMe$_2$ substitutent, i.e. those rotamers that have the aryl's plane close to or exactly perpendicular to the Li...Li axis. It must be expected that it is also this aryl orientation which provides optimum orbital interaction in a three center, two electron C(1)Li$_2$ bond, cf, ref. 30a.

This novel idea concerning the influence of ortho substituents on the aggregate stability of aryllithium compounds is further substantiated by the following observations:

  i. The presence of two ortho−CH$_2$NMe$_2$ substituents as in *15* (see Table 1) stabilizes the dinuclear aryllithium structure. The aryl groups are three center, two electron bonded to the Li$_2$ pair like in *14* (For a figure, see ref. 10). Both N donor atoms coordinate to lithium. Their excellent positioning for this coordination is reflected by the fact that neither Et$_2$O nor THF can compete for the coordination sites at the Li atoms.

  ii. The preference for the dinuclear structure in the presence of coordinating solvents is less pronounced for unsubstituted phenyllithium. Even for o-tolyllithium equilibrium mixtures of the tetra- and dinuclear aggregates are observed at low temperature. However, when two ortho groups are present, as in xylyllithium, tetranuclear aggregates can not be detected at all and in THF the dinuclear aggregate Li$_2$(xylyl)$_2$·4THF is observed.

Full details of this study will be published shortly (14).

B. Arylmetal IB Compounds (3)

Structural data in the solid exist for Cu$_4$(C$_6$H$_3$CH$_2$NMe$_2$−2−Me−5)$_4$, *5b,* and a schematic structure is shown in Figure 3. The actual structure contains the four copper atoms in a butterfly arrangement with a short bridged Cu...Cu distances of 2.37 Å (3,31). The aryl groups are three center, two electron bonded and the N donor atoms coordinate only weakly to the Cu centers.

Reasons for the observed differences in stereochemistry at C(1) (i.e. 4c,2e vs. 3c,2e bridging in *1* and *5b,* respectively) and at the metal atoms between these aryllithium and -copper(I) species are not apparent. Earlier we proposed (10) as a possible factor the much stronger preference of Li for N coordination that would thus stabilize the Li$_4$C$_4$ core of *1*. This explanation seems now to have been rendered invalid by the recent structure of unsubstituted phenyllithium etherate (13) and the

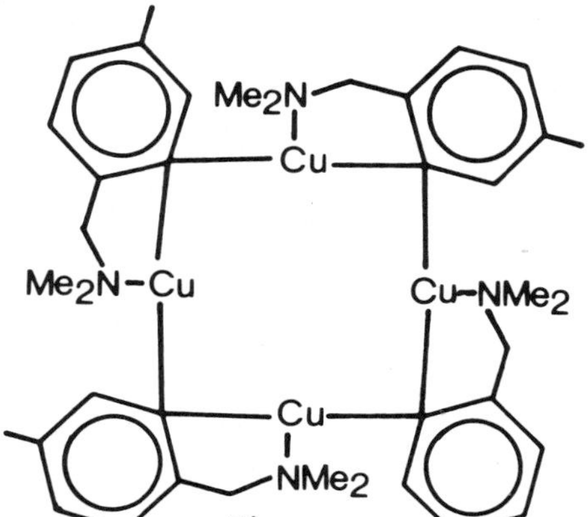

Figure 3. Schematic structures of two arylmetal IB compounds *5b* (for X-ray see ref. 31) and *7* (20).

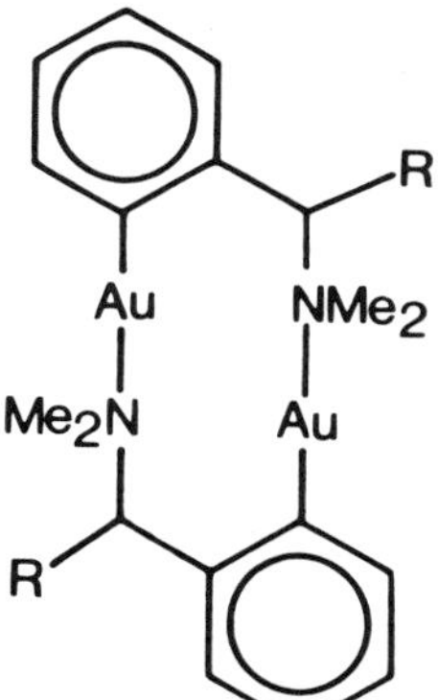

results of our NMR study of the solution behaviour of various aryllithium compounds, vide supra.

Comparison of the known aryllithium and -copper structures shows that although both Li and Cu(I) have vacant s and p orbitals for bonding it is the Li atom which favours the higher number of bonding interactions, cf. Figures 2 and 3. This is a generally observed phenomenon since tetrahedral structures (with four center, two electron bonded organo groups) for various other alkyl- (24) and alkynyllithium (26) compounds have also been reported. In contrast in most of the known arylcopper(I) structures (as well as $Cu_4(CH_2SiMe_3)_4$) (32) the copper(I) atoms show linear bonding and three center, two electron bonded aryl groups, e.g. in Cu_5(mesityl)$_5$ (33), while in a few cases three bonding interactions are present, e.g. in *5b* and in $Cu_6Br_2(C_6H_4NMe_2-2)_4$ (16).

It must be noted that in a three center, two electron bonding situation the aryl ring is perpendicular to the Cu...Cu axis. This is the groundstate situation especially preferred when ortho-substituents are present because in this rotamer the interaction between these substitutents and the bridged Cu atoms is at its minimum, see discussions in refs. 3 and 34. Accordingly, it is not the (weak) (34b) coordination of the donor atom with the Cu atom that stabilizes the Cu−C bond in *1*. It is more particularly the bulkiness of this ortho-substituent which stabilizes the perpendicular rotamer and thus the $C(1)Cu_2$ bonding. This is nicely reflected in the structures of recently reported mesityl metal IB compounds. Both linear bonding at each metal IB atom and the perpendicular mesityl groups are present and this leads to the flat $M_nC(1)_n$ (M=Cu,Ag or Au) cores in these M_n(mesityl)$_n$ structures (33).

Finally it is tempting to speculate as to whether the structure of $Li_4(C_6H_4CH_2NMe_2-2)_4$, *1a*, mimics the transition state of an intramolecular exchange route for the aryl groups in $Cu_4(C_6H_3CH_2NMe_2-2-R-5)_4$, *5*. This process would involve folding of the butterfly Cu_4 arrangement into a tetrahedral one (cf. *1a* in Figure 2) and concomitant change of the aryl bonding from a three center, two electron into a four center, two electron one. The reversed process, but now involving opening of a different set of Cu_2 edges, would lead to intramolecular exchange.

The aryl silver species (*6*) have most probably Ag_4R_4 structures similar to those found for the corresponding copper compounds *5*. The gold compound $AuC_6H_4CH_2NMe_2-2$, *7*, has a dinuclear structure. Based on molecular weight measurements, ¹H and ¹³C NMR data and on ¹⁹⁷Au Mössbauer data the structure shown in Figure 3 has been proposed (20).

C. Arylmetal IB Lithium (Ate) Compounds

The tetranuclear structures, $M_2Li_2R_4$, have been proposed for the neutral ate compounds *2-4, 10* and *11* in solution (see Figure 4) on the basis of molecular weight data (cryoscopic in benzene) as well as ¹H and ¹³C NMR data (10,11,20,30b).

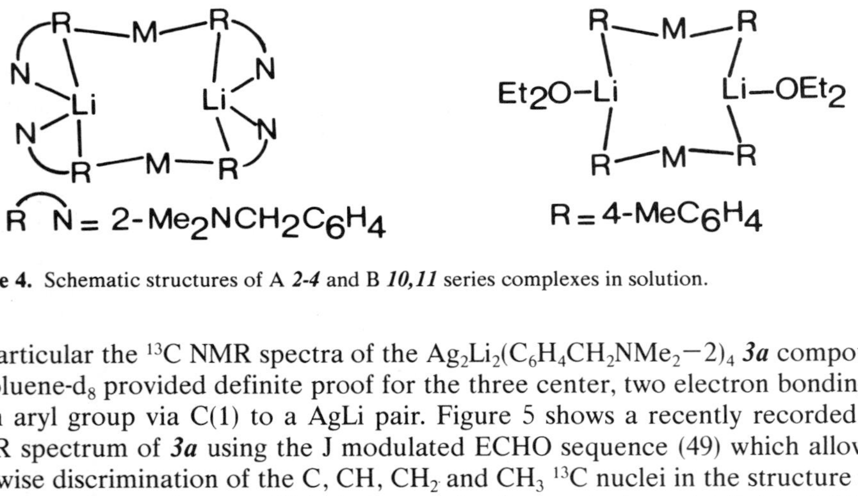

$$\widehat{R \quad N} = 2\text{-}Me_2NCH_2C_6H_4 \qquad\qquad R = 4\text{-}MeC_6H_4$$

Figure 4. Schematic structures of A *2-4* and B *10,11* series complexes in solution.

In particular the ¹³C NMR spectra of the $Ag_2Li_2(C_6H_4CH_2NMe_2-2)_4$ *3a* compound in toluene-d_8 provided definite proof for the three center, two electron bonding of each aryl group via C(1) to a AgLi pair. Figure 5 shows a recently recorded ¹³C NMR spectrum of *3a* using the J modulated ECHO sequence (49) which allows a pairwise discrimination of the C, CH, CH_2 and CH_3 ¹³C nuclei in the structure and thus a complete assignment (35). An interesting feature is the multiplicity of C(1) as a result of $J(^{107}Ag,^{13}C(1))$, $J(^{109}Ag,^{13}C(1))$, and $J(^7Li, ^{13}C(1))$ (see also ref. 21).

Furthermore, $J(^{107,109}Ag, ^{13}C)$ (36) is also present on C(2), C(6) and even on the benzylic C resonance.

The ¹⁰⁹Ag INEPT NMR spectrum (37) using the $^3J(^{107,109}Ag, ^1H(6))$ (−7.1 Hz) (21) is shown in Figure 6a. It reveals a single line which is in accord with the proposed structure in which Ag...Ag interactions are absent (38) The coupling pattern of

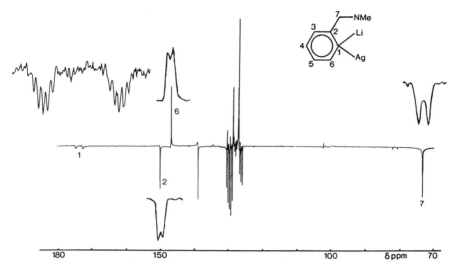

Figure 5. J modulated ECHO ^{13}C NMR spectrum of $Ag_2Li_2(C_6H_4CH_2NMe_2-2)_4$ *3a* at 293 K. $J(^{109}Ag, ^{13}C(1))$ is 136.0 ± 0.8; $J(^7Li, ^{13}C(1))$ is 7.2 ± 0.2 Hz.

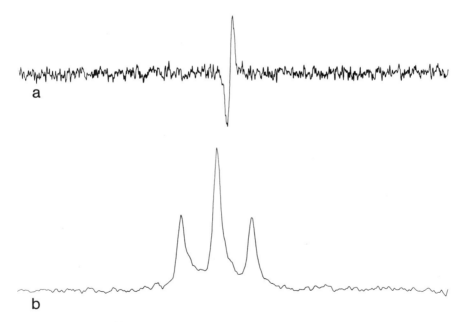

Figure 6. a. ^{1}H coupled ^{109}Ag INEPT NMR spectrum of *3a* in toluene-d_8 at 293 K. δ^{109}Ag is 897.7 ppm (1 M AgNO$_3$/D$_2$O external reference). b. ^{6}Li NMR spectrum of *3a* in toluene-d_8 at 293 K. δ^6Li is -0.10 ppm (1M LiCl/D$_2$O external reference), $J(^{107,109}Ag,^7Li)$ is 3.91 and $J(^{107,109}Ag,^6Li)$ is 1.46 Hz.

^{109}Ag with Li is not observed because of line broadening of the Ag resonance due to small long range ^{109}Ag$-^1$H couplings and to the multiplicity of the ^{109}Ag$-^6$Li.

However, when we recorded the ^{6}Li NMR spectrum of *3a* the triplet pattern shown in Figure 6b was obtained. The 1:2:1 intensity ratio arises from coupling of the Li nuclei with two neighboring ^{107,109}Ag (38) nuclei (vide infra).

The importance of these results goes beyond the confirmation of the structural features of these ate complexes in solution. It demonstrates clearly the power of the multinuclear NMR approach for the study of cluster structures in solution. Even in the present case where a heavy metal nucleus like Ag with a low γ value (e.g. γ ^{109}Ag is −1.2449) is involved.

After many attempts (39) we succeeded in growing single crystals of the cuprate *2a* and aurate *4a,* which were suitable for an X-ray structure determination. Both structures are shown in Figure 7 together with some relevant bond distances and angles.

To our knowledge these structures are the first examples of a structural investigation of a neutral cuprate with characteristic 1/1 Cu/Li atomic ratio (see Introduction) as well as of a neutral aurate. Two other cuprate structures have been reported, i.e. [Cu$_5$Ph$_6$][LiTF$_4$] which in fact is an anionic arylcopper structure (7b,41) and [Li$_2$Cu$_3$Ph$_6$]$_2$[Li$_4$Cl$_2$(Et$_2$O)$_{10}$] in which the Cu/Li ratio in the anionic cluster is 3/2 (7a). The present discussion will be concentrated on the structural features of the cuprate *2* in the solid because the aurate *4* has been the subject of a recent communication (42).

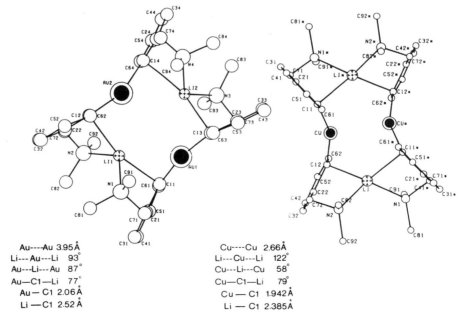

Au----Au 3.95Å	Cu----Cu 2.66Å
Li---Au---Li 93°	Li---Cu---Li 122°
Au---Li---Au 87°	Cu---Li---Cu 58°
Au—C1—Li 77°	Cu—C1—Li 79°
Au—C1 2.06Å	Cu—C1 1.942Å
Li—C1 2.52Å	Li—C1 2.385Å

Figure 7. Structures of the neutral cuprate *2a* and aurate *4a* in the solid. ⊙ is the metal IB nucleus and ⊕ the lithium.

The copper and lithium atoms in *2* are in one plane with Cu—Li distances of 2.755 Å (mean). The aryl groups each bridge a CuLi pair with expected Cu—C(1) and Li—C(1) bond lengths (see Figure 7). These values are comparable with those distances found in the $Cu_3Li_2Ph_6$ anion (7a) (Cu—C(1) 1.923 Å and Li—C(1) 2.240 Å). The four N-donor atoms are exclusively coordinated to lithium with a Li—N distance of 2.139(6) Å.

The bridging configuration of the aryl groups in the various homonuclear aryllithium and -copper compounds is essentially perpendicular (about 80-85°) to the M...M vectors. This has also been found for the $[Cu_5Ph_6]$-anion in which the aryl groups are likewise bridging equivalent metal atoms. The symmetric configuration of the metal-aryl-metal bridges is as expected from the proposed bonding scheme (see Figure 8: A and B): (31,34b) i.e., a combination of three center interactions consisting of the two metal centers and the carbon sp^2 orbital (A) and an antibonding combination of the metal orbitals and the carbon p orbital (B). It is the contribution of the latter interaction B which stabilizes the aryl-M_2 bonding (cf. the role of ortho-substituents in aryllithium and -copper compounds).

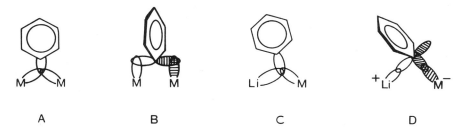

Figure 8. The various bonding interactions of the aryl C(1) sp^2 and metal orbitals M=Cu(I), Ag(I) or Au(I).

The cuprate structure of *2* shows a less symmetric configuration for the aryl bridges. This is as expected when the different orbital sizes and energies of copper and lithium are taken into account. The tilting of the aryl ring into the direction of the lithium indicates a better overlap of the carbon sp^2 and copper orbitals (C). However, it must be noted that any contribution of interaction C still implies a bonding between the carbon sp^2 and lithium orbitals. This is supported by the $J(^{13}C(1),^7Li)$ of 7.0 Hz indicating that s electron density is still present in the C—Li interaction of *2*. Furthermore, interaction C comprises a bonding combination of M and Li orbitals which is reflected by the $J(^{107,109}Ag,Li)$ (see Figure 6) observed in the Li spectra of the neutral silver lithium compound *3*.

The same asymmetric bridging configuration for the aryl bridges has been found in $[Cu_3Li_2Ph_6]$ cuprate anion (7a) and it is plausible to assume that this will be a general feature of bridging organo groups (e.g. alkyls, aryls, alkynyls, etc) in cuprates. Accordingly, we propose that $Cu_2Li_2(p\text{-tolyl})_4\cdot2Et_2O$ (see Figure 4) has structural features similar to those observed for *2a* (see Figure 7): i.e. a planar Cu_2Li_2 arrangement with the p-tolyl groups asymmetrically bridging between Cu and Li. Since coordinating substituents are absent coordination of a solvent molecule to each of the lithium centers is required. In this respect it is relevant to recall our observation described above for the dissolution of $Cu_2Li_2(p\text{-tolyl})_4$ in toluene on addition of 2 equivalents of diethyl ether (i.e. formation of $Cu_2Li_2(p\text{-Tol})_4 \cdot 2Et_2O$; see eqn. (7)). Strong coordination of these Et_2O molecules is indicated by the large ^1H NMR chemical shift changes of the ether's CH_2 and CH_3 protons (22). Likewise the structure of $Cu_2Li_2Me_4$ in Et_2O most probably consists of the same basic $Cu_2Li_2C(1)_4 \cdot 2Et_2O$ framework present in *2a*, i.e., a planar Cu_2Li_2 arrangement with the methyl groups bridging asymmetrically between Cu and Li via a three center, two electron interaction. It is interesting to note here that Pearson et al. (43) reported that using solution X-ray scattering data the Cu...Cu distances in $Cu_2Li_2Me_4$ in diethyl ether can be estimated at 4.4 Å. This is not at all in agreement with the Cu...Cu distance of 2.6660(8) Å (44) in our cuprate *2*, thus substantiating earlier questioning (47) of the interpretation of these X-ray scattering data.

There is strong evidence that in coordinating solvents the neutral lithium cuprate structure disintegrates. This is caused by solvent coordination of the free lithium cation which competes with the intramolecular stabilization of the cationic lithium centers in the neutral cuprate structures. This leads to the anionic cuprate species with Cu/Li ratios larger than one, see eqns. 9-11:

$$\text{From CuBr + excess PhLi} \xrightarrow{\text{THF}} \text{crystallizes} \quad (Cu_5Ph_6)(LiTHF_4) \qquad (9)$$

$$\text{From CuCN + 2PhLi} \xrightarrow{Et_2O} \text{crystallizes(20\%)} \quad 2(Cu_3Li_2Ph_6) \cdot (Li_4Cl_2(Et_2O)_{10}) \qquad (10)$$
$$\text{(containing 6-7\% Cl}^-\text{)}$$

$$\text{From CuI + [LiTHF}_4][Li\{C(SiMe_3)_3\}_2] \xrightarrow{Et_2O} \text{cristallizes (20\%)}$$
$$[LiTHF_4][(Me_3Si)_3CCuC(SiMe_3)_3] \qquad (11)$$

In the latter example (45) the monomeric linear structure with two center, two electron Cu−C bonding is most likely due to the steric bulk of the $C(SiMe_3)_3$ groups which prevents bridge bonding.

In a recent study (14) of the solution behaviour of $Cu_2Li_2(C_6H_4CH_2NMe_2-2)_4$, *2a*, we have found that in toluene the tetranuclear structure remains whereas in THF this complex also exists as an anionic $[Cu(C_6H_4CH_2NMe_2-2)_2]$ species with $[LiTHF_4]$ cations (46). However, on crystallization of *2a* from THF the tetranuclear species was recovered. These results indicate that the role of the N donors in the aryl cuprate *2a* on the structure is that of a well-positioned "intramolecular solvent" for which Li coordination has a favourable entropy factor.

Comparison of the cuprate and aurate structures *2a* and *4a*, see Figure 7, shows that the lithium-aryl-metal IB bridge becomes increasingly asymmetric going down the series Cu(I), Ag(I) to Au(I). For the Au(I) compound *4a* this aryl-metal interaction (in the solid) is better described as a two center, two electron aryl-gold(I) interaction; i.e. in this structure the aryl sp^2 lone pairs are almost exclusively bonded to the Au atoms (see Figure 8D). The lithium sites are the electropositive centers to which the heteroatoms are coordinated. This bonding description is supported by the trend in ^{6}Li chemical shift data of the series $M_2Li_2(C_6H_4CH_2NMe_2-2)_4$, *2a-4a* (14).

In toluene-d_8 *2a-4a* give a single line whose chemical shift was temperature independent (-60-$30°$). Whereas δ^6Li of $Li_4(C_6H_3NMe_2-2-Me-5)_4$, was observed at 3.58 ppm the resonances of the ate complexes appeared upfield ranging from 0.35 for *2a,* -0.10 for 3a to -1.25 ppm for the aurate *4a.* There is also a marked difference in $J(^{13}C(1), ^7Li)$ values of these species, i.e., 7.0 *2a,* 7.2 *3a* and 4 Hz for the aurate *4a.* Both results strongly suggest that the lithium centers become increasingly cationic going from Cu(I) and Ag(I) to the Au(I) lithium species. However, further work is clearly needed to further substantiate these observations.

The neutral cuprate and aurate structures, *2a* and *4a,* are interesting models for, on the one hand, the reactive organocuprates and, on the other hand, the transient (organocuprate-substrate) species that are postulated (47) to be formed in reactions of simple organocuprates (e.g. $Cu_2Li_2Me_4$) with, for example, α,β-unsaturated ketones. Structural changes from C to D (see Figure 8) which enhance the nucleophilicity of the copper center are feasible with retention of the square-planar Li_2M_2 structure. The present results suggest that such ketones anchor via the O donor to the lithium center in the neutral cuprate. However, alternative mechanisms have been proposed and the results of a recent ^{13}C NMR study of the $Cu_2Li_2Me_4$/t-butyl-cinnamate system were interpreted in terms of an initial formation of an olefin-copper(I) π-complex (48).

References and Footnotes

1. Address correspondence to this author at Anorganisch Chemisch Laboratorium, J.H. van't Hoff Instituut, Universiteit van Amsterdam, Nieuwe Achtergracht 166, 1018 WV Amsterdam, The Netherlands.
2. (a) E.g. G.H. Posner in *Organic Reactions, Substitution reactions using organocopper reagents,* Vol. *22,* Chapter 2, 253 (1980); (b) J.K. Kochi, *Organometallic mechanisms and catalysis,* New York, 1978.
3. G. van Koten and J.G. Noltes in *Comprehensive Organometallic Chemistry, Copper and Silver, Ch. 14,* Ed. G. Wilkinson, F.G.A. Stone and E.W. Abel, Oxford, p. 710 (1982).
4. R.L. Kieft and T.L. Brown, *J. Organometal. Chem., 77,* 289 (1974); J.S. Fillippo Jr., *Inorg. Chem., 17,* 275 (1978); E.C. Ashby and J.J. Watkins, *J. Amer. Chem. Soc., 99,* 5312 (1977), *J. Org. Chem., 48,* 2125 (1983); H. Westmijze, A.V.E. George and P. Vermeer, *Recl. Trav. Chim. Pays-Bas, 102,* 322 (1983).
5. D.E. Bergbreiter, T.J. Lynch and S. Shimazu, *Organometallics, 2,* 1354 (1983).
6. G. van Koten and J.G. Noltes, *J. Chem. Soc., Chem. Commun.,* 940 (1972) and *J. Amer. Chem. Soc., 101,* 6593 (1979) and references therein.
7. (a) H. Hope, D. Oram and P.P. Power, *J. Amer. Chem. Soc., 106,* 1149 (1984); (b) P.G. Edwards, R.W. Gellert, M.W. Marks and R. Bau, *J. Amer. Chem. Soc., 104,* 2072 (1982).
8. (a) E.g. G.J. Lambert, R.P. Duffley, H.C. Dalzell and R.K. Razdan, *J. Org. Chem., 47,* 3350 (1982); (b) F.E. Ziegler, I. Chliwner, K.W. Fowler, S.J. Kanfer, S.J. Kuo and N.D. Sinha, *J. Amer. Chem. Soc., 102,* 790 (1980).
9. (a) In contrast to the suggestion that pure aryllithium compounds are difficult to synthesize we have found that the methodology developed and followed in our laboratory for the production of lithium salt-free aryllithium compounds, e.g. synthesis of *1* (10), is straightforward; (b) H. Hope and P.P. Power, *J. Amer. Chem. Soc., 10,* 5320 (1983).
10. J.T.B.H. Jastrzebski, G. van Koten, M. Konijn and C.H. Stam, *J. Amer. Chem. Soc., 104,* 5490 (1982).
11. G. van Koten and J.G. Noltes, *J. Organometal. Chem., 174,* 367 (1979) and references cited therein.
12. J.T.B.H. Jastrzebski and G. van Koten in *Inorganic Synthesis,* Ed. H. Kaesz, Vol. *25,* to be published.

13. In a forthcoming paper these syntheses will be described (see ref. 14).

14. J.T.B.H. Jastrzebski and G. van Koten, to be published.

15. G. van Koten and J.G. Noltes, *J. Organometal. Chem., 84,* 419 (1975).

16. G. van Koten and J.G. Noltes, *J. Organometal. Chem., 102,* 551 (1975).

17. R.W.M. ten Hoedt, G. van Koten and J.G. Noltes, *J. Organometal. Chem., 179,* 227 (1979).

18. P. Leoni, M. Pasquali and C.A. Ghilardi, *J. Chem. Soc. Chem. Commun.,* 241 (1983).

19. G. van Koten and J. G. Noltes, *J. Chem. Soc. Chem. Commun.,* 452 (1972) and *J. Organometal. Chem., 159,* 441 (1978).

20. G. van Koten, C. A. Schaap, J.T.B.H. Jastrzebski, *J. Organometal. Chem., 186,* 427 (1980).

21. A.J. Leusink, G. van Koten, J.W. Marsman and J.G. Noltes, *J. Organometal. Chem., 55,* 419 (1973).

22. G. van Koten, J.T.B.H. Jastrzebski and J.G. Noltes, *J. Organometal. Chem., 140,* C23 (1977).

23. Extensive studies have been reported of the NMR features of a series of alkyl- (24), alkenyl- (24,25), and alkynyllithium (26) compounds.

24. L.D. McKeever and R.J. Waack, *J. Chem. Soc. Chem. Commun.,* 750 (1969).

25. D. Seebach, R. Hässig and J. Gabriel, *Helv. Chim. Acta, 66,* 308 (1983).

26. G. Fraenkel and P. Pramanik, *J. Chem. Soc. Chem. Commun.,* 1527 (1983); B. Schubert and E. Weiss, *Chem. Ber., 116,* 3212 (1983); Ibid., *Angew. Chem., 95,* 499 (1983).

27. The importance of steric requirements of the chelate rings formed is indicated by the *dinuclear* structure of $Li_2(naphthylNMe_2-8)_2 \cdot 2Et_2O$; J.T.B.H. Jastrzebski, G. van Koten, K. Goubitz, C. Arlen and M. Pfeffer, *J. Organometal. Chem., 246,* C75 (1983).

28. D. Thoennes and E. Weiss, *Chem. Ber., 111,* 3157 (1978).

29. The aryl ring can rotate around the $C(1)\text{---}C(4)$ axis, see refs. 3 and 30 and also Figure 8 (A and B).

30. (a) See Figure 8 (A and B) and the accompanying text in the section on the structural aspects of the ate complexes; (b) It has been established that intermolecular exchange of groups between arylcopper species occurs in solution (3). In the case of the arylcopper compounds **5a** and **5b** this was shown by mass spectrometry (31), see eqn.:

$$Cu_4R_4 + Cu_4R_4' \underset{C_6H_6}{\rightleftarrows} Cu_4R_3R' + Cu_4R_2R_2' + Cu_4RR_3'$$
$$\textbf{5a} \qquad \textbf{5b}$$

The formation of octanuclear intermediates $R_nR'_{8-n}Cu_8$ were proposed as a possible route for this exchange.

31. G. van Koten and J.G. Noltes, *J. Organometal. Chem., 84,* 129 (1975); J.M. Guss, R. Mason, A.I. Søtofte, G. van Koten and J.G. Noltes, *J. Chem. Soc. Chem. Commun.,* 446 (1972).

32. J.A.J. Jarvis, R. Pearce and M.F. Lappert, *J. Chem. Soc. Dalton Trans.,* 999 (1977)

33. S. Gambarotta, C. Floriani, A. Chiesi-Villa and C. Guastini, *J. Chem. Soc. Chem. Commun.,* 1156 (1983); ibid, 1087 (1983).

34. (a) G. van Koten, J.T.B.H. Jastrzebski and J.G. Noltes, *J. Organometal. Chem., 142,* 2047 (1977); (b) G. van Koten and J.G. Noltes, *J. Amer. Chem. Soc., 101,* 6593 (1979).

35. J.T.B.H. Jastrzebski, G. van Koten and C. Brevard., to be published.

36. For small $J(^{107}Ag, {}^{13}C)$ and $J(^{109}Ag, {}^{13}C)$ values the doublets are overlapping because of the small $^{109}Ag/^{107}Ag$ frequency ratio of 1.14.

37. C. Brevard, G.C. van Stein and G. van Koten, *J. Amer. Chem. Soc., 103,* 6746 (1981).

38. For the Ag_2Li_2 cores containing on ^{107}Ag and one ^{109}Ag nucleus a $J(^{107}Ag,^{109}Ag)$ is expected. (Nat. abund. $^{107}Ag=51.82\%$ and of $^{109}Ag=48.18\%$. Both isotopes have $I=\frac{1}{2}$).

39. In one case the attempted crystallization of **2** from diethyl ether resulted in the formation of crystals of the lithium enolate $Li_4(2-H_2C=C(O)C_6H_4CH_2NMe_2)_4$; (40) i.e. the product of an acetylation reaction at C(1). The structure consists of a cubane Li_4O_4 structure with Li—N coordination. A similar enolate structure has been reported by R. Amstutz, W.B. Schweizer, D. Seebach and J.D. Dunitz, *Helv. Chim. Acta, 264,* 2617 (1981).

40. J.T.B.H. Jastrzebski, G. van Koten, M.J.N. Christophersen, F. Muller and C.H. Stam, *J. Organometal. Chem.,* in press.

41. See eqn. 9 in this paper.

42. G. van Koten, J.T.B.H. Jastrzebski, C.H. Stam and N.C. Niemann, *J. Amer. Chem. Soc., 106,* 1880 (1984).

43. R.G. Pearson and C.D. Gregory, *J. Amer. Chem. Soc., 98,* 4098 (1976).

44. This rather short Cu−Cu distance is not indicative of metal-metal bonding but is a consequence of the asymmetric configuration of the aryl bridges in this structure.

45. C. Eaborn, P.B. Hitchcock, J.D. Smith and A.C. Sullivan, *J. Organometal. Chem., 263,* C23 (1984).

46. *2a* in toluene-d_8 at 293 K: δ^{13}C (ppm) C(1) 169.4, C(2) 148.8, C(6) 144.7, NCH$_2$ 71.5 and NCH$_3$ 47.5.
2a in THF-d_8 at 293 K: δ^{13}C (ppm) C(1) 175.6, C(2) 149.0, C(6) 141.2, NCH$_2$ 72.5 and NCH$_3$ 46.3.

47. H.O. House, *Accounts of Chem. Res., 9,* 59 (1976); K.R. Stewart, J.R. Lever and M.H. Whoangbo, *J. Org. Chem., 47,* 1472 (1982); S.R. Krauss and S.G. Smith, *J. Amer. Chem. Soc., 103,* 141 (1981).

48. G. Hallnemo, T. Olsson and C. Ullenius, *J. Organometal. Chem., 265,* C22 (1984).

49. C. Lecocq and J.Y. Lallemand, *J. Chem. Soc. Chem. Commun.,* 950(1981).